Weeds of the
North Central States

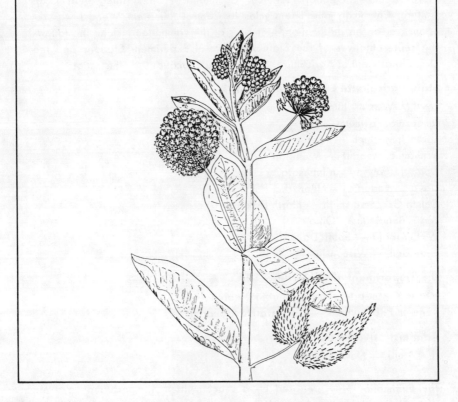

Agricultural Experiment Stations of Illinois, Indiana, Iowa, Kansas, Michigan, Minnesota, Missouri, Nebraska, North Dakota, Ohio, South Dakota, and Wisconsin, and the U.S. Department of Agriculture cooperating

Urbana, Illinois
April, 1981

Sponsored by the Agricultural Experiment Stations of Illinois, Indiana, Iowa, Kansas, Kentucky, Michigan, Minnesota, Missouri, Nebraska, North Dakota, Ohio, Oklahoma, South Dakota, and Wisconsin, and by the U.S. Department of Agriculture, Science and Education Administration — Agricultural Research and Cooperative Research.

North Central Regional Technical Committee NC-121 (Integrating Crop Culture, Chemicals and Life Cycles to Control Persistent Weeds) was responsible for this publication. Members of the committee include the following representatives of the State Agricultural Experiment Stations and the U.S. Department of Agriculture, Science and Education Administration:

State Agricultural Experiment Stations

Loyd M. Wax — Illinois
Richard S. Fawcett — Iowa
Loren J. Moshier — Kansas
William F. Meggitt — Michigan
Donald L. Wyse — Minnesota
Lloyd C. Haderlie — Nebraska
Calvin G. Messersmith — North Dakota
Leo E. Bendixen — Ohio
W. E. Arnold — South Dakota
Jerry Doll — Wisconsin

U.S. Department of Agriculture, SEA

Melvin K. McCarty — Agricultural Research
Kenneth P. Dorschner — Cooperative Research

Administrative Advisor

H. R. Lund — North Dakota

The publication was prepared by a subcommittee that included Loyd M. Wax, University of Illinois and U.S. Department of Agriculture, SEA (Chairman) and Richard S. Fawcett and Duane Isely, Iowa State University.

The participating Agricultural Experiment Stations and government agencies provide equal opportunities in programs and employment.

FOREWORD

Weeds of the North Central States was originally published in 1954 as North Central Regional Publication 36 and Illinois Agricultural Experiment Station Circular 718. Members of the Regional Technical Committee of Project NC-10, including representatives of the Agricultural Experiment Stations of the twelve North Central states and Oklahoma, contributed to the original edition. The editorial subcommittee that prepared the material for publication was made up of K. P. Buchholtz, Wisconsin (Chairman); B. H. Grigsby, Michigan; O. C. Lee, Indiana; F. W. Slife, Illinois; C. J. Willard, Ohio; and N. J. Volk, Indiana, Administrative Advisor.

A revised, enlarged edition was published in 1960. The editorial subcommittee that prepared the revision consisted of Professors Slife (Chairman) and Buchholtz from the initial subcommittee, together with Thor Kommedahl, Minnesota.

The present edition was prepared by the editorial subcommittee of the North Central Regional Technical Committee NC-121. Members of the subcommittee are: Loyd M. Wax, University of Illinois and U.S. Department of Agriculture, Science and Education Administration (Chairman); and Richard S. Fawcett and Duane Isely, Iowa State University.

This edition includes all the weeds that were in the 1960 edition, with some changes in nomenclature, updating of distribution maps, and minor revisions of the descriptions. In addition, 19 weeds have been added, the original keys have been expanded, and a new key for common weed seedlings in corn and soybean fields has been included.

CONTENTS

ACKNOWLEDGMENTS

Illustrations were obtained from many sources. Credit for illustrations that appeared in the first two editions of this publication, as well as in the present edition, is due the following institutions: California State Department of Agriculture (*Weeds of California*), Iowa State Department of Agriculture (Bul. 81-A), Michigan Agricultural Experiment Station (Bul. 267 and Spec. Bul. 304), University of Minnesota (illustrations prepared under W.P.A. project 65-1-71-140), Missouri Agricultural Experiment Station (Bul. 433), Nebraska State Department of Agriculture (Bul. 101), South Dakota State Weed Board (Publication No. 5), U.S. Department of Agriculture (Misc. Pub. 200).

The editorial subcommittee that prepared the present edition appreciates the suggestions and guidance given by members of the Project NC-121 Regional Technical Committee. Special thanks for texts, drawings, and maps for species added in 1981 are given to personnel from the following institutions: University of Minnesota, South Dakota State University, Kansas State University, University of Wisconsin, University of Nebraska, North Dakota State University, and University of Illinois.

A LL THE WEEDS commonly found in the North Central Region, as well as a good many that are less common, are illustrated and described in this book. Detailed pictures have been given for most of the weeds, and wherever possible in the descriptions common terms have been substituted for technical ones. People with a minimum of botanical knowledge should therefore be able to identify almost every weed they are likely to find.

What is a weed? Although we all have a general concept as to what a weed is, it is sometimes hard to determine whether a particular plant is a weed or not. Some crop plants, for example, can become weeds when they appear where they are not wanted. On the other hand, a number of plants usually thought of as weeds may actually be useful under some conditions or in some areas. They may help to control soil erosion or may serve as foods for wild animals and birds. Sometimes certain weeds are used as forages for farm animals.

With these points in mind, we can define a weed as a plant not intentionally sown, whose undesirable qualities outweigh its good points. This definition eliminates the many plants — often native — that grow uncultivated in every locality but seldom have weedy tendencies. They are not aggressive enough to be troublesome in cropland or pastures. Since they do not interfere with agricultural production they should be allowed to grow undisturbed. In fact, many of these plants have such colorful flowers and interesting habits that they are well worth preserving.

How weeds are troublesome. Weeds reduce crop yields by depriving the crops of the water, light, and soil nutrients they need. Weeds may also produce allelopathic substances that are toxic to crop plants. The work of controlling weeds in crops and pastures increases production costs. If weeds are present at crop maturity, they may cause harvesting problems.

Weeds often serve as hosts for crop diseases; and they may provide a place for insects attacking crop plants to overwinter. Some weeds detract from the quality of crops and of animal products; wild garlic, for example, reduces the value of wheat and taints the milk of cows that graze it.

The harmful effects of some common weeds on the health of animals and people are well known. Farm animals become ill and sometimes die from eating poisonous weeds. Thousands of people who suffer from hay fever can attest to the annoyance caused by the pollen from many plants, especially ragweed.

Control is difficult. The seeds of many weeds remain dormant in the soil for years and then germinate when conditions are favorable. Some weeds have extensive root systems and underground stems that help the weed to spread and persist. Perennial weeds store reserve foods in their root systems and continue to sprout again and again after the tops are destroyed. These characteristics of weeds make control a problem.

Even though control is often difficult, the proper selection and use of herbicides can give excellent results with most of the common weeds. For best results, however, it is necessary to identify the weed problem correctly before selecting herbicides. Many herbicides are rather specific in their action and may control only one or a few species of weeds. The same thing is often true of other control measures. If control measures are applied haphazardly, they may not only fail to control weeds, but they may also injure the crop.

Recommendations for the control of weeds vary from locality to locality, and may change fairly rapidly as new herbicides and new combinations become available. Thus no attempt is made in this publication to describe control measures. Precise, up-to-date recommendations for your situation are best obtained locally. This type of information is available from agricultural experiment stations, county agents or extension advisors, agricultural teachers, and other agricultural leaders.

How to identify weeds. A particular weed may be identified in several ways. Always, however, you need a reasonably good specimen. Identification will be easier if you have the entire plant with leaves, roots, and flowers. Fresh plants are always more easily identified than wilted or dried ones.

If you believe the unidentified weed belongs to a particular family, such as the grass or mustard family, you have a head start in identifying it. Since plants are arranged by families in this bulletin, you can compare your plant with the different illustrations and descriptions in the family until you find what you're looking for. (A special index to families is given on page 303.) Check the flower color, flower shape, leaf arrangement and shape, type of growth, and other characteristics, to make sure the identification is correct.

Sometimes several closely related weeds are grouped together on a page, with only one being described in detail. If the weed you are trying to identify is in such a group, it may not correspond exactly with the one described. It may differ in size, leaf shape, leaf color, and other minor characteristics. However, the description usually mentions if these related forms of a weed are likely to be found.

If the weed is entirely unfamiliar to you, you may have to compare the specimen with the various illustrations in the bulletin until you find the correct one. However, this may be a long process. A better way is usually to go to the key at the back of the bulletin. Directions for using the key are given on page 243. Some practice is needed to use it rapidly, but it usually offers the quickest way of identifying an unknown plant.

At times it is necessary to make a tentative identification of weeds while they are still in the seedling stage. For this purpose, beginning on page 289, we have included vegetative keys that will help in identifying young seedlings of the most common grass and broadleaf weeds found in corn and soybean fields in the North Central region. While it is difficult to identify these young seedlings positively, practice with these keys can result in a correct identification much of the time.

Many plants that are occasionally found in the region are not illustrated in this publication. These may be identified by consulting local or state authorities or botanical manuals.

Maps show distribution. With each weed illustration there is a small outline map that indicates the general prevalence of the weed. The maps are based on a study of herbarium samples and, perhaps more importantly, on the opinions of weed scientists from throughout the region. Changes are required from time to time as species advance to new areas or decline in others as the result of changes in cropping practices, tillage methods, and herbicide use. The following illustration gives the significance of the shadings used on the maps.

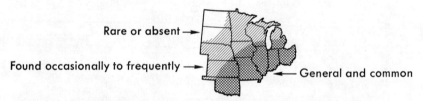

Rare or absent →

Found occasionally to frequently →

← General and common

Names of weeds vary. Common names of weeds vary considerably in different localities. One weed may have several different names, or several weeds may be known by the same name. The names used in this bulletin have been selected because they seem to be the ones in most general use and because they avoid unnecessary duplication. For the most part, these common names are based on the Composite List of Weeds that was published in *Weed Science* 19:435-476, 1971.

Scientific names of plants are more uniform than common names, but they sometimes vary according to the authority. Moreover, the names of some plants may be changed as the result of continuing taxonomic studies. In general, the scientific names used in this book follow those used in the Composite List of Weeds mentioned above, as well as in the following publications.

Manual of the Grasses of the United States, by A. S. Hitchcock, revised by Agnes Chase. U.S. Department of Agriculture, Miscellaneous Publication 200. 1950.

Gray's Manual of Botany, eighth edition, revised by M. L. Fernald. American Book Company. 1950.

Manual of Vascular Plants of Northeastern United States and Adjacent Canada, by H. A. Gleason and A. Cronquist. D. Van Nostrand Co., Inc. 1963.

Atlas of the Flora of the Great Plains, edited by T. M. Barkley. Iowa State University Press. 1977.

In some instances, if authorities differed or if recent taxonomic studies indicated the need for a changed name, decisions were made to use different scientific names than those given in previous editions of *Weeds of the North Central States.*

Suggestions will be welcome. The subcommittee responsible for this publication would appreciate comments and suggestions, so that they may be considered for future editions. New weed problems are continuously developing in the region while others seem to diminish. Thus information about needed changes in distribution maps would be especially helpful. We would also welcome suggestions as to possible changes in names of plants.

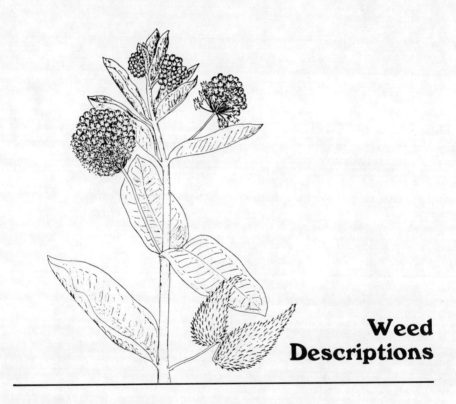

**Weed
Descriptions**

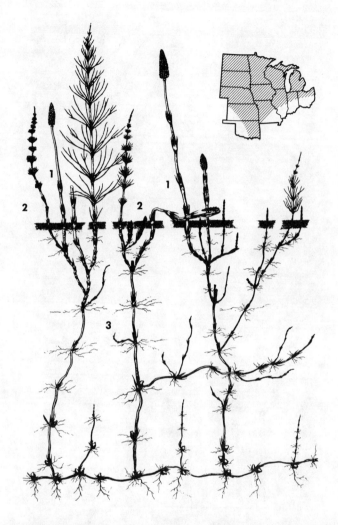

FIELD HORSETAIL, *Equisetum arvense* L. **1**, fertile or reproductive shoots; **2**, sterile or vegetative shoots; **3**, rhizomes. **Perennial**, reproducing by spores instead of seeds, and by rhizomes, to which are attached small tubers. **Stems** tough and wiry, hollow, jointed, and of two types: *fertile*, producing fruiting heads and having large, easily separable joints, not branched; *sterile or vegetative*, having much smaller joints, with lateral branches in whorls around the main stem. **Leaves** on sterile stems only, in the form of cup-shaped toothed sheaths at the joints. **Fruiting heads** contain masses of tiny pale greenish spores in small pine-cone-like structure. **Found** mostly on wet, sandy, or gravelly soil. It is poisonous to livestock when eaten in large quantities. There are several species of *Equisetum* in the area, all of which can be recognized as horsetails from this illustration.

FERN FAMILY, *Polypodiaceae*

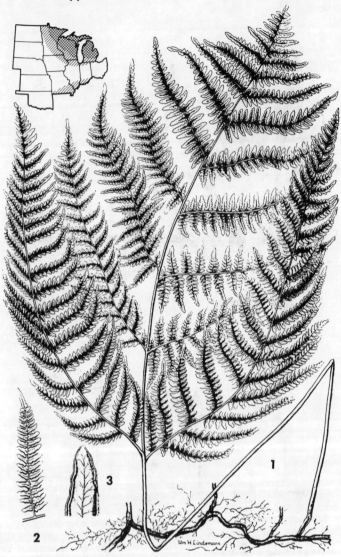

BRACKEN, *Pteridium aquilinum* (L.) Kuhn. **1,** plant showing leaves and rhizomes; **2,** segmented leaflet; **3,** undersurface of leaflet showing spore-bearing margin. **Perennial,** growing 1 to 4 feet (0.3 to 1.2 m) tall. Reproduces by spores or by shoots from a thick, black, scaly rhizome that may grow to a length of 20 feet (6 m). **Leaves** or fronds arise directly from the rhizome, with many branches, each branch being made up of numerous leaflets which in turn are segmented. **Spores** are borne on the underside of each leaflet in a narrow, brownish marginal band. **Found** in open pastures, woodlands, and hillsides, particularly on acid soils. The plant is poisonous if consumed over time, but is not usually eaten unless feed is very short.

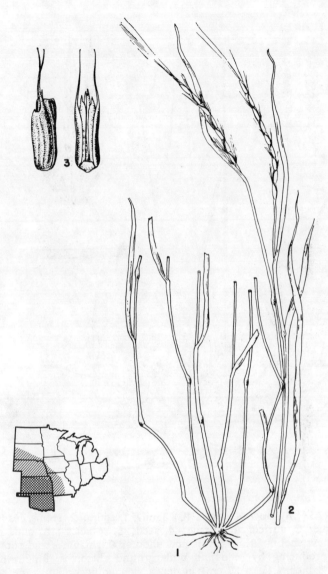

JOINTED GOATGRASS, *Aegilops cylindrica* Host. **1,** lower part of plant showing fibrous roots; **2,** upper portion with spike; **3,** seeds. **Winter annual,** reproducing by seeds. **Root** system fibrous. **Stems** erect, branching at base. **Leaves** alternate, simple, with auricles at the base of the blade, smooth or, in one variety, hairy. **Spikes** with spikelets arranged in a compact cylinder, bearded, longest beards at top of head. **Seeds** ripening ahead of wheat, shattering easily. **Found** principally in wheat fields, from which it spreads to roadsides and waste places. Very difficult to control where wheat is grown continuously.

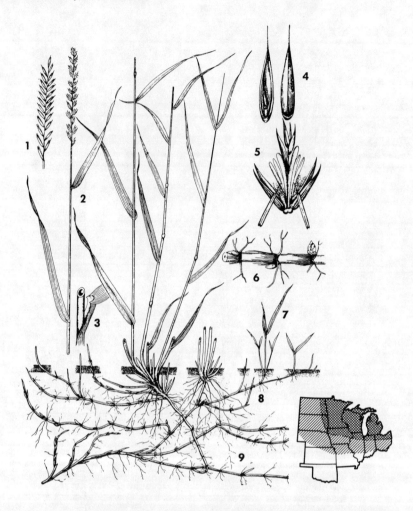

QUACKGRASS, *Agropyron repens* (L.) Beauv. **1,** spike; **2,** stems, leaves, and inflorescence; **3,** auricle and ligule; **4,** seed; **5,** spikelets; **6,** buds on rhizome; **7,** new shoots; **8,** origin of new shoots; **9,** rhizomes and roots. **Perennial,** reproducing by seed and underground rhizomes. **Rhizomes** vary from 2 to 8 inches (5 to 20 cm) in depth, depending on soil type and soil treatment. Individual rhizomes live only two summers and one winter but new ones develop from buds in the axils of reduced leaves. Roots arise only at nodes. **Stems** 1½ to 3 feet (45 to 90 cm) tall, with smooth culms and 3 to 6 joints. Leaves have auricles, ligule 1/32 inch (0.8 mm) long, hairy lower sheaths, upper sheaths smooth or nearly so. **Spike** has 3 to 7 short-awned florets in a spikelet. **Found** in open waste places, pastures, and most cropped areas. It requires special control methods because of its weedy habits. Although it is considered a primary noxious weed in most states, it can often be used for pasture or hay.

BROOMSEDGE, *Andropogon virginicus* L. **1**, stems and root system; **2**, part of inflorescence; **3**, single spikelet and rachis segment. **Perennial**, growing in small erect clumps or bunches, reddish-brown when dry. **Roots** densely fibrous. **Stems** several in a tuft, slightly flattened, 1 to 3 feet (30 to 90 cm) tall, upper part branched. **Leaves** 6 to 12 inches (15 to 30 cm) long, flat or folded, very hairy on upper surface where attached to stem. **Panicle** consists of 2 to 4 fingerlike clusters, each ¾ to 1½ inches (1.9 to 3.8 cm) long, bearing tufts of conspicuous white hairs, enclosed by reddish-brown leaves. **Seeds** about ⅛ inch (3 mm) long, brown, bearded. **Found** mostly on poor run-down pastures and open meadows. A serious problem in pastures on marginal lands, it disappears under fertilization and adequate grazing.

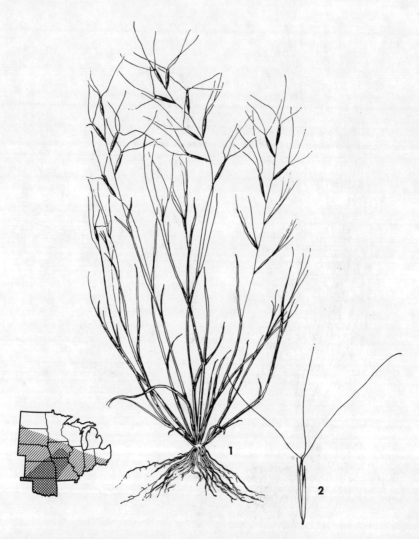

PRAIRIE THREEAWN, *Aristida oligantha* Michx. **1,** entire plant showing habit; **2,** glumes and floret. **Annual,** reproducing by seeds. **Roots** fibrous. **Stems** branched near surface of ground, wiry, 12 to 26 inches (30 to 65 cm) high, smooth or sometimes slightly rough. **Leaves** very narrow, flat, smooth, tapering to fine point. **Panicle** loose, terminal, each containing a few short-pediceled, narrow, 1-flowered spikelets. **Seeds** bear a triple awn with bristles of nearly equal length. Awns 1 to 3 inches (2.5 to 7.5 cm) long, somewhat spirally curved at base. **Found** generally on open, dry, sterile soil, especially overgrazed prairies and abandoned land that was formerly cultivated. Awns cause irritation in mouth and nostrils of livestock. Several other species of threeawn grasses are found and can be recognized as belonging to the genus *Aristida* from this illustration.

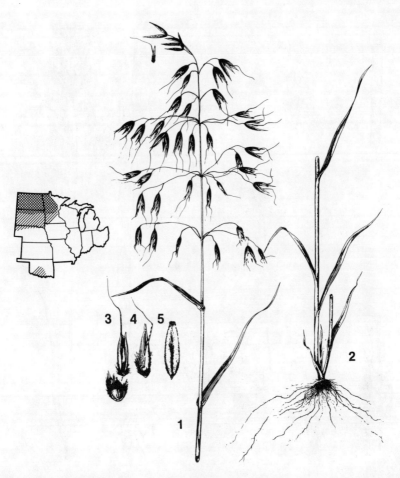

WILD OAT, *Avena fatua* L. **1**, panicle; **2**, portion of lower stem, crown, and roots; **3, 4**, seeds with hull and enlargement of "sucker-mouth" base; **5**, kernel without hull. **Annual,** reproducing by seed. **Root system** extensive and fibrous. **Stems** smooth, stout, 1 to 4 feet (0.3 to 1.2 m) high. Leaves 3 to 8 inches (7.5 to 20 cm) long, resembling those of tame oats. **Panicle** usually more open than that of tame oats. **Spikelets** distinguished by long, dark awns, the lower parts twisted, the upper parts bent sharply at right angles to twisted parts. **Seeds** vary from white to yellow, brown, gray, or black; are usually hairy, especially near base. Distinguished from cultivated oats by the round "sucker-mouth" callus at base of the grain. **Seeds** usually ripen earlier than most cereals and many drop to ground before time to harvest cultivated cereals. **Found** especially in fields under continuous cropping to small grains and flax. Probably the most harmful annual weed in the hard red spring wheat area. Recently it has become a problem in the southern part of the hard red winter wheat area, where it acts as a winter annual.

17

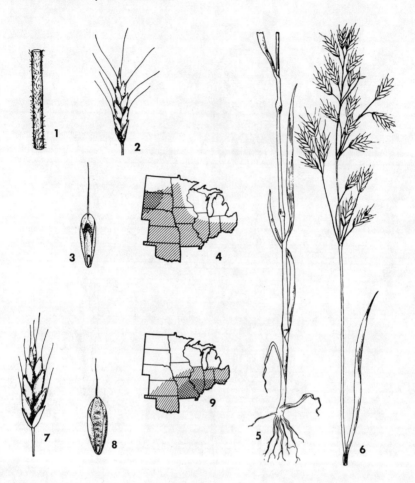

JAPANESE BROME, *Bromus japonicus* Thunb. **1,** part of hairy stem; **2,** mature spikelet; **3,** seed, inner surface; **4,** distribution. **Winter annual** or **annual,** reproducing by seeds. **Stems** erect, 10 to 30 inches (25 to 75 cm) tall. **Leaves,** both blades and sheaths, covered with soft hairs. **Inflorescence** a panicle. Spikelets about ½ inch (13 mm) long, somewhat hairy, borne on long, drooping stalks. **Seeds** mature May-June, have a stiff beard ¼ to ½ inch (6 to 13 mm) long, bend conspicuously outward at maturity. **Found** in grain fields, meadows, wasteland.

CHEAT, *Bromus secalinus* L. **5,** lower part of stem; **6,** panicle; **7,** mature spikelet; **8,** seed; **9,** distribution. **Winter annual** or **annual,** reproducing by seed. **Stems** erect, 12 to 24 inches (30 to 60 cm) high. **Leaves,** both blades and sheaths, smooth or slightly hairy. **Inflorescence** a panicle. Spikelets borne on shorter, more upright stalks than Japanese brome. **Seeds** bearing a short beard (⅛ to ¼ inch; 3 to 6 mm), or none at all, broader and shorter than Japanese brome. **Found** in grain fields, meadows, and waste places.

DOWNY BROME, *Bromus tectorum* L. **1**, mature plant with fibrous root system; **2**, mature seed; **3**, panicle; **4**, spikelet. **Winter annual** or **annual** reproducing by seeds. **Stems** erect or spreading, slender, 6 to 24 inches (15 to 60 cm) high. **Leaves**, both blades and sheaths, light green, covered with long soft hairs. **Panicle** rather dense, soft, very drooping, often purplish, flowering in April-May. **Seeds** long and narrow, bearing long beard (½ to ¾ inch; 12 to 19 mm), maturing in May-June. **Found** in meadows, pastures, small grain, wasteland.

19

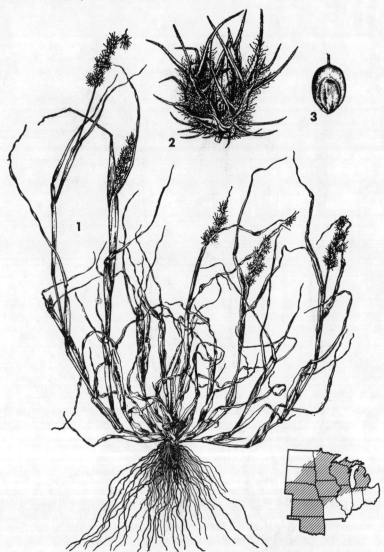

LONGSPINE SANDBUR, *Cenchrus longispinus* (Hack.) Fern. **1,** mature plant showing burs in terminal spikes; **2,** bur; **3,** a single seed from a bur. **Annual,** reproducing by seed. **Roots** fibrous. Rooting may occur at the nodes of the stems when they come in contact with the soil. **Stems** erect, or sometimes spreading and matlike, 6 inches to 2 feet (15 to 60 cm) long. **Leaves** smooth, twisted, 2 to 5 inches (5 to 12.5 cm) long. **Spike** short, composed of spikelets enclosed in sharp spiny burs. **Burs** each contain 1 to 3 seeds, usually 2. **Found** mostly on sandy soil. Is troublesome in garden crops, lawns, and fields mainly because the spiny burs cause discomfort to persons and livestock.

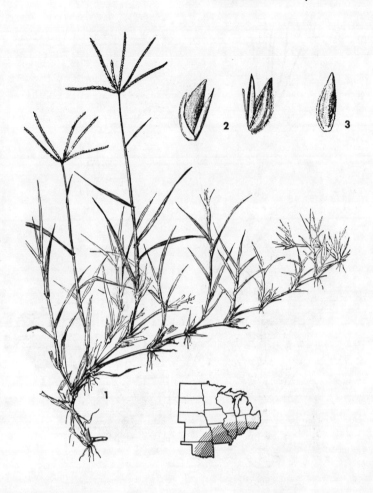

BERMUDAGRASS, *Cynodon dactylon* (L.) Pers. **1**, plant; **2**, spikelets; **3**, seed. **Perennial,** reproducing by seed (although rarely in our region), rhizomes, and stolons. **Rhizomes** hard, scaly, sharp-pointed, forming dense heavy sod. **Stolons** flat, hairless, extensively creeping, bearing at each joint the dead, bladeless sheaths that make the "dog's teeth" giving the plant its Latin name (Cynodon — dog's tooth). **Flowering stems** erect or ascending, 6 to 18 inches (15 to 45 cm) tall. **Leaf** blades ⅛ inch (3 mm) wide, gray-green, slightly hairy or glabrous except for a fringe of long hair at edge just above collar; sheath sparsely hairy or hairless, strongly flattened, ligule a ring of white hairs. **Flowers** borne in "finger-branched" inflorescence of 3 to 7, usually 5, parts. Spikelets in 2 rows tightly appressed to rachis. **Seeds** resemble those of timothy. **Found** in open places, pastures, and most cropped areas. A very persistent weed when established, it seems to have entered our territory primarily in nursery stock or by being sown as a lawn; is definitely spreading northward.

21

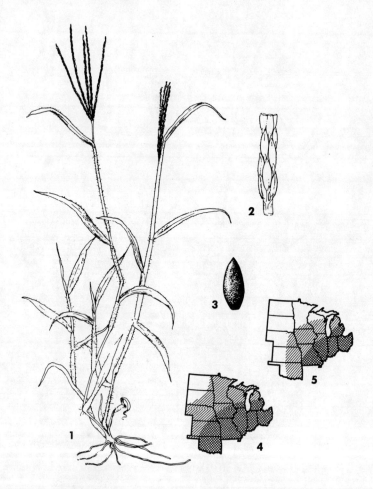

LARGE CRABGRASS, *Digitaria sanguinalis* (L.) Scop. **1,** plant; **2,** section of spike showing spikelets; **3,** seed; **4,** distribution. **Annual,** reproducing by seed. **Stems** stout, smooth, up to 3 feet long; when prostrate, rooting at the joints. **Leaf** blades usually at least somewhat hairy, ¼ to ⅓ inch (6 to 8 mm) wide; leaf sheaths, especially the lower ones, densely long-hairy. **Inflorescence** has 3 to 10 segments, in whorls at top of stem. **Seeds** 3/32 inch (2.4 mm) long, alternate on the branches of the inflorescence. **Found** in lawns, gardens, and fields. The most troublesome lawn weed in southern part of region. Starts late, when ground is quite warm; grows well under dry, hot conditions; flowers August-September. Also commonly known as hairy crabgrass.

SMOOTH CRABGRASS, *Digitaria ischaemum* (Schreb.) Muhl. **5,** distribution. Similar to above but not so coarse or tall, without hairs, more purplish or bluish. **Found** in same places as large crabgrass, but most commonly in lawns.

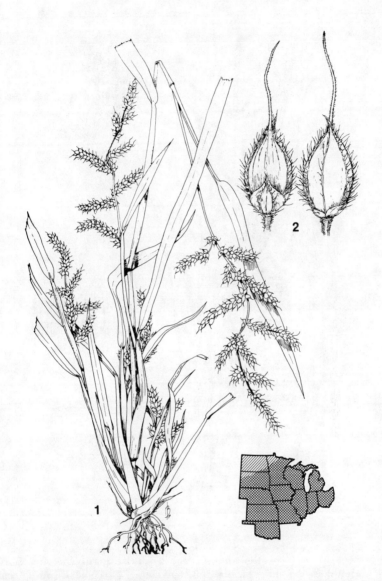

BARNYARDGRASS, *Echinochloa crusgalli* (L.) Beauv. **1**, plant; **2**, two views of spikelet. **Annual** with fibrous, rather shallow roots. **Stems** 1 to 4 feet (0.3 to 1.2 m) tall, thick, coarse, mostly erect, smooth, branching at the base. **Leaves,** both sheaths and blades, smooth. Blades ⅜ to ⅝ inch (9 to 15 mm) wide, light green. **Panicle** bearing several rather compact side branches, green or purplish in color. **Florets** covered with conspicuous short stiff bristles, bearded. **Seeds** tan to brown, oval with longitudinal ridges on the convex surface. **Found** in most cropped areas in late summer or fall.

23

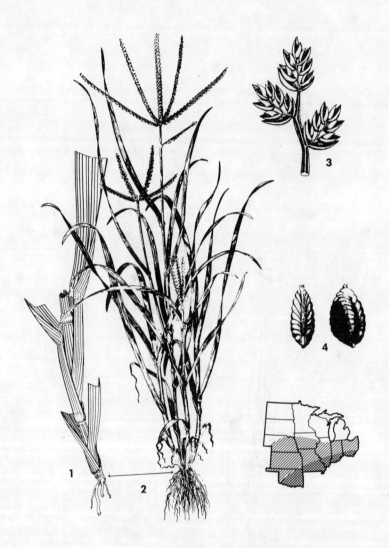

GOOSEGRASS, *Eleusine indica* (L.) Gaertn. **1,** close-up of a tiller showing arrangement of leaf sheaths and blades; **2,** entire plant showing fibrous roots and finger-like inflorescence; **3,** spikelets; **4,** seeds. **Annual,** reproducing by seeds. **Roots** fibrous. **Stems** smooth, sometimes upright but usually nearly prostrate, 6 inches to 2 feet (15 to 60 cm) long. **Leaves** smooth, blades 3 to 12 inches (7.5 to 30 cm) long, sometimes slightly roughened. **Inflorescence** fingerlike, similar to crabgrass, with 2 to 10 segments 1 to 3 inches (2.5 to 7.5 cm) long. Spikelets 3- to 6-seeded along the edges of the rachis. **Seeds** very small, reddish-brown, rough, ridged. **Found** in lawns, gardens, roadsides, and waste places. A common weed, it is sometimes confused with crabgrass but is darker green and grows only in tufts.

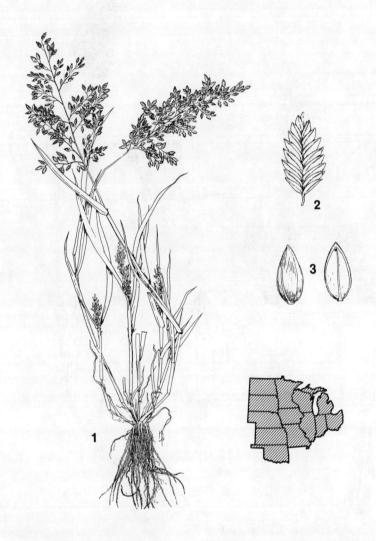

STINKGRASS, *Eragrostis cilianensis* (All.) Lutati. **1,** plant; **2,** spikelet; **3,** seed. **Annual** with shallow fibrous roots. **Stems** slender, smooth, 1 to 2 feet (30 to 60 cm) tall, branched at top — several usually arising from root crown. **Leaves** have smooth sheaths except for hairs on upper portion, and flat, smooth blades, 1/16 to 5/16 inch (1.5 to 7.5 mm) wide. **Panicles** branched, the branches moderately spreading, bearing numerous spikelets ¼ to ⅝ inch (6 to 15 mm) long. Spikelets flat, containing 20 to 40 florets or seeds; dark gray-green to purple. **Seeds** egg-shaped, 1/32 inch (0.8 mm) in diameter, orange-red. **Found** in cultivated fields and waste places. A moderately troublesome weed. Plant has disagreeable odor.

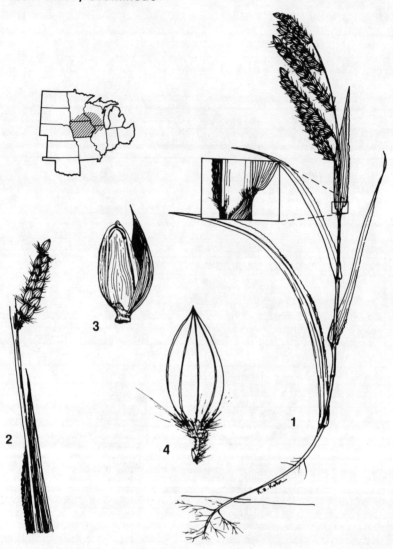

WOOLLY CUPGRASS, *Eriochloa villosa* (Thunb.) Kunth. **1,** entire plant; **2,** portion of stem, leaf, and raceme; **3,** spikelet; **4,** seed. **Annual,** reproducing by seed. **Root** system fibrous. **Stems** 3 to 5 feet (0.9 to 1.5 m) tall, erect but sometimes decumbent at base, lower portion often purplish, especially in young plants. **Leaves** dark green, covered with a fine pubescence, one leaf margin often distinctly crinkled. **Inflorescence** of several racemes, the rachises and pedicels very woolly; rachis narrow, with spikelets in 2 rows on one side. **Seed** varies in color from tan to brown to green, with bulbous base, large (to 3/16 inch or 4.5 mm long). **Found** on moist soils in corn, soybean, small grain, and forage crops.

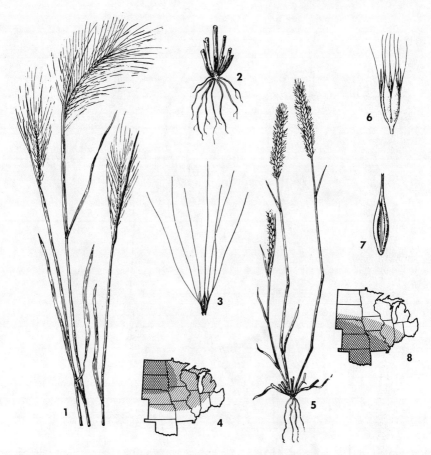

FOXTAIL BARLEY, *Hordeum jubatum* L. **1,** upper portions of stems with spikes; **2,** base of plant; **3,** seed with awns; **4,** distribution. **Perennial,** growing in clumps. **Roots** densely fibrous. **Stems** usually erect, 1 to 2 feet (30 to 60 cm) high. **Leaves** alternate, sheaths smooth, blades ⅛ to ¼ inch (3 to 6 mm) wide, rough on upper surface. **Spike** 2 to 5 inches (5 to 12.5 cm) long, nodding, with rather soft, yellowish-green or purplish bristles about 2 inches (5 cm) long. **Seeds** about ⅛ inch (3 mm) long, yellow, hairy. **Found** in pastures, where it is especially troublesome, and other noncultivated areas. Bristles may injure mouths of livestock.

LITTLE BARLEY, *Hordeum pusillum* Nutt. **5,** part of whole plant; **6,** group of spikelets or seeds; **7,** seed; **8,** distribution. **Winter annual** or **annual. Roots** shallow and fibrous. **Stems** smooth, 4 to 15 inches (10 to 37.5 cm) tall, bent slightly at each node. **Leaves** erect, ¾ to 2¾ inches (1.9 to 6.9 cm) long, rough on upper surfaces. **Spike** resembles small dense head of rye, 1¼ to 3¼ inches (3 to 8 cm) long, with short, stiff bristles (5/16 to ⅝ inch or 7.5 to 15 mm). **Seed** ⅛ to ¼ inch (3 to 6 mm) long, hairy at apex, yellow. **Found** in same places as above.

27

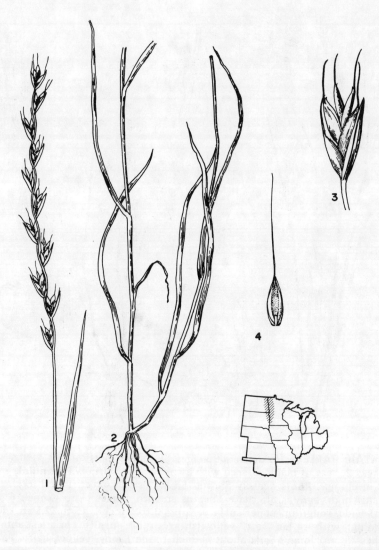

DARNEL, *Lolium temulentum* L. **1**, spike; **2**, lower portion of plant; **3**, spikelet (note long single outer glume on the right); **4**, seed. **Annual**, reproducing by seeds. **Roots** fibrous. **Stems** about 1½ to 2 feet (45 to 60 cm) tall. **Leaf** sheaths smooth, overlapping on one another. Leaf blades ⅛ to ¼ inch (3 to 6 mm) wide, flat, slightly rough on upper surfaces. **Spikes** long and narrow with 2 rows of small, flattened spikelets placed edgewise to the stem. Outer glume of spikelet as long as or longer than spikelet, sharp-pointed. **Seed** ⅛ to ¼ inch (3 to 6 mm) long, narrowly oval, brownish, usually short-bearded at the tip. **Found** in grain fields, pastures, roadsides, and waste places. Usually not a serious problem.

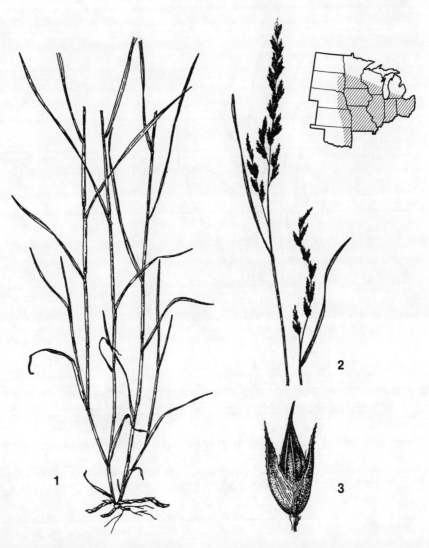

WIRESTEM MUHLY, *Muhlenbergia frondosa* (Poir.) Fern. **1,** lower part of plant; **2,** upper portions of stems with panicles; **3,** spikelet. **Perennial,** reproducing by seeds, rhizome growth, and rhizome fragments. **Rhizomes** short, creeping, very scaly. **Stems** erect or decumbent, 2 to 3 feet (60 to 90 cm) tall, smooth below joints, very tough, leafy, freely branched, rooting at lower nodes. **Leaves** flat, rough, pale green, scattered along the stem and dense near the tip, giving a bushy appearance. **Panicles** terminal and axillary, barely protruding from the leaf sheaths. **Seeds** tightly enclosed in the lemma, which may or may not be awned. **Found** in fence rows and along roadsides; sometimes persists in cultivated fields. Growth starts in late spring.

29

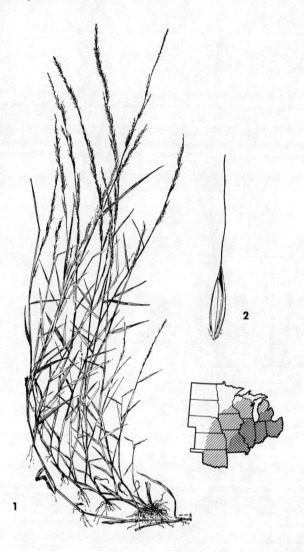

NIMBLEWILL, *Muhlenbergia schreberi* J. F. Gmel. **1,** plant showing rooting at lower nodes; **2,** spikelet. **Perennial,** reproducing by seed and numerous fine stolons. **Stems** not hairy, very slender, spreading, branching, decumbent at base and rooting at lower nodes, forming dense patches 1 foot (30 cm) or more in diameter from a single plant. **Leaf** blades flat, short (½ to 2 inches or 1.3 to 5 cm), not hairy except for occasional marginal hairs at the base; ligule short, membranous; collar not hairy, leaf sheath loose, not hairy. **Inflorescence** a fine slender panicle, 2 to 6 inches (5 to 15 cm) long, appearing in September. **Seeds** very small, about the size of redtop. **Found** generally in lawns, fence rows, and noncultivated areas. Often confused with crabgrass and Bermudagrass in lawns.

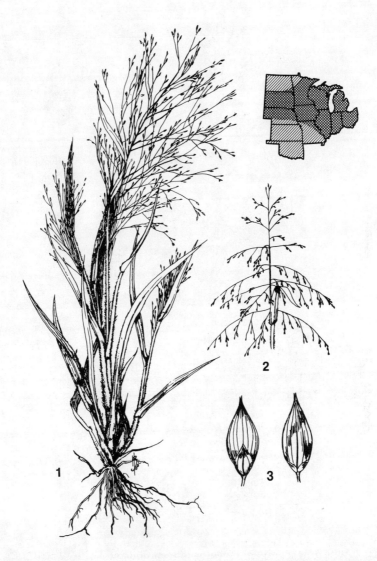

WITCHGRASS, *Panicum capillare* L. **1**, entire plant; **2**, panicle; **3**, seeds. **Annual** with fibrous roots, reproducing by seeds. **Stems** 10 to 30 inches (25 to 75 cm) tall, often spreading and branched. **Leaves** and especially the leaf sheaths covered with dense soft hairs. **Panicle** much branched, becoming spreading and open at maturity, often breaking from stem and blown about by wind. **Seeds** 1/16 inch (1.5 mm) long, greenish or grayish, shiny, smooth, readily separated from hulls when ripe. **Found** in small grain stubble, cultivated fields, meadows, gardens, and waste areas. Seed frequently spread in small-seeded crop seeds.

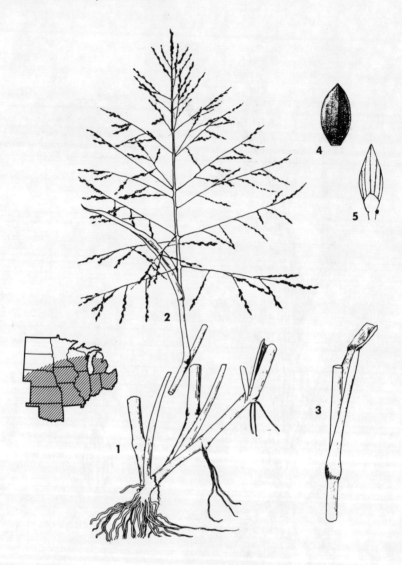

FALL PANICUM, *Panicum dichotomiflorum* Michx. **1,** lower part of plant showing root system; **2,** panicle; **3,** section of stem; **4,** seed; **5,** seed with hull. **Annual** with fibrous roots, reproducing by seeds. **Stems** 20 to 50 inches (0.5 to 1.3 m) long, smooth, spreading, often partly flat on the ground. Lower nodes swollen, often rooting. **Leaves** smooth or sparsely hairy. Leaf sheaths heavy, short, smooth, loose, often purplish. **Panicle** more compact and shorter than that of witchgrass. **Seeds** about 1/16 inch (1.5 mm) long, yellow, smooth, dull, readily separated from hulls when ripe. **Found** in gardens, cultivated fields, waste places, and low areas. Often common in corn and soybean fields in the fall.

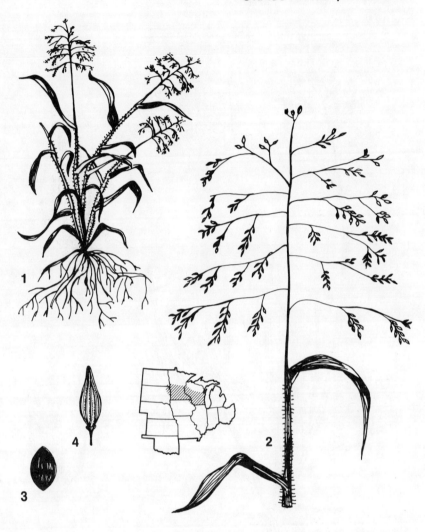

WILD PROSO MILLET, *Panicum miliaceum* L. **1**, entire plant; **2**, enlarged section of upper stem with panicle; **3**, seed; **4**, seed with hull. **Annual** with fibrous roots, reproducing by seeds. **Stems** 20 to 60 inches (0.5 to 1.5 m) tall, either spreading or erect, branched. **Leaves** and especially leaf sheaths covered with dense, stiff hairs. **Panicle** resembling fall panicum but larger. **Seeds** 3/32 to ⅛ inch (2.4 to 3 mm) long, oval, brown to black, shiny, smooth, readily separated from hulls, resembling domestic proso millet or "bird seed" but darker. **Found** in cultivated fields, particularly field and sweet corn. Grows rapidly; is particularly well adapted to sandy or drouthy soils and hot weather. Large seedling resembles volunteer corn but hairy. Prolific seed producer. Seed shatters easily and is often spread on harvest equipment.

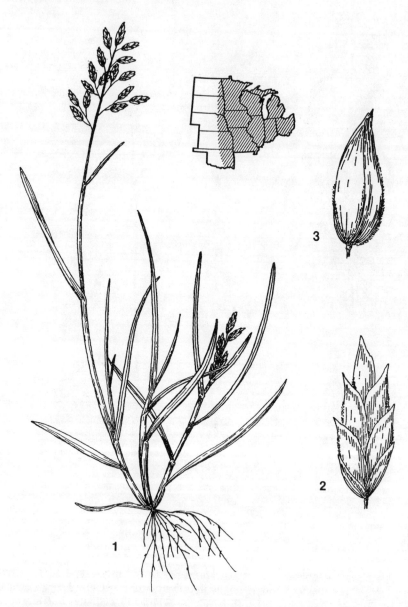

ANNUAL BLUEGRASS, *Poa annua* L. **1**, entire plant; **2**, spikelet; **3**, seed. **Annual** in the North Central states. Grows well in cool weather but is not winter hardy. **Roots** shallow, easily pulled from the soil. **Stems** 1 to 12 inches (2.5 to 30 cm) tall, often decumbent at base, sometimes rooting at lower joints. **Leaves** a soft, light green. **Panicles** very small in clipped lawns; plants flower during the entire growing season. **Prevalent** in lawns and gardens, particularly those with moist, rich soils.

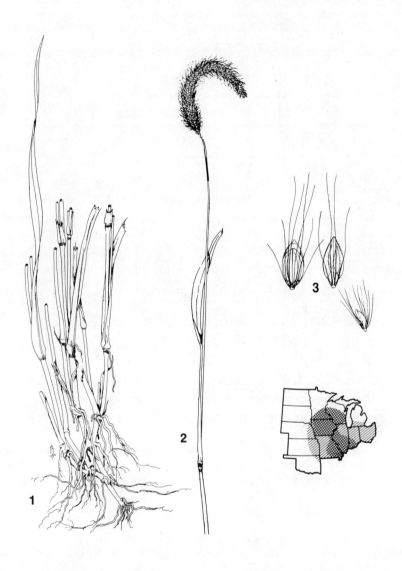

GIANT FOXTAIL, *Setaria faberi* Herrm. **1,** lower part of plant; **2,** stem with panicle; **3,** spikelets with bristles attached. **Annual,** reproducing by seed. **Stems** 3 to 7 feet (0.9 to 2 m) tall, so weak that plants may lodge unless supported by each other or by other vegetation. **Leaves** covered with short hairs on upper surface. **Panicle** dense, 3 to 8 inches (7.5 to 20 cm) long, bending near base so that head is drooping. Three to six bristles extend from base of each spikelet. **Seed** mostly greenish, about 1/16 inch (1.5 mm) long, intermediate in size between seeds of green and yellow foxtail. **Found** in cultivated crops, where it is extremely troublesome.

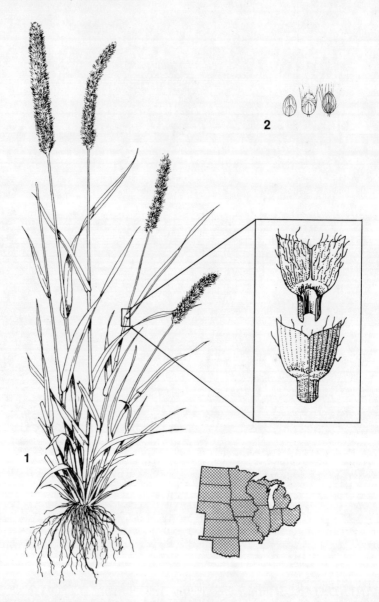

YELLOW FOXTAIL, *Setaria lutescens* (Weigel) Hubb. **1,** entire plant; **2,** seeds. **Annual,** reproducing by seeds. **Stems** erect, 1 to 2 feet (30 to 60 cm) tall. **Leaves** flat, often having a spiral twist, with many long hairs on the upper surface near the base. **Panicle** dense, erect. **Spikelets** with 5 or more bristles. **Seed** about 1/12 inch (2 mm) long, mostly yellowish but some dark brown. **Found** in all places except woods. A serious weed. Also commonly known as pigeon grass.

BRISTLY FOXTAIL, *Setaria verticillata* (L.) Beauv. **1,** lower part of plant; **2,** seeds; **3,** upper part of stem with panicle. **Annual,** reproducing by seeds. **Stems** 1 to 4 feet (0.3 to 1.2 m) tall, erect but branching more than those of other foxtails. **Panicle** dense, 2 to 4 inches (5 to 10 cm) long, with 1 bristle at the base of each spikelet, rarely 2 or 3. Bristles barbed, causing seed heads to be carried great distances by man and animals. **Seed** greenish, similar to that of green foxtail in shape and size. Found in gardens, orchards and other noncultivated areas as well as in some cultivated fields. Irritating to humans and animals because of sticky habit.

GREEN FOXTAIL, *Setaria viridis* (L.) Beauv. **1,** entire plant; **2,** seeds. **Annual,** similar to giant foxtail but smaller, usually growing 1 to 3 feet (0.3 to 0.9 m) tall. **Stems** erect. **Leaves** hairless. **Panicle** dense, 1 to 3 inches (2.5 to 7.5 cm) long, erect, except near tip, which bends slightly. One to three bristles below each spikelet. **Seed** green, about 1/16 inch (1.5 mm) long, but uniformly smaller than that of giant foxtail. **Found** generally throughout region. One of the most widespread grass weeds. Several types of *S. viridis* in the region vary greatly from the above description. They may grow to 6 or 7 feet (1.8 to 2 m) tall and may have panicles as large as or larger than those of giant foxtail. Some types may have purple bristles. The seed, however, is always smaller than that of giant foxtail. Some authors have separated these types of *S. viridis* into varieties and refer to them by such names as giant green, robust white, and robust purple foxtails.

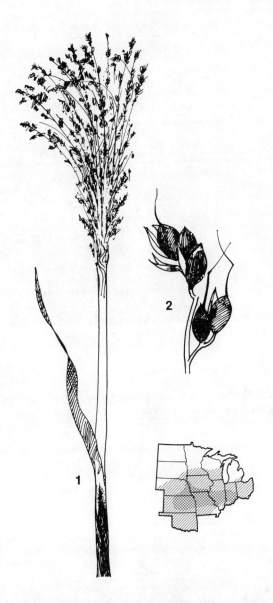

SHATTERCANE, *Sorghum bicolor* (L.) Moench. **1,** upper portion of stem with panicle of racemes; **2,** group of spikelets. **Annual,** reproducing by seed. Root system fibrous. **Stems** erect, smooth, 4 to 8 feet (1.2 to 2.4 m) high; tillers readily produced from crown. **Leaves** resemble those of forage sorghum or sudan. **Seeds** resemble forage sorghum seed, enclosed in black to red, shiny glumes; seeds shatter very easily and remain viable in soil 2 to 3 years. **Found** only in cultivated fields, where it reseeds itself.

39

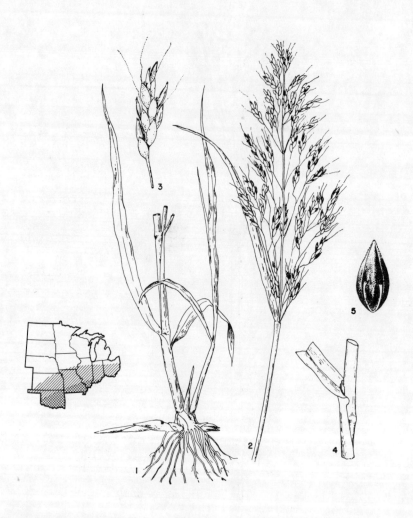

JOHNSONGRASS, *Sorghum halepense* (L.) Pers. **1,** stout stem base, roots, and a young rhizome; **2,** panicle; **3,** group of spikelets; **4,** section of stem showing base of leaf; **5,** seed. **Perennial,** reproducing by large rhizomes and seeds. **Root** system freely branching, fibrous. Rhizomes stout, creeping, with purple spots, usually with scales at the nodes. **Stems** erect, stout, from 1½ to 6 feet (0.45 to 1.8 m) or more tall. **Leaves** alternate, simple, smooth, 6 to 20 inches (15 to 50 cm) long, about ½ to 1½ inches (1.3 to 3.8 cm) wide. **Panicles** large, purplish, hairy. **Seed** nearly ⅛ inch (3 mm) long, oval, reddish-brown, marked with fine lines on surface, bearing a conspicuous awn easily broken off. **Found** especially on rich soil. Troublesome in corn and soybeans on overflow bottoms. Difficult to control or eradicate. Listed as noxious weed in states where found.

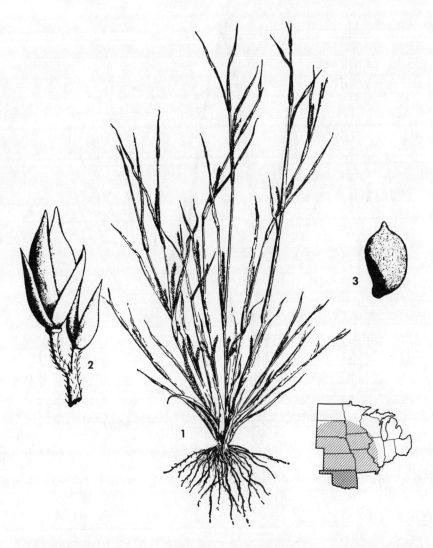

ANNUAL DROPSEED, *Sporobolus neglectus* Nash. **1**, plant; **2**, spikelets; **3**, seed. **Annual**, reproducing by seeds. **Root** system fibrous. **Stems** erect or base prostrate, 6 to 12 inches (15 to 30 cm) high, smooth, slender, branching at base. **Leaves** very slender, long and tapering, smooth, hairy at base, 1 to 3 inches (2.5 to 7.5 cm) long. **Panicles** slender, at first more or less hidden in the sheath. Awnless, slender spikelets. **Seeds** small, nearly transparent with a dark gray or brown spot for the germ, separated easily from white chaffy hull. **Found** in old alfalfa fields, pastures, lawns, and waste places on dry, sandy soil. It appears late in the season and has little forage value. Becomes objectionable in grassed areas as it leaves bare spots each spring and white spots after fall frosts.

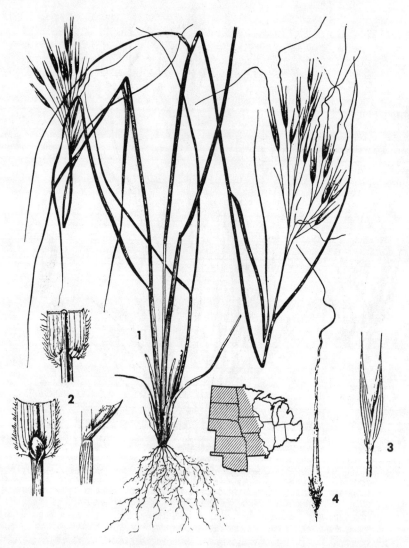

PORCUPINEGRASS, *Stipa spartea* Trin. **1**, entire plant; **2**, several views of leaf base; **3**, glumes; **4**, seed. **Perennial**, reproducing by seeds only. **Stems** smooth, 2 to 4 feet (0.6 to 1.2 m) high, in clumps. **Leaves** smooth beneath, rough on top, slightly rolled, 6 to 12 inches (15 to 30 cm) long, tapering to a fine point. **Seeds** brown, shiny, ¼ to ½ inch (6 to 13 mm) long, borne in a panicle 3 to 6 inches (7.5 to 15 cm) long. One end of seed has a sharp point with a ring of soft hairs and the other end, a twisted awn 3 to 5 inches (7.5 to 12.5 cm) in length. Moisture untwists the awn, forcing the sharply pointed end into the ground or into the flesh of animals. A valuable forage grass if properly handled to prevent seed formation. **Found** in range land and waste places.

HOP SEDGE, *Carex lupulina* Muhl. **Perennial,** reproducing by seeds and rhizomes. **Root** system shallow and fibrous. **Stems** smooth, 2 to 2½ feet (60 to 75 cm) tall, 3-sided, filled with pith, with few nodes and internodes, ending in a spike. The plant grows in dense mats. **Leaves** 3-ranked, without hairs but harsh, mostly basal with long blades and short sheaths. The relatively few stem leaves have long, narrow, V-shaped blades, pronounced midribs, closed sheaths, no auricles, and much reduced ligules. **Spikes** 1 to 3 inches (2.5 to 7.5 cm) long, bearing male and female flowers on the same plant, with male flowers uppermost on inflorescence. Bloom in July and August. **Seeds** brown, 3-sided, ⅛ inch (3 mm) thick and ½ inch (13 mm) long. **Found** in swamps, ditches, and other poorly drained areas. Not an important weed.

43

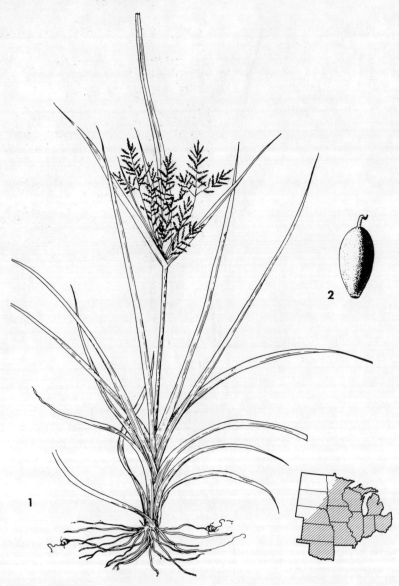

YELLOW NUTSEDGE, *Cyperus esculentus* L. **1**, whole plant; **2**, seed. **Perennial,** reproducing by seed and by tubers produced at the tips of scaly rhizomes. **Root** system fibrous. **Stems** erect, triangular, yellow-green. **Leaves** 3-ranked, narrow, grasslike, basal. **Flowers** yellowish or yellowish-brown, small, arranged in narrow spikelets on umbel-like inflorescence. **Seeds** yellowish-brown, 3-angled, small, about 1/16 inch (1.5 mm) long, with blunt ends. **Found** primarily on low, damp soils. Often troublesome in cultivated fields and pastures, especially on low land. Usually considered a serious weed.

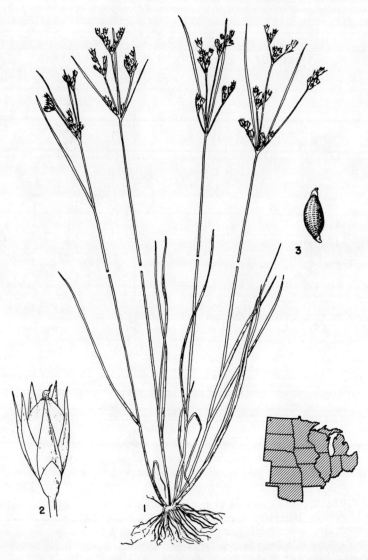

SLENDER RUSH, *Juncus tenuis* Willd. **1**, entire plant; **2**, flower with immature seed pod; **3**, seed. **Perennial,** reproducing by seeds. **Roots** fibrous, tufted. **Stems** 6 to 24 inches (15 to 60 cm) tall, slender, round, hollow, wiry, dark green, branching at the top, not jointed. **Leaves** very narrow, grasslike, mostly at the base of the stems. **Flowers** small, greenish-brown, with 6 scalelike bracts surrounding the seed pod; borne in clusters of 3 at the tips of the stems. **Seed pod** nearly egg-shaped, brown, splitting into 3 sections when mature. **Seeds** brown, small, about ⅛ inch (3 mm) long, with minute crossline markings. **Found** along paths, in pastures, roadsides, and waste places.

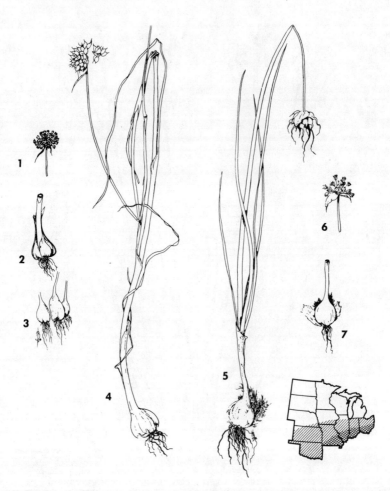

WILD GARLIC, *Allium vineale* L. **1,** flower cluster; **2,** old bulb and bulblets; **3,** underground bulblets; **4,** entire plant. **Perennial,** reproducing from seed, aerial bulblets, and underground bulblets. **Stems** 1 to 3 feet (30 to 90 cm) tall, smooth, and waxy. **Leaves** slender, hollow, nearly round, attached to lower half of stem. **Aerial bulblets** form in a cluster at top of stem, are oval and smooth with shiny covering. **Flowers** greenish-white, small, on short stems above aerial bulblets. **Seeds** black, flat on one side, about 1/8 inch (3 mm) long; formed only occasionally. **Found** in grain fields and pastures; serious in the humid winter wheat area of the region.

WILD ONION, *Allium canadense* L. **5,** entire plant; **6,** flower cluster; **7,** old bulb. Similar to above species but does not produce underground bulblets. **Stems** 1 to 2 feet (30 to 60 cm) tall. **Leaves** flat, not hollow, arising from base of plant only. The old bulb coat of wild onion is fibrous-matted while in wild garlic it is thin and membranous. **Found** in same places as above.

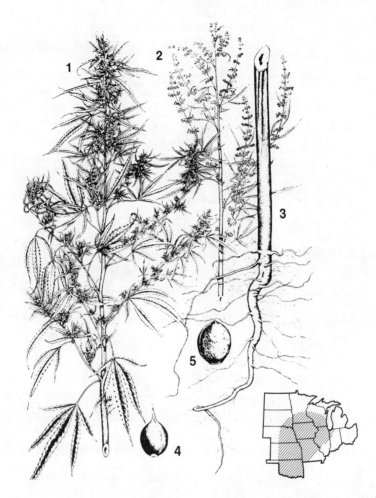

HEMP, *Cannabis sativa* L. **1,** upper part of female plant; **2,** upper part of male plant; **3,** root; **4,** flower from female plant; **5,** seed. **Annual,** reproducing by seed, with much-branched taproot. **Stems** 2 to 10 feet (0.6 to 3 m) tall, coarse, somewhat grooved, rough, and hairy. Plants usually bushy unless crowded. Hairs on the upper parts exude a sticky resin with a characteristic odor. **Leaves** palmately divided, consisting of 5 to 9 hairy leaflets with notched edges. **Flowers** of two kinds; male and female flowers borne on separate plants. Pollen-producing flowers have no petals and are borne in clusters from the axils of upper leaves. Male plants turn yellow and die after shedding pollen. Seed-producing flowers are without petals and are located in the axils of the leaves. Female plants are vigorous and dark green until frost. **Seed** oval, mottled brown, about ⅛ inch (3 mm) long. Plants are prolific seed and pollen producers. **Found** along ditches, fences, roadsides, and on wastelands with moist, fertile soil. Cultivated varieties are grown as fiber crop. Also commonly known as marijuana.

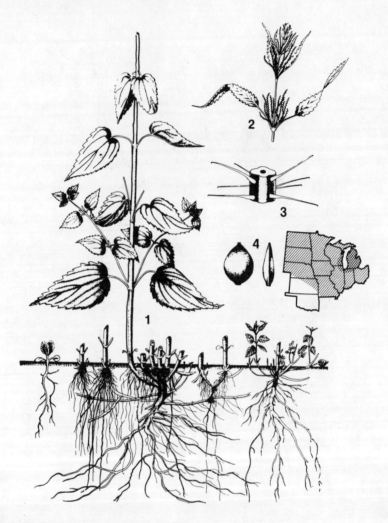

STINGING NETTLE, *Urtica dioica* L. **1**, lower part of plant; **2**, upper part of plant with flowers; **3**, section of stem with hairs; **4**, seed. **Perennial**, reproducing by seeds and underground rootstocks. **Stems** 2 to 7 feet (0.6 to 2 m) tall, slightly branched near the top, slender, rigid, covered with numerous stinging hairs. **Leaves** dark green, coarse, opposite, 3 to 6 inches (7.5 to 15 cm) long, pointed with saw-toothed margins, sometimes rounded at base, covered with stinging hairs. **Flowers** are greenish without petals and produced in clusters in the leaf axils. Male and female flowers borne separately but on the same plant. **Seed pod** 1-seeded. **Seeds** small, egg-shaped, slightly rough, yellow to grayish-tan. **Found** in barnyards, fence rows, thickets, waste places, and roadsides; generally in damp rich soil. When this plant comes in contact with the skin it causes welts or inflammation.

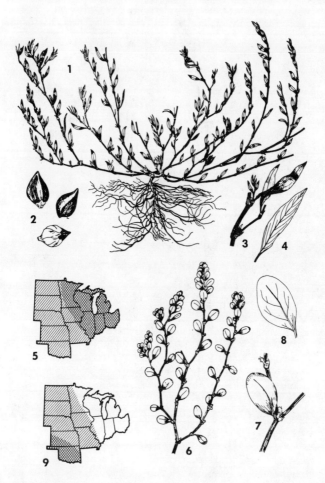

PROSTRATE KNOTWEED, *Polygonum aviculare* L. **1**, entire plant; **2**, seeds; **3**, portion of stem and leaves; **4**, single leaf; **5**, distribution. **Annual**, reproducing by seed. **Stems** bluish-green, leafy, wiry, extending 4 to 24 inches (10 to 60 cm) in all directions from the small taproot and forming a dense mat. Each joint or node covered with a thin papery sheath. **Leaves** bluish-green, alternate, oblong, narrowed at base, pointed at tip. **Flowers** very small, yellow or white, borne in clusters in the leaf axils. **Seeds** small, slender, reddish-brown, triangular. **Found** in hard trampled areas in yards, lawns, waste places, and along roadways or paths.

ERECT KNOTWEED, *Polygonum erectum* L. **6**, branch of plant; **7**, portion of stem and leaf; **8**, leaf; **9**, distribution. **Annual**, reproducing by seed. **Stem** erect, 8 to 24 inches (20 to 60 cm) high, branched near top, smooth, yellowish-green, slightly rigid. **Leaves** light green, oval, alternate, ¼ to 1 inch (0.6 to 2.5 cm) long, sometimes covered with mildew. **Flowers** and **seed** similar to those above. **Found** in same areas as prostrate knotweed.

49

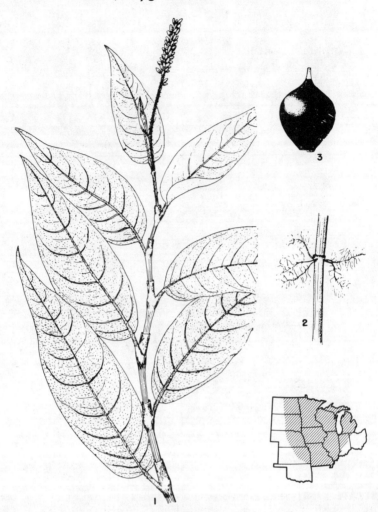

SWAMP SMARTWEED, *Polygonum coccineum* Muhl. **1**, upper part of plant; **2**, portion of rhizome; **3**, seed. **Perennial**, reproducing by long, creeping, tough, woody, horizontal rhizomes and by seed. **Stems** erect, 1 to 3 feet (0.3 to 0.9 m) long, enlarged at nodes, usually unbranched; may produce roots at nodes. **Leaves** alternate, oblong, 2½ to 8 inches (6.3 to 20 cm) long, pointed at tip, rounded at base with prominent veins. A sheath at base of each leaf surrounds stem. **Flowers** rose in color and produced in compact erect spike 1 to 3 inches (2.5 to 7.5 cm) long. **Seeds** oval, flattened on one side, black, shiny, and slightly rough; however, not usually produced in northern areas. **Found** usually in low, wet places in fields, gardens, or roadsides, but may be present elsewhere. The extensive root system makes it a strong competitor with other plants and difficult to kill. Also commonly known as tanweed and devil's shoestring.

50

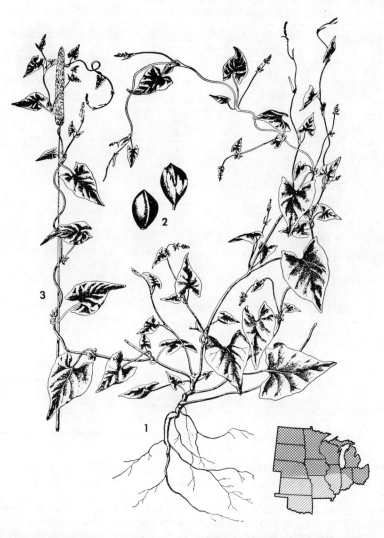

WILD BUCKWHEAT, *Polygonum convolvulus* L. **1,** entire plant; **2,** mature seed; **3,** vine entwined around stem of grass. **Annual,** reproducing by seed. **Stems** smooth, slender, twining or creeping, branched at base. **Leaves** alternate, heart-shaped, pointed with smooth edges. **Flowers** small, greenish-white, borne in clusters in leaf axils. **Seeds** triangular, somewhat shiny, black; often covered with a dull brown, rough hull. **Found** in noncultivated areas and under most cropping systems. It is often mistaken for field bindweed (page 139), but the annual habit, black, shiny 3-cornered seeds, heart-shaped leaf, and minute flowers set it apart. It is a serious weed and often reduces crop yields and quality; its seeds are difficult to remove from crop seeds.

BUCKWHEAT FAMILY, *Polygonaceae*

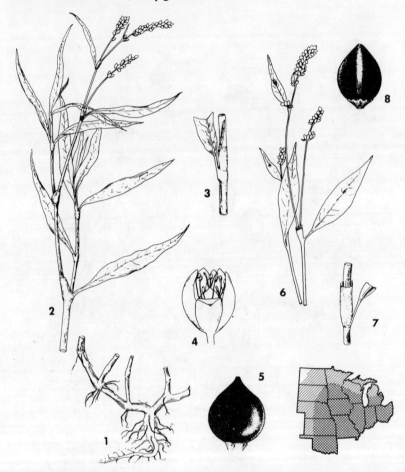

PENNSYLVANIA SMARTWEED, *Polygonum pensylvanicum* L. **1**, lower part of plant; **2**, upper part of plant; **3**, section of stem, leaf, and leaf sheath; **4**, flower; **5**, seed. **Annual**, reproducing by seeds. **Stems** smooth, swollen at nodes, branching, 1 to 4 feet (0.3 to 1.2 m) tall. **Leaves** smooth, pointed, alternate, 2 to 6 inches (5 to 15 cm) long, with a sheath at the base extending around the stem. **Flowers** bright pink or rose, 5-parted, arranged in a short spike. **Seeds** shiny, black, smooth, flattened, almost circular. **Found** in cultivated ground and waste places, and along ditches.

LADYSTHUMB, *Polygonum persicaria* L. **6**, upper part of plant; **7**, section of stem, leaf, and leaf sheath; **8**, seed. **Annual**, reproducing by seeds. **Stems** smooth, sometimes hairy, much-branched, 6 inches to 3 feet (15 to 90 cm) tall. **Leaves** alternate, pointed at both ends, 1 to 6 inches (2.5 to 15 cm) long, with smooth edges and usually a dark spot in the middle. **Sheath** at base of the leaf fringed with short bristles. **Flowers** pink or purplish. **Seeds** almost circular, flattened or 3-sided, smooth, black, shiny. **Found** in same areas as above.

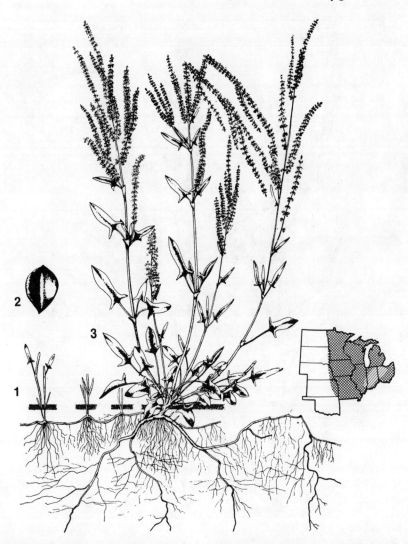

RED SORREL, *Rumex acetosella* L. **1**, young plant; **2**, seed; **3**, entire plant.
Perennial, reproducing by creeping rootstocks and seeds. **Roots** and rootstocks extensive but rather shallow. **Stems** 6 to 18 inches (15 to 45 cm) high,
slender, upright, branched at top. Several stems may arise from 1 crown.
Leaves are arrow-shaped, 1 to 3 inches (2.5 to 7.5 cm) long, thick, smooth,
acid to the taste. Early growth consists of a rosette of basal leaves. **Flowers**
yellow to red, borne on a raceme near top of plant. Male and female
flowers borne on different plants. **Seeds** 3-sided, reddish-brown, shiny. Hull
reddish-brown, rough, often adhering to the seed. **Found** mainly in pastures
and meadows, sometimes in lawns. Persists in areas of poor drainage, low
soil fertility, and little competition.

53

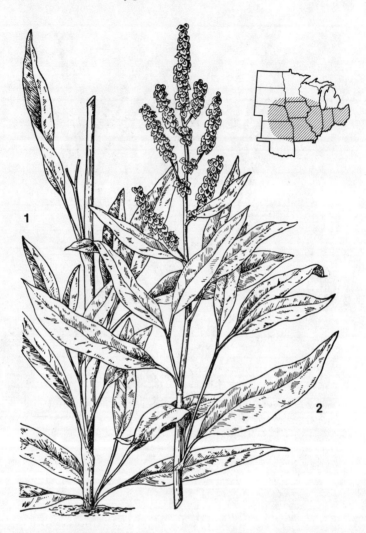

PALE DOCK, *Rumex altissimus* Wood. **1**, lower part of plant; **2**, upper part of plant with seed head. **Perennial**, with large taproot, reproducing by seed. **Stems** 2 to 4 feet (0.6 to 1.2 m) tall, erect or ascending, smooth, branched, arising singly or in groups from a fleshy crown. **Leaves** at first in a dense rosette, 6 to 12 inches (15 to 30 cm) long, flat, ovate, with smooth margins. Leaves on stem smaller, alternate, with heavy midribs, smooth margins, and short petioles bearing papery sheaths surrounding the stem. **Flowers** in clusters on branches at tip of stem, without petals, small, greenish, becoming brown at maturity. **Seeds** 3-sided, brown, shiny, surrounded by 3 heart-shaped bracts with smooth edges. **Found** along roadsides, in pastures and new hayfields, especially in places with moist rich soil. Also commonly known as smooth dock.

CURLY DOCK, *Rumex crispus* L. **1**, lower part of plant; **2**, upper part of plant; **3**, seed; **4**, distribution. **Perennial**, with large, yellow, somewhat branched taproot, reproducing by seed. **Stems** smooth, erect, 1 to 4 feet (0.3 to 1.2 m) tall, single or in groups from the root crown. **Leaves** mostly basal, smooth, 6 to 12 inches (15 to 30 cm) long, lanceolate, with wavy-curled edges. Upper leaves alternate, the base of the short petiole having a papery sheath surrounding the stem. **Flowers** in dense clusters on branches at tip of stem, without petals, small, greenish, becoming reddish-brown at maturity. **Seeds** brown, shiny, triangular, and sharp-edged, surrounded with 3 heart-shaped bracts with smooth edges. **Found** in pastures, roadsides, new hay fields, and waste areas.

BROADLEAF DOCK, *Rumex obtusifolius* L. **5**, seed; **6**, leaf; **7**, distribution. Similar to curly dock. Leaves broad and flat with a heart-shaped base. Bracts surrounding seed with toothed edges.

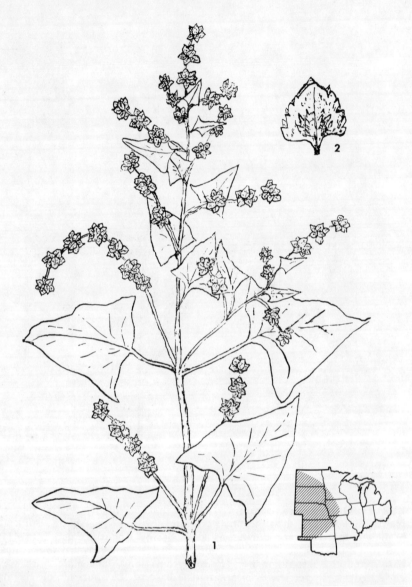

SPREADING ORACH, *Atriplex patula* L. **1,** flowering branch; **2,** female flower. **Annual,** reproducing by seed. **Stem** smooth, slender, 1 to 4 feet (0.3 to 1.2 m) long, with numerous spreading branches. **Leaves** petioled, fleshy, triangular, lanceolate or linear, mostly opposite, usually mealy, especially on lower surface. **Flowers** small without petals; male and female flowers borne separately on the same plant in scattered spikes at ends of branches and in axils of upper leaves. **Seed** round, gray, borne between 2 triangular green bracts. **Found** in damp saline soil. Seldom a troublesome weed.

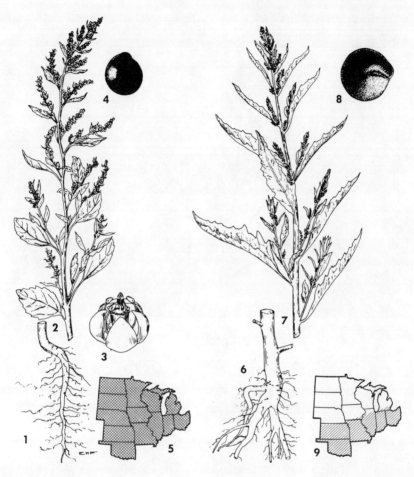

COMMON LAMBSQUARTERS, *Chenopodium album* L. **1**, roots; **2**, leaves and flowers; **3**, flower; **4**, seed; **5**, distribution. **Annual**, reproducing by seeds. **Taproot** short and much branched. **Stems** 3 to 4 feet (0.9 to 1.2 m) tall, smooth, grooved, often with red or light green striations. Branching varies from little to much, depending on competition. **Leaves** alternate, 1 to 3 inches (2.5 to 7.5 cm) long, smooth, usually white mealy-coated, especially on underside and in early stages, and with edges more or less toothed. **Flowers** small, green, without petals, borne at the ends of branches and in the axils of leaves. **Seed** shiny, black, disk-shaped, 1/16 inch (1.5 mm) in diameter, with a gray hull. **Found** in cultivated crops.

MEXICANTEA, *Chenopodium ambrosioides* L. **6**, roots; **7**, leaves and flowers; **8**, seed; **9**, distribution. Somewhat similar to above with longer, narrower, wavy-edged leaves, not mealy, and with unpleasant, pungent, aromatic odor. Widely distributed but almost uncommon compared to lambsquarters.

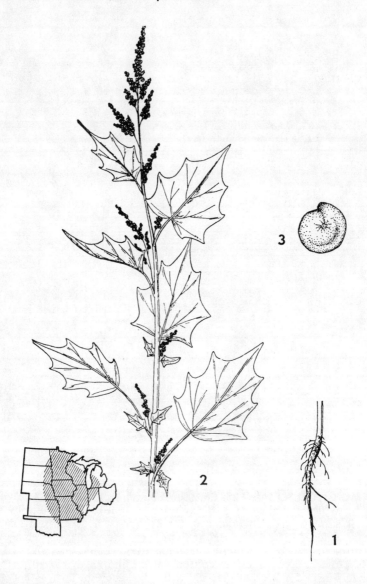

MAPLELEAF GOOSEFOOT, *Chenopodium hybridum* L. **1**, root; **2**, upper portion of stem with flowers; **3**, seed. **Annual. Stem** ridged, upright, widely branched, as much as 5 feet (1.5 m) tall. **Leaves** alternate, thin, light green, long-petioled, as broad as wide, with 1 to 4 large teeth on margins, free of mealiness on lower surface, easily detached from stem. **Flowers** greenish, inconspicuous, in a loose terminal panicle. **Seeds** dull black, lens-shaped, 1/16 inch (1.5 mm) or more in diameter, and covered with thin tissue that rubs off. **Found** in fence rows and waste areas.

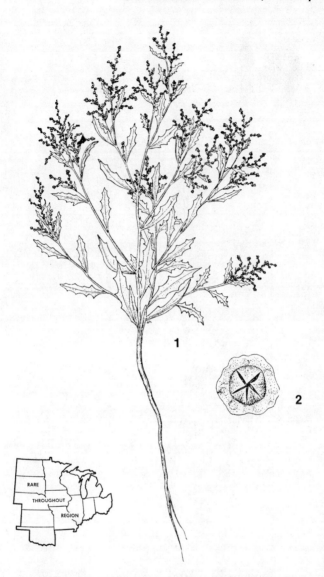

WINGED PIGWEED, *Cycloloma atriplicifolium* (Spreng.) Coult. **1,** upper portion of stem with flowers; **2,** seed. **Annual,** bushy, much-branched plant. **Stems** ½ to 2 feet (15 to 60 cm) tall, smooth, without hairs after seedling stage, often turning red during the fall. **Leaves** alternate, ½ to 2 inches (1.3 to 5 cm) long, with scalloped edges, falling early. **Flowers** numerous, sessile, greenish, borne singly on the nearly leafless upper branches. **Seeds** flat, round, about ⅛ to 3/16 inch (3 to 4.5 mm) in diameter, with a prominent circular wing, often red or purple in the fall. **Found** in cultivated fields and in row crops. Often prevalent in sandy soils.

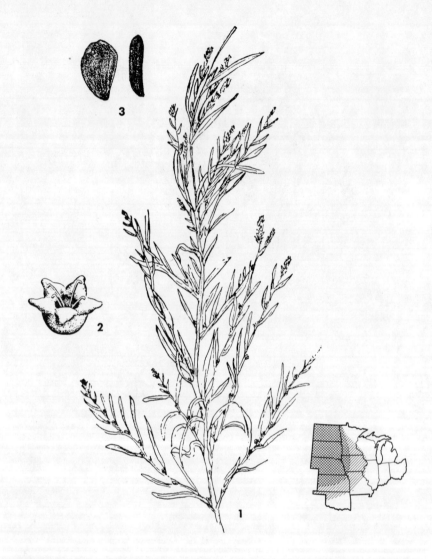

KOCHIA, *Kochia scoparia* (L.) Schrad. **1**, entire plant; **2**, individual flower; **3**, seeds. **Annual**, reproducing from seeds. **Stems** smooth, green, much branched, from a few inches to over 6 feet (1.8 m) high, growing from a taproot. **Leaves** alternate, simple, hairy, 1 to 2 inches (2.5 to 5 cm) long, pointed, without petioles. **Flowers** small, greenish, without petals, in axils of upper leaves and in terminal panicles. Seeds about 1/16 inch (1.5 mm) long, oval, flattened with groove on each side, finely granular, surface dull, brown with yellow markings. Fragile star-shaped hull may enclose seed. **Found** in cropland, dry pastures, and rangeland, where it is a serious weed. Also commonly known as Mexican fireweed.

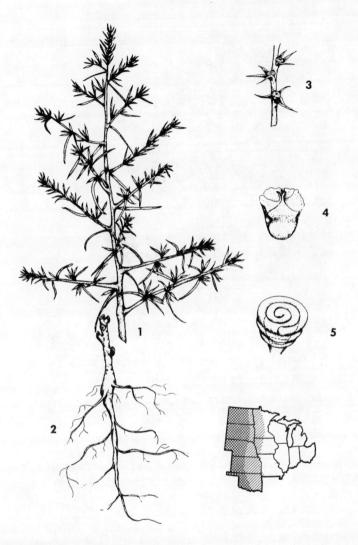

RUSSIAN THISTLE, *Salsola kali* L. var. *tenuifolia* Tausch. **1**, branch; **2**, root; **3**, portion of older branch; **4**, seed in hull; **5**, seed, hull removed. **Annual,** reproducing by seed. **Stem** profusely branched, 1 to 3 feet (30 to 90 cm) high, forming typical ball-like tumbleweed at maturity. Young plants soft, succulent; mature plants stiff and woody. **Leaves** cylindrical or awl-shaped. Young leaves long, soft. Later leaves short, stiff, prickle-pointed. **Flowers** numerous, small, without petals, axillary on upper branches. At maturity, entire plant may be splashed with red color; stem breaks from root and moves freely across open fields with winds scattering the seed. **Found** in spring grain and legume seedings. An important annual weed, it is most troublesome in dry years.

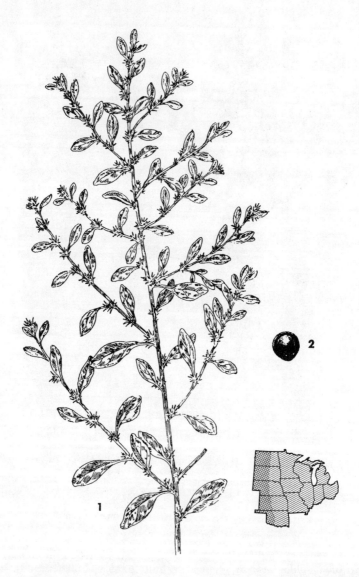

TUMBLE PIGWEED, *Amaranthus albus* L. **1**, fruiting branch; **2**, seed. **Annual**, reproducing by seed. **Stem** pale green, with numerous ascending branches making more or less globular plant, 1 to 3 feet (30 to 90 cm) tall. Breaks off at ground at maturity and is rolled over open fields by wind, distributing the seeds. **Leaves** spatulate, short-petioled, ½ to 1 inch (1.3 to 2.5 cm) long. **Flowers** small, greenish, in axillary clusters. **Seed** small, round, shiny, black, each contained in a bladderlike hull. **Found** in cultivated and fallow land. Dried plants often observed in piles against fences and hedge rows after windstorms.

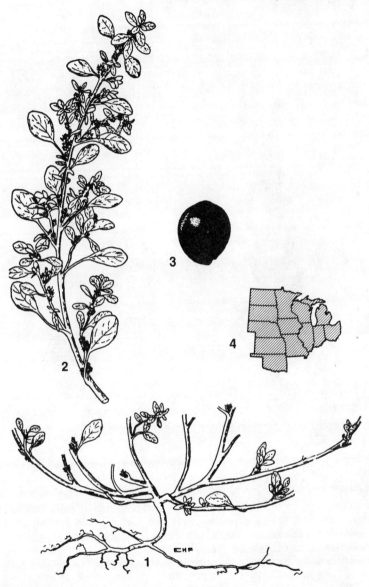

PROSTRATE PIGWEED, *Amaranthus blitoides* S. Wats. **1,** lower portion of plant showing spreading habit; **2,** upper part of plant with flowers; **3,** seed; **4,** distribution. **Annual,** reproducing by seeds. **Stems** 1 to 3 feet (30 to 90 cm) long, nearly smooth, reddish, spreading flat over the ground, mostly erect at the tips. **Leaves** small, alternate, simple, egg-shaped, broadest near tip. **Flowers** without petals, small, inconspicuous in axils of leaves. **Seeds** flattened, shiny, black, nearly circular, 1/16 inch (1.5 mm) in diameter. **Found** in fields, gardens, unused yards, and similar places.

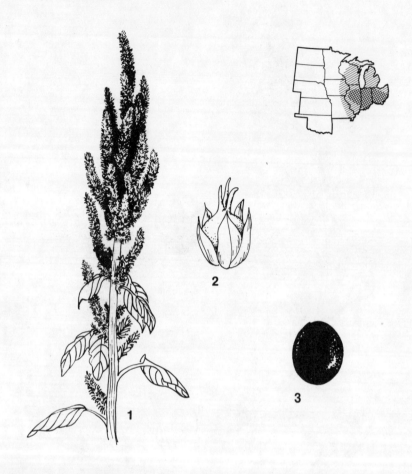

SMOOTH PIGWEED, *Amaranthus hybridus* L. **1,** upper stem with leaves and flower clusters; **2,** flower; **3,** seed. **Annual,** reproducing by seeds. **Taproot** shallow, reddish. **Stems** erect, up to 8 feet (2.4 m) tall, branching freely if not crowded. **Leaves** dull green, usually at least 6 inches (15 cm) long when mature, ovate to lanceolate. **Flowers** green, small, in slender, lax, panicle-like spikes with many short, crowded lateral branches. Bracts and sepals slightly longer than utricles. Sepals straight and acute. **Seeds** shiny black, lens-shaped, ovate, notched at narrow end, about 1 mm in diameter. **Found** in cultivated fields, yards, fence rows, and other waste places. Other species such as redroot pigweed (page 65) and Powell amaranth (*Amaranthus powellii* S. Wats) are similar to smooth pigweed in morphology and weedy habits, and may often be found in the same area. Powell amaranth has longer floral bracts than smooth pigweed; has straight, acute sepals that are longer than the utricle; has a stiff terminal inflorescence that either is simple or has a few widely spaced, long lateral branches; and is found mainly in northern part of region.

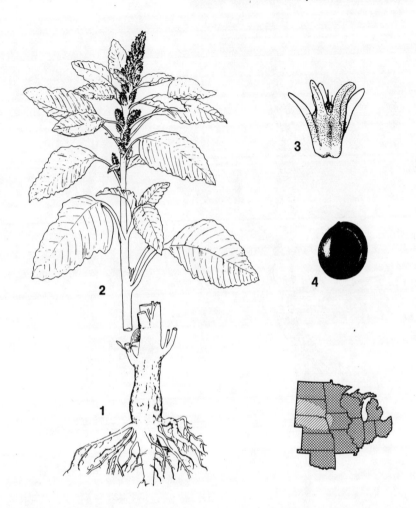

REDROOT PIGWEED, *Amaranthus retroflexus* L. **1**, lower stem and roots; **2**, upper stem with leaves and flower clusters; **3**, flower; **4**, seed. **Annual**, reproducing by seeds. **Taproot** shallow, reddish. **Stems** erect, up to 6 feet (1.8 m) high, rough, branching freely if not crowded. **Leaves** dull green, usually at least 6 inches (15 cm) long when mature, ovate to lanceolate. **Flowers** green, small, in thick, stiff, paniclelike terminal spikes with many short, crowded lateral branches. Bracts much longer than sepals and utricles. Sepals longer than utricle, curved, rounded, often with small notch at end. **Seeds** shiny black, lens-shaped, ovate, notched at the narrow end, about 1 mm in diameter. **Found** in cultivated fields, yards, fence rows, and other waste places. Other species, such as smooth pigweed and Powell amaranth (page 64), are similar to redroot pigweed in morphology and weedy habits, and may often be found in the same area. Redroot pigweed is also commonly known as rough pigweed.

65

SPINY AMARANTH, *Amaranthus spinosus* L. **1**, upper portion of plant showing leaves, spines, and flowers; **2**, flower; **3**, seed. **Annual**, reproducing by
seeds. **Stems** upright, branched, up to 3 feet (0.9 m) tall, reddish, bearing
spines at the bases of the leaf stalks. **Leaves** alternate, simple, dull green,
ovate-lanceolate to ovate. **Flowers** small, green, in numerous long spikes.
Terminal spike often wholly or chiefly staminate; axillary flower clusters
mostly pistillate. **Seeds** egg-shaped, shiny black, notched at one end, about
0.7 to 1 mm wide. **Found** in fields, gardens, unused yards, and similar places.

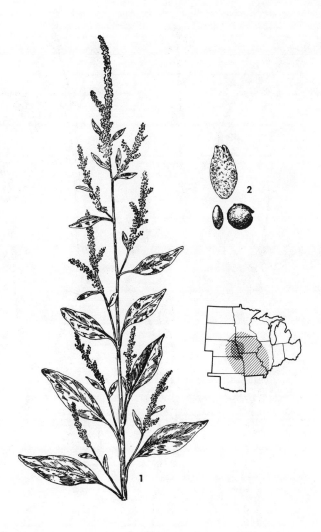

TALL WATERHEMP, *Amaranthus tuberculatus* (Moq.) Sauer. **1,** top of plant in flower; **2,** seed in the hull and dehulled. **Annual,** reproducing by seed. **Stem** smooth, erect, ascending or somewhat prostrate, stout or slender, 3 feet (0.9 m) up to 8 feet (2.4 m) tall. **Leaves** narrowly ovate to lanceolate, long-petioled, alternate, 3 to 6 inches (7.6 to 15 cm) long. **Flowers** small, greenish, surrounded by small bracts, in loose terminal and axillary spikes; male and female flowers borne on separate plants. **Seeds** oval, reddish-black, each contained in a bladderlike hull. **Found** chiefly in cultivated crops or waste areas, especially on low ground. Other very similar species, *Amaranthus tamariscinus* (Nutt.) Wood and *Amaranthus arenicola* I. M. Johnston, also occur in the region. Some waterhemp in the region is probably a hybrid complex among these various species.

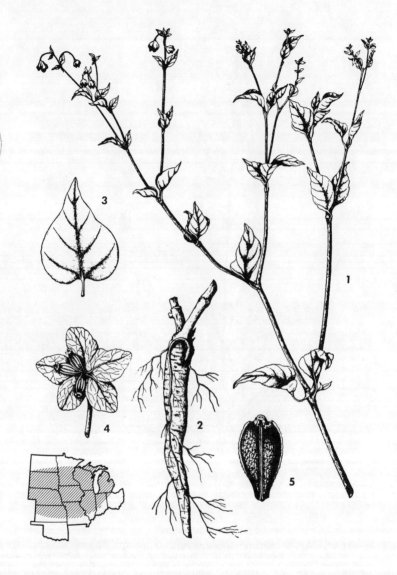

WILD FOUR-O'CLOCK, *Mirabilis nyctaginea* (Michx.) MacM. **1,** upper part of plant in flower; **2,** fleshy taproot; **3,** leaf; **4,** flower; **5,** seed. **Perennial,** with large, tough taproot. Reproduces by seeds. **Stems** smooth, bushy, often 4-sided, 1 to 3 feet (30 to 90 cm) tall. **Leaves** heart-shaped, 2 to 4 inches (5 to 10 cm) long by 1 to 3 inches (2.5 to 7.5 cm) wide, smooth, opposite, with smooth margins. **Flowers** bloom from June to October; are red, small, with 1 to 5 in a cluster. **Seeds** hairy, oblong, grayish-brown, with 5 ridges. **Found** rather generally along roadsides, in gardens, meadows, pastures, and waste places. Not usually troublesome in cultivated land.

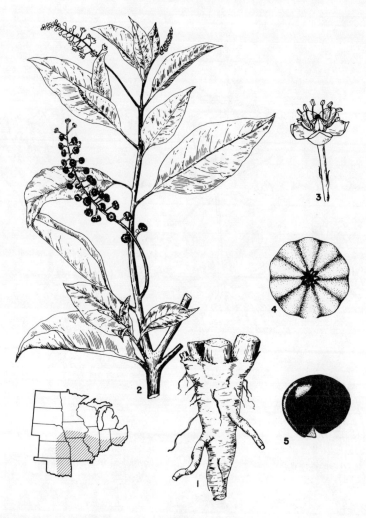

COMMON POKEWEED, *Phytolacca americana* L. **1**, part of fleshy taproot; **2**, branch with flower raceme and berries; **3**, flower; **4**, upper surface of berry; **5**, seed. **Perennial**, from a very large, poisonous taproot, often 6 inches (15 cm) across in older plants. **Stems** stout, erect, 3 to 9 feet (0.9 to 2.7 m) high, smooth, branching above, often reddish, dying to the ground each winter. **Leaves** alternate, large but smaller toward top of plant, with short to long petioles. **Flowers** small, white, in long, rather narrow, unbranched racemes from ends of stems and from upper branches. **Fruit** a dark purple, many-seeded berry with red juice. **Seeds** small, flattened, round in outline, shiny black, about ⅛ inch (3 mm) in diameter. **Found** in rich, low-ground pastures, roadsides, borders of fields, and similar places. The root is the most poisonous part of the plant. Poisoning from leaves and berries is occasional.

69

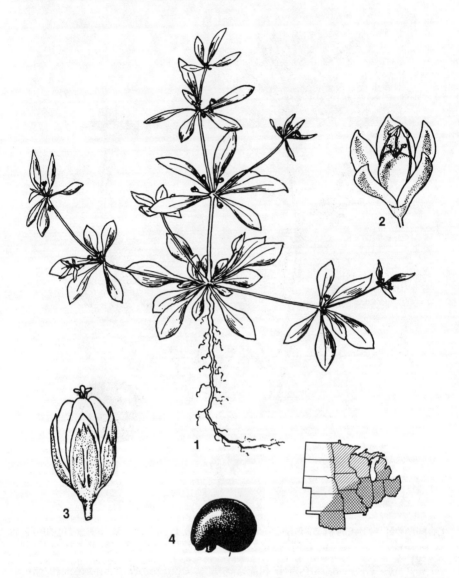

CARPETWEED, *Mollugo verticillata* L. **1,** small plant, showing habit of growth; **2,** flower; **3,** young seed pod in calyx; **4,** seed. **Annual,** reproducing by seed, with little-branched taproot. **Stems** green, smooth, branching along the ground in all directions from the root, making flat circular mats on the soil surface. **Leaves** in circles of 5 or 6 at each joint of the stems, smooth, tonguelike. **Flowers** small, white, several at each joint. **Seeds** very small, orange-red, somewhat kidney-shaped. **Found** in gardens, tilled crops, lawns, and wasteland. A late-starting, quick-growing summer annual, it will quickly cover any fertile bare soil where it starts.

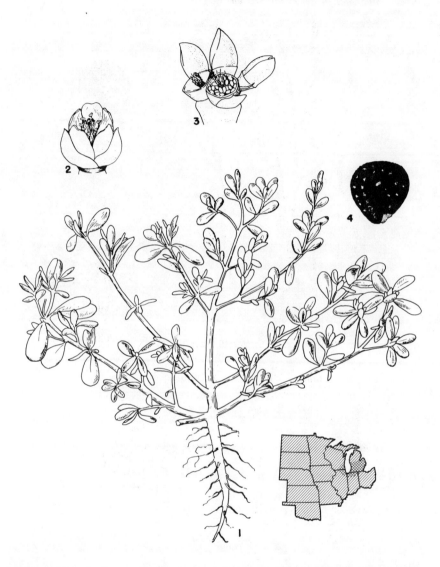

PURSLANE, *Portulaca oleracea* L. **1,** entire plant showing fleshy stems, prostrate growth habit; **2,** flower; **3,** pods; **4,** seed. **Annual,** reproducing by seed. **Root system** fibrous. **Stems** juicy, smooth, often reddish, either completely prostrate or turned up at the ends, sometimes forming mats 1 foot (30 cm) or more in diameter. **Leaves** alternate or clustered, simple, juicy, and smooth. **Flowers** small, yellow, in axils of leaves and branches. **Seeds** small, flattened, broadly oval, glossy black. Seeds require warm soil to germinate. **Found** in fields and waste places. Especially troublesome in gardens and truck crops. The fleshy stems and leaves make this plant drouth-resistant, difficult to kill.

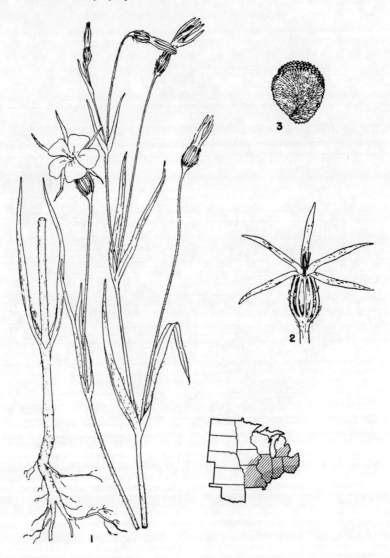

CORN COCKLE, *Agrostemma githago* L. **1**, plant in flower; **2**, seed pod enclosed by the ribbed calyx; **3**, seed. **Winter annual**, reproducing by seed. **Taprooted**, shallow. **Stems** rough, hairy, erect, 2 to 3 feet (60 to 90 cm) tall, swollen at joints, branching slightly. **Leaves** opposite and joined at base, slender, hairy. **Flowers** large, purple, with narrow, green sepals longer than colored petals. **Seed pod** holding several seeds, enclosed in a 10-ribbed urn-like calyx. **Seeds** black, about ⅛ inch (3 mm) in diameter, triangular, covered with rows of sharp tubercles. Seeds poisonous and therefore highly objectionable in grain used for milling or feed. **Found** especially on cultivated land and in association with fall-sown grain crops.

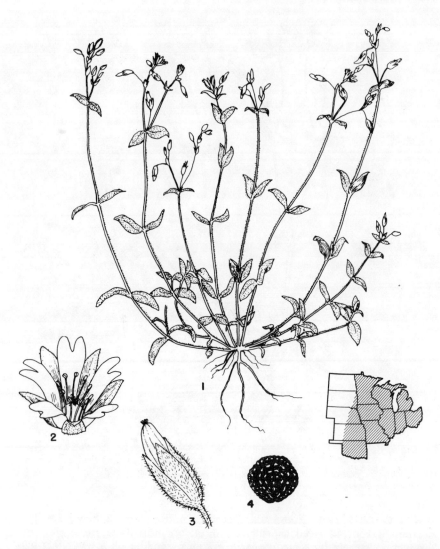

MOUSE-EAR CHICKWEED, *Cerastium vulgatum* L. **1**, plant; **2**, flower; **3**, seed pod enclosed in calyx; **4**, seed. **Perennial**, reproducing by seeds, occasionally by root development on lower branches. **Roots** shallow, branched, fibrous. **Stems** hairy, slender, partly spreading to erect. **Leaves** small, very hairy, opposite, attached directly to the stem. **Flowers** small, with 5 white petals notched at the tips, surrounded by an equal number of hairy sepals. **Seed pods** very small, cylinder-like, located at tips of the stems, containing many seeds. **Seeds** brown, very small, circular, flattened with a rounded back bearing irregular knobs. Seeds long-lived, often remaining dormant in the soil over several seasons. **Found** in lawns, pastures, and abandoned cultivated land.

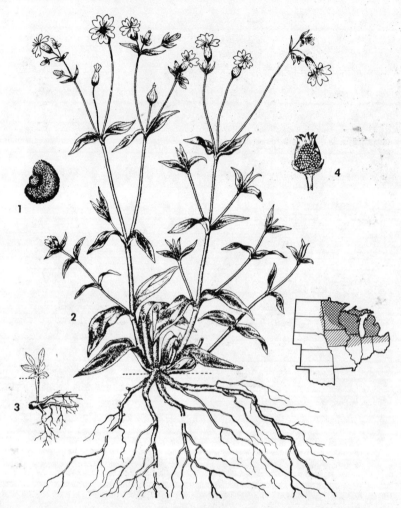

WHITE COCKLE, *Lychnis alba* Mill. **1,** seed; **2,** entire plant; **3,** new plant from portion of root; **4,** seed capsule. **Biennial,** or **short-lived perennial.** Reproduction largely by seeds. **Rootstocks** thick, sending up a few short barren shoots and long, branching, flowering stems. **Stems** erect, branched, stout, quite hairy and sticky, 1 to 2½ feet (30 to 75 cm) tall. **Leaves** opposite, long and narrow, not petioled, covered with short hair, pointed at the tip and rather light green. **Flowers** fragrant, white to pink, about ¾ inch (1.9 cm) in diameter with 5 notched petals; borne on erect stems in leaf axils or loose panicles; open in evening. Male and female flowers on separate plants. **Seed pod** swollen, ovoid with 10 short teeth at top, in hairy inflated calyx. **Seeds** numerous, flat, nearly round, pale gray, covered with small knobs, and about 1/16 inch (1.5 mm) in diameter. **Found** along roadsides, borders of fields, and in waste places; may become troublesome in grain and legume fields.

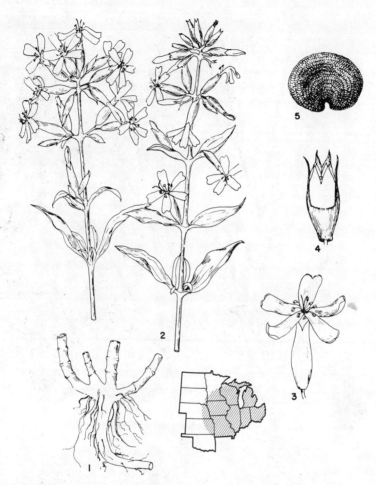

BOUNCINGBET, *Saponaria officinalis* L. **1,** lower part of plant; **2,** flowering stems; **3,** flower; **4,** mature seed pod with part of calyx removed; **5,** seed. **Perennial,** reproducing by seeds and short rhizomes. **Stems** stout, jointed, erect, 12 to 24 inches (30 to 60 cm) tall, clustered, smooth, and usually unbranched. **Leaves** opposite, smooth, entire, 2 to 3 inches (5 to 7.5 cm) long, about 1 inch (2.5 cm) wide, without petioles. **Flowers** in conspicuous clusters at the tops of the stems; about 1 inch (2.5 cm) across with 5 pink or white petals, and with base enclosed in a tubular calyx about ¾ inch (1.9 cm) long. **Seed pod** narrowly egg-shaped, pointed, containing numerous seeds, enclosed by calyx. **Seeds** flattened, dull black, kidney-shaped, about 1/16 inch (1.5 mm) long, surface covered by curved rows of minute knobs. **Found** along roadsides, in waste places, and on ditch banks. Originally grown in gardens as an ornamental, from which it has spread. In pioneer days, used as a soap substitute, the stems and rhizomes making a foamy solution when bruised in water.

75

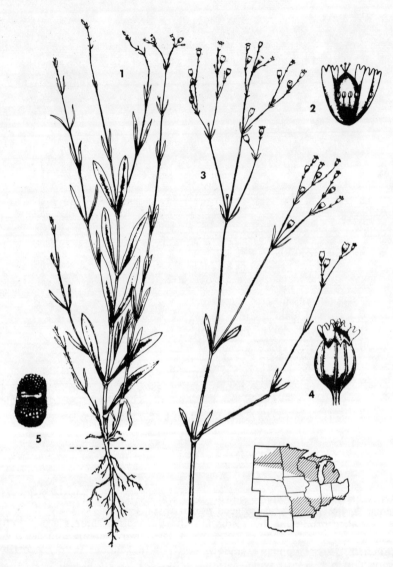

SLEEPY CATCHFLY, *Silene antirrhina* L. **1**, plant; **2**, flower with pod; **3**, upper portion of stem; **4**, flower enclosed by calyx; **5**, seed. **Annual**, reproduced by seeds only. **Stem** slender, erect, 1 to 2½ feet (30 to 75 cm) high, sparingly branched, upper part often of darker color and sticky. **Leaves** opposite, not petioled, linear, although those at base are somewhat broader. **Flowers** small, ⅛ inch (3 mm) across, pink with 5 petals, enclosed at base by ovoid calyx. **Seeds** kidney-shaped, very small, lead-colored, covered with knobs. **Found** especially on dry, light soil. Important weed in clover seed fields, because seeds are difficult to remove from the clover seed.

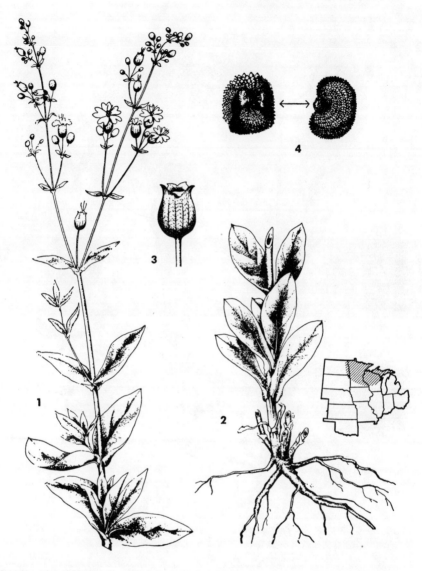

BLADDER CAMPION, *Silene cucubalus* Wibel. **1,** upper part of plant in bloom; **2,** root and base of plant; **3,** seed pod; **4,** seed. **Perennial,** propagated by seeds and creeping rhizomes. **Stems** 1 to 1½ feet (30 to 45 cm) tall, smooth, decumbent from base. **Leaves** opposite, elliptical, smooth-edged, not hairy. **Flowers** white, 1 inch (2.5 cm) wide with 5 notched petals, borne in loose panicles, often drooping. **Seed pod** enclosed by a thin, inflated, 5-toothed calyx. **Seeds** blackish, round and flattened, covered with knobs, about 1/16 inch (1.5 mm) in diameter. **Found** in waste places and fields.

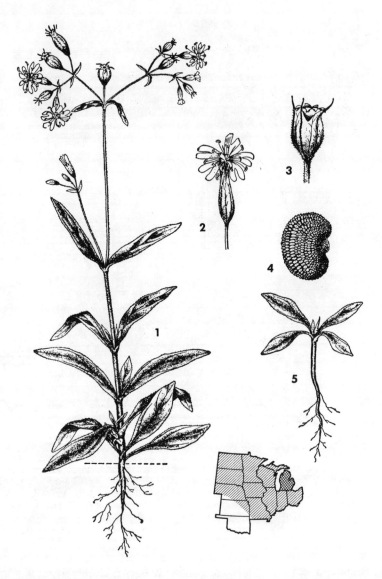

NIGHT-FLOWERING CATCHFLY, *Silene noctiflora* L. **1,** plant in bloom; **2,** flower; **3,** seed pod; **4,** seed; **5,** seedling. **Annual,** reproducing by seed. **Stems** 1 to 3 feet (30 to 90 cm) high, erect, densely covered with sticky hairs. **Leaves** oblong, 2 to 5 inches (5 to 12.5 cm) long, smooth-edged. **Flowers** white, shading into pink, about ¾ inch (1.9 cm) across with 5 petals. **Seed pod** enclosed by calyx with 5 teeth. **Seeds** rounded, 1/16 inch (1.5 mm) in diameter, gray, with knobs covering surface. Seed is common impurity in clover seed. **Found** in fields and waste places.

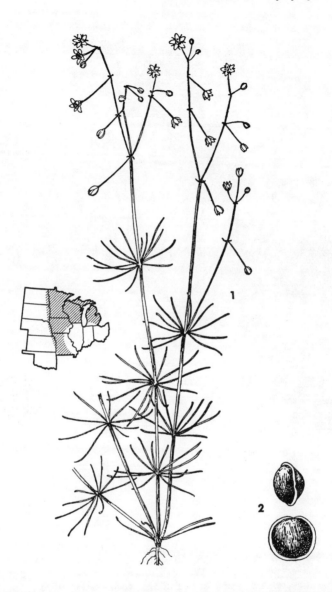

CORN SPURRY, *Spergula arvensis* L. **1**, plant in bloom; **2**, seeds. **Annual,** reproducing by seeds. **Stems** erect or ascending, 6 to 18 inches (15 to 45 cm) high, not hairy or only slightly so, slender, branching. **Leaves** bright green, threadlike, ½ to 1 inch (1.3 to 2.5 cm) long, in whorls around each joint of the stem. **Flowers** small, white, with 5 petals, in terminal clusters. **Seed pod** round, breaking into 5 sections, containing many seeds. **Seeds** lens-shaped, dull black with a conspicuous white wing. **Found** locally in small grains and other annual crops.

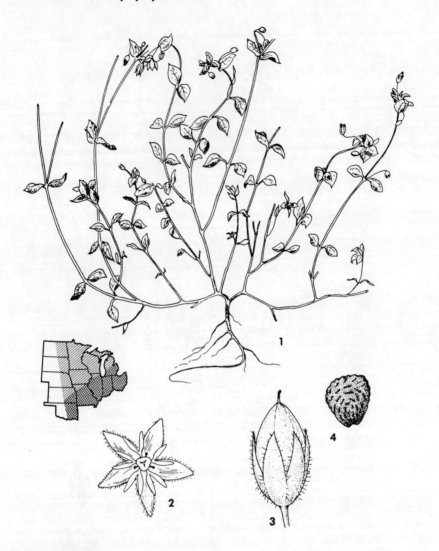

COMMON CHICKWEED, *Stellaria media* (L.) Cyrillo. **1**, plant in flower; **2**, flower; **3**, seed pod; **4**, seed. **Winter annual** or **annual**, reproducing by seed and creeping stems, rooting at the nodes. **Root** system fibrous, shallow. **Stem** is much branched, creeping or ascending, resulting in low spreading plant 4 to 12 inches (10 to 30 cm) high. **Leaves** small, opposite, simple, broadly ovate, pointed at the tips, smooth; petioles have a line of hairs on one side. **Flowers** small, white, with 5 deeply notched petals. **Seed pod** cylindrical, breaking into 5 segments at maturity, containing many seeds. **Seed** small, dull reddish-brown, somewhat heart-shaped but nearly round, roughened by curved rows of minute tubercules. **Found** in lawns, gardens, alfalfa, strawberry beds, nurseries.

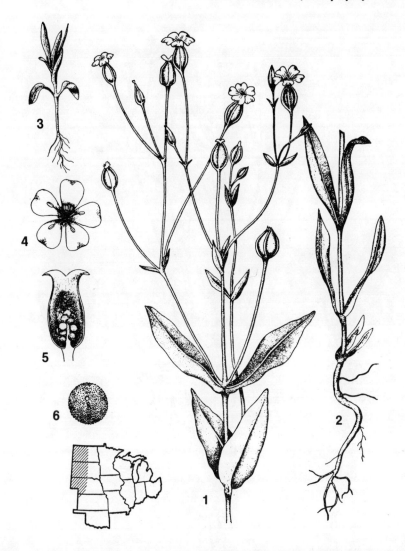

COW COCKLE, *Vaccaria segetalis* (Neck.) Garcke. **1**, plant in flower; **2**, root and basal portion of stem; **3**, seedling plant; **4**, flower; **5**, pod; **6**, seed. **Annual**, reproducing by seed. **Stem** erect, branched, smooth, whitish, 1 to 3 feet (30 to 90 cm) high. **Leaves** opposite, not petioled, ovate to lanceolate, smooth-edged. **Flowers** deep pink, about ½ inch (13 mm) across, with 5 petals. **Seed pod** a capsule with many seeds, enclosed by an angular calyx. **Seeds** globular, about 1/16 inch (1.5 mm) in diameter, dull black, covered with minute tubercles, and having circular whitish seed scar. **Found** in wheat and other crops, feedlots, and waste places, mainly in spring wheat area. Seeds are poisonous to animals and if concentrated in screenings make such feed unsafe to use.

81

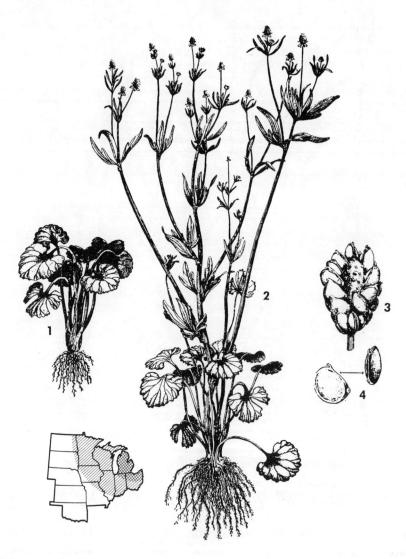

SMALLFLOWER BUTTERCUP, *Ranunculus abortivus* L. **1**, young plant; **2**, plant in bloom; **3**, mature receptacle bearing seeds; **4**, seeds. **Annual** or **biennial**, reproducing by seeds. **Stems** slightly hairy, slender, branched from base, 6 to 20 inches (15 to 50 cm) tall. **Lower leaves** round, bright green with round-toothed margins, borne on long petioles coming from base of plant. Upper leaves on shorter petioles, divided into 3 to 5 leaflets with somewhat toothed margins. **Flowers** small, yellow, with small oblong petals. **Seeds** produced in round heads, numerous, flattened with very small curved beak, dull, wrinkled, yellowish-brown. **Found** in lowland meadows, pastures, and fields. The plant has no forage value and may poison livestock.

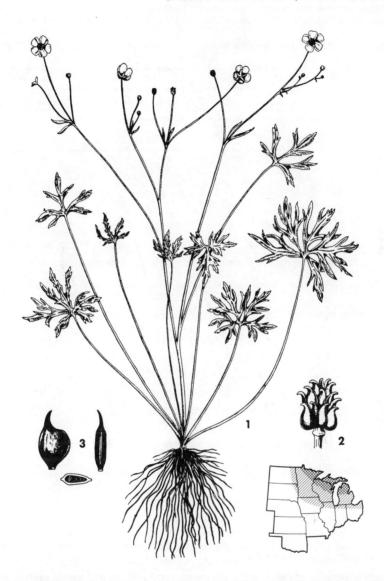

TALL BUTTERCUP, *Ranunculus acris* L. **1**, plant in bloom; **2**, seed head; **3**, seeds. **Perennial**, reproducing by seeds. **Stems** erect, branched above, hairy, 1 to 3½ feet (30 to 106 cm) tall. **Leaves** alternate, hairy, palmately divided into narrow segments. **Flowers** usually bright yellow but sometimes cream-colored, with 5 to 7 petals. **Seeds** numerous, dark brown, about ⅛ inch (3 mm) long, minutely pitted, flattened, with hooked beak; formed in a rounded head. **Found** in pastures; does not persist in cultivated crops. This plant contains an acrid juice which is somewhat poisonous if eaten by livestock, often blistering the mouth and intestinal tract.

83

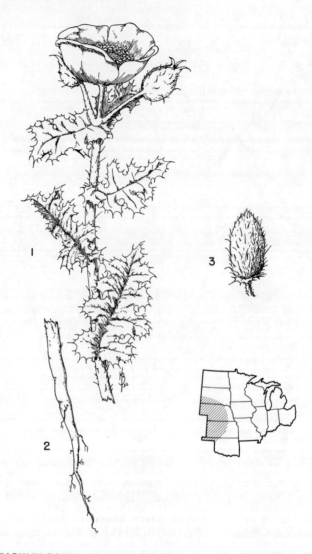

BLUESTEM PRICKLEPOPPY, *Argemone intermedia* Sweet. **1,** plant in flower; **2,** root system; **3,** seed pod. **Annual,** reproducing by seed. **Stems** stout, prickly, not branched, 1 to 2 feet (30 to 60 cm) high. **Leaves** bluish-green with spiny margins and prickly surfaces, alternate, clasping the stem. Sap in stems and leaves orange-colored. **Flowers** large, white, 2 to 3 inches (5 to 7.5 cm) across, petals dropping off quickly. **Seed pod** oblong, about 1 inch (2.5 cm) in length, spiny, containing many seeds. **Seeds** globular, about 1/16 inch (1.5 mm) in diameter, dark brown, rough with narrow ridge along one side, short pointed tip on one end. **Found** on prairies and uncultivated areas. Plant is poisonous to cattle but they don't eat it because of its prickliness.

ROCKY MOUNTAIN BEEPLANT, *Cleome serrulata* Pursh. **1,** upper part of plant; **2,** lower part of plant; **3,** seed. **Annual,** reproducing by seeds. **Stems** 2 to 8 feet (0.6 to 2.4 m) tall, pale, smooth, branched at summit. **Leaves** alternate, compound, with 3 pointed leaflets per leaf; surface and margins smooth, with strong fetid odor. **Flowers** in terminal racemes, 4 white or pink petals per flower, each petal about ⅜ inch (9 mm) long and separate, some petals notched. **Seeds** in pods (capsules) which are 1 to 2 inches (2.5 to 5 cm) long and have projections at the base that are as long as the pedicels; each seed is ⅛ inch (3 mm) long, rough, dull, grayish-brown, grooved on each side. **Found** in pastures, prairies, ranges, fields, and waste places, often on sandy soils.

85

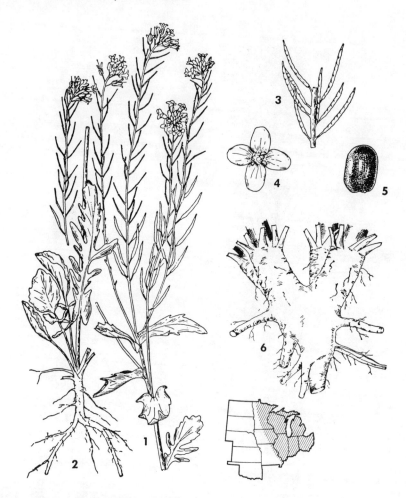

YELLOW ROCKET, *Barbarea vulgaris* R. Br. **1**, upper part of plant; **2**, lower part of plant; **3**, pods; **4**, flower; **5**, seed; **6**, root. **Winter annual, biennial,** or **perennial,** reproducing by seed, taprooted. **Stems** numerous, growing from a crown, upright, 1 to 2 feet (30 to 60 cm) tall, branched near top, smooth, and angular or ridged. **Leaves** pinnately divided; basal leaves have a large terminal lobe, are 2 to 8 inches (5 to 20 cm) long, and form a dense rosette; stem leaves become progressively shorter with top leaves about 1 inch (2.5 cm) long and less deeply lobed. **Flowers** bright lemon-yellow, 4-petaled (typical mustard flower), borne in spikelike racemes on end of each branch. Bloom in late April and early May. **Pods** about 1 inch (2.5 cm) long, about 3/32 inch (2.4 mm) in diameter, nearly square in cross section. **Seeds** light yellow to yellowish-brown, 1/32 inch (0.8 mm) long, ripening in May and early June. **Found** along roadsides, in pastures, and in timothy, clover, and alfalfa fields, where it matures before the crop is cut. Seeds live several years in the soil. Also known as winter cress.

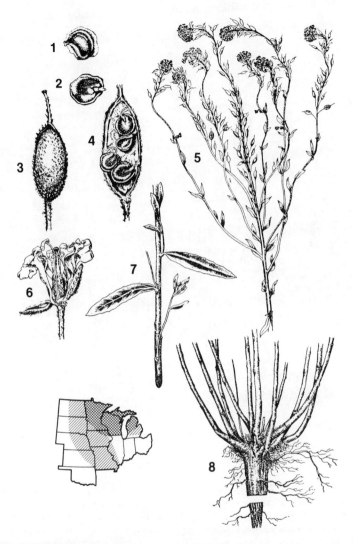

HOARY ALYSSUM, *Berteroa incana* (L.) DC. **1,2**, seed; **3**, seed pod; **4**, seed pod split open; **5**, upper part of flowering plant; **6**, flower; **7**, stem; **8**, lower part of plant. **Annual, biennial**, or **perennial**, reproducing by seeds. The name "hoary" indicates many rough hairs on stems, leaves, and seed pods. **Stems** gray-green, hairy, 1 to 3 feet (30 to 90 cm) tall, with many branches near the top. **Leaves** gray-green, hairy, alternate, oblong, narrow, ½ to 3 inches (1.3 to 7.5 cm) long, with smooth edges. **Flowers** white, with 4 deeply divided petals, produced in long raceme. **Seed pods** hairy, swollen, oblong with short beak on the end. **Seeds** oblong, rough, dull gray-brown. **Found** in meadows, pastures, and waste places. Emerges early in the year, continues to grow throughout season, producing seeds until frost.

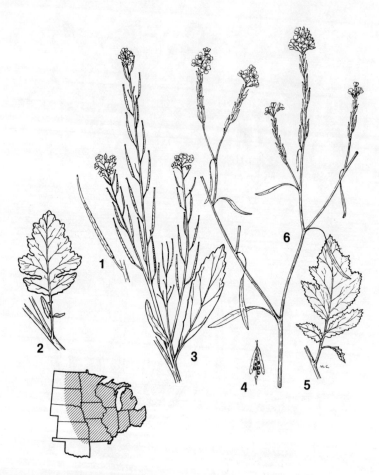

INDIAN MUSTARD, *Brassica juncea* (L.) Coss. **1,** seed pod; **2,** lower leaf; **3,** upper part of plant. **Annual** or **winter annual** with taproot. **Stems** smooth, erect, usually growing 2 to 3 feet (60 to 90 cm) tall. **Leaves:** upper ones short-petioled, lance-shaped, tapering gradually from a broad base; lower ones petioled, deeply lobed, leaf margins coarsely toothed. **Flowers** yellow, with 4 petals. **Seed pods** 1 to 2 inches long, tips conical. **Seeds** rounded, reddish-brown, surface pitted. **Found** in small grain and legume fields.

BLACK MUSTARD, *Brassica nigra* (L.) Koch. **4,** seed pod; **5,** lower leaf; **6,** upper part of plant. **Annual,** with taproot. **Stems** erect, branched, growing commonly between 3 and 6 feet (0.9 and 1.8 m) tall; lower parts somewhat hairy. **Leaves** also somewhat hairy. Upper leaves narrow with elongated petiolelike base. Lower leaves petioled, divided, with large terminal lobe, leaf margins fine-toothed. **Flowers** yellow, with 4 petals. **Seed pods** ½ to ¾ inch (1.3 to 1.9 cm) long, lying along stem. **Seeds** somewhat oval, dark reddish-brown, their surface pitted. **Found** commonly in waste areas and fields.

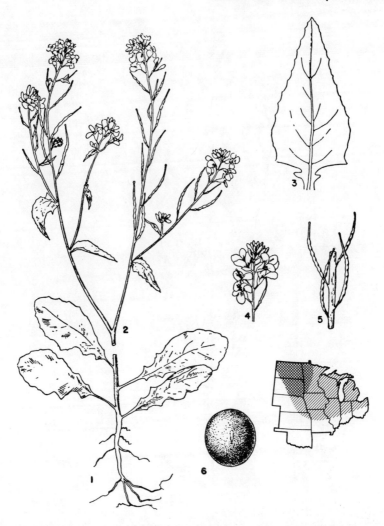

WILD MUSTARD, *Brassica kaber* (DC.) Wheeler. **1,** lower part of plant; **2,** upper part of plant; **3,** leaf from upper part of stem; **4,** flower cluster; **5,** seed pods; **6,** seed. **Annual** or **winter annual,** reproducing by seeds. **Stems** erect, branched near top, with a few bristly hairs. **Leaves:** lower ones irregularly lobed, toothed, with petioles and with bristly hairs; upper leaves smaller, often not lobed, alternate, with no petioles or short ones. **Flowers** conspicuous, with 4 yellow petals, in clusters at the ends of branches. **Seed pod** slender, on a spreading stalk; 1 inch (2.5 cm) or more long, about ⅓ of length being an angular beak at the tip. **Seeds** round, black, bluish, or brown, smooth and hard, about 1/16 inch (1.5 mm) in diameter. **Found** commonly in grain fields and occasionally in other cultivated crops. A troublesome weed in many areas. Seeds live in the soil for many years. Also commonly known as charlock.

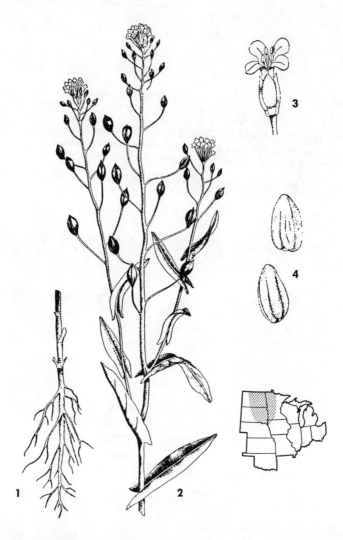

LARGESEED FALSEFLAX, *Camelina sativa* (L.) Crantz. **1,** roots; **2,** upper stem with seed pods and flowers; **3,** flowers; **4,** seeds. **Annual** or **winter annual,** reproducing by seeds. **Stems** 1 to 3 feet (30 to 90 cm) tall, smooth or hairy, branched, becoming woody at maturity. **Leaves** arrow-shaped, sharp-pointed, 2 to 3 inches (5 to 7.5 cm) long, with smooth edges. **Flowers** small, pale yellow or greenish-yellow with 4 petals. **Seed pods** ¼ to ½ inch (6 to 13 mm) long, pear-shaped, slightly flattened. **Seeds** small, pale yellow-brown, oblong, rough, with ridged surface. **Found** chiefly in flax-growing areas.

SMALLSEED FALSEFLAX, *Camelina microcarpa* Andrz. Similar to the above but smaller. **Stems** 1 to 2 feet (30 to 60 cm) tall. **Pods** ⅛ to ¼ inch (3 to 6 mm) long. **Found** in flax-growing areas.

SHEPHERD'S PURSE, *Capsella bursa-pastoris* (L.) Medic. **1**, entire plant; **2**, root; **3**, flower; **4**, pods; **5**, seeds. **Annual** and **winter annual**, reproducing by seed, with a branched taproot. **Stems** erect, 1 to 1½ feet (30 to 45 cm) tall, covered with gray hairs. **Leaves** in rosette at base are coarsely lobed; those clasping stem have pointed lobes, are coarsely serrate, and 2 to 4 inches (5 to 10 cm) long. **Flowers** are small, white, 4-petaled (typical mustard), borne in elongated racemes at ends of branches. **Seed pod** triangular, 2-parted, about ¼ inch (6 mm) long. **Seeds** small, yellowish, shiny. **Found** widely in practically all crops as well as in noncultivated areas. Seeds are long-lived in the soil.

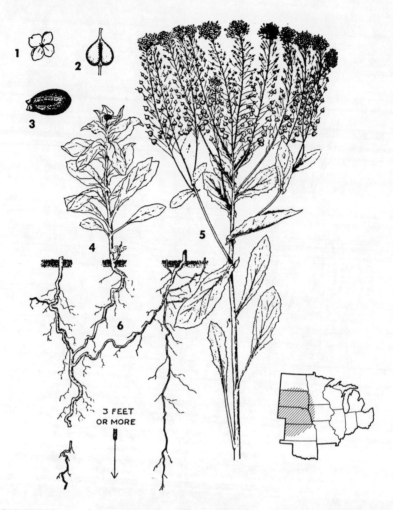

HOARY CRESS, *Cardaria draba* (L.) Desv. **1,** flower; **2,** mature pod; **3,** seed; **4,** new shoot; **5,** plant in bloom; **6,** root system. **Perennial,** reproducing by seeds and rootstocks. **Roots** deep, penetrating, slender, extending horizontally and vertically as much as 10 feet (3 m). **Stems** 1 to 1½ feet (30 to 45 cm) tall, branching little except at top, covered with whitish hairs. **Leaves** on lower stem spatulate, tapering to a slender base; upper leaves sessile, clasping stem. Leaf margins wavy with shallow indentations. Leaves covered with whitish pubescence. **Flowers** white, 4-petaled, borne in flat-topped clusters. **Seed pods** 2-parted, heart-shaped, borne on racemes 2 to 4 inches (5 to 10 cm) long. **Seeds** oval, rough, about 1/16 inch (1.5 mm) long, reddish-brown, seed coat marked by many small netlike depressions. **Found** in dry areas, in all crops where established, especially pastures and meadows, and on sandy ridges. It is very persistent and hard to eradicate. There is another species of *Cardaria* similar to the above plant.

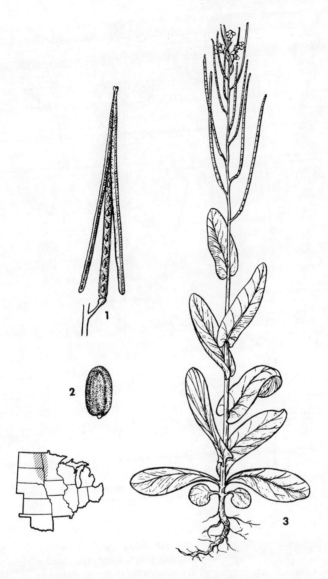

HARE'S EAR MUSTARD, *Conringia orientalis* (L.) Dumort. **1**, open seed pod; **2**, seed; **3**, entire plant. **Annual** or **winter annual**, with taproots, reproducing by seed. **Stem** erect, growing from 1 to 3 feet (30 to 90 cm) tall, branching little if at all, becoming stiff and wiry with age. **Leaves** smooth, alternate, elliptic in shape, 1 to 3 inches (2.5 to 7.5 cm) long, base clasping the stem with heart-shaped lobes. **Flowers** small, pale yellow, 4-petaled. **Pods** erect, narrow, 2 to 4 inches (5 to 10 cm) long. **Seeds** dark mahogany, oblong, circular in cross section, surface roughened with minute shallow pits. **Found** in small-grain and legume fields.

93

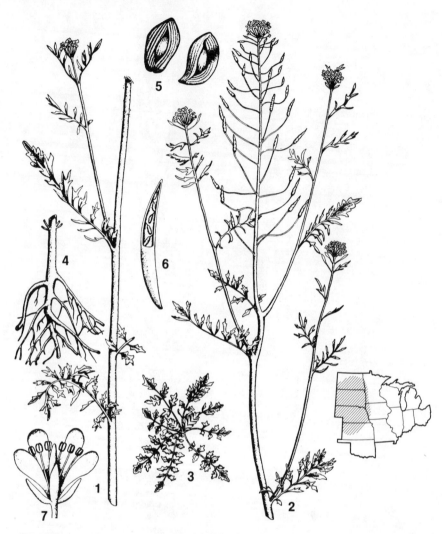

TANSY MUSTARD, *Descurainia pinnata* (Walt.) Britt. **1**, stem; **2**, upper portion of flowering plant; **3**, young plant; **4**, lower stem and roots; **5**, seed;
6, seed pod; **7**, flower. **Annual** or **biennial**, reproducing by seeds. **Stems**
erect, slightly hairy, 1 to 3 feet (30 to 90 cm) high, much branched above.
Leaves light green, alternate, 2 to 4 inches (5 to 10 cm) long, finely divided,
almost fernlike. **Flowers** small, pale yellow, produced on elongated racemes.
Seed pods narrow, smooth, slightly curved, ½ to ¾ inch (1.3 to 1.9 cm)
long, 2-celled, many-seeded. **Seeds** small, oblong to 3-angled with a groove
on one side, dull red or light brown. **Found** in cultivated fields, pastures,
meadows, waste places, and roadsides. The plant can produce a rank growth,
crowding out grain and reducing crop yields. A similar species, flixweed
(*Descurainia sophia*), is also found in abundance in much of the same area.

WORMSEED MUSTARD, *Erysimum cheiranthoides* L. **1**, plant; **2**, flower; **3**, seed pod; **4**, seed. **Annual** or **winter annual**, reproducing by seed. **Stem** erect, simple or sparingly branched, 1 to 2 feet (30 to 60 cm) tall, green or slightly grayish. **Leaves** numerous, alternate, lanceolate, tapering to the base, slightly toothed, finely pubescent. **Flowers** bright yellow, small, 4-petaled. **Seed pods** somewhat 4-angled, elongate, pedicels spreading at 45° angle from stem. **Seeds** small, oblong, brownish **Found** on moist soils in corn, soybeans, small grains, or noncultivated areas.

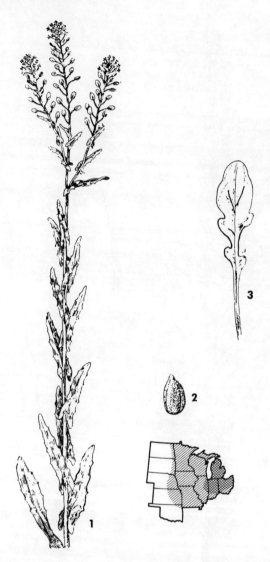

FIELD PEPPERWEED, *Lepidium campestre* (L.) R. Br. **1**, upper portion of stem; **2**, seed; **3**, basal leaf. **Winter annual** (south) or **biennial** (north), reproducing by seed. **Stems** hoary-pubescent or, rarely, hairless, 6 to 24 inches (15 to 60 cm) high, very leafy. **Leaves** on stem alternate, covered with soft hairs, arrow-shaped, bases clasping the stem; basal leaves lyrate, deeply cut at base. **Flowers** inconspicuous, white or greenish with 4 petals, borne in rather dense racemes at top of plant. **Seed pods** boat-shaped, containing 2 seeds. **Seeds** dark brown, rough-coated, pointed at tip, shaped like grape seeds, often an impurity in winter wheat. **Found** in winter wheat, first-year meadows, wasteland.

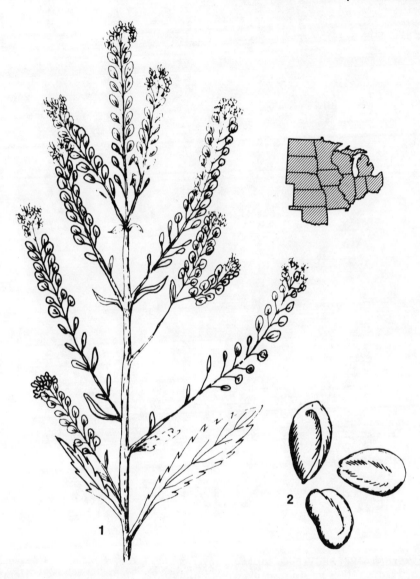

GREENFLOWER PEPPERWEED, *Lepidium densiflorum* Schrad. **1,** plant with flower pods; **2,** seeds. **Annual** or **winter annual**, reproducing by seed. **Root** a short, straight taproot. **Stems** erect, 4 to 15 inches (10 to 38 cm) high, without branches on lower part but with several spreading flowering branches on upper part. **Leaves** oblong, 1 to 2 inches (2.5 to 5 cm) long, with short sharp teeth or sometimes deeply cut. **Flowers** greenish. **Seed pod** round to oblong, somewhat flattened. **Seeds** small, reddish, oblong, twice as long as wide. **Found** in fields, pastures, roadsides.

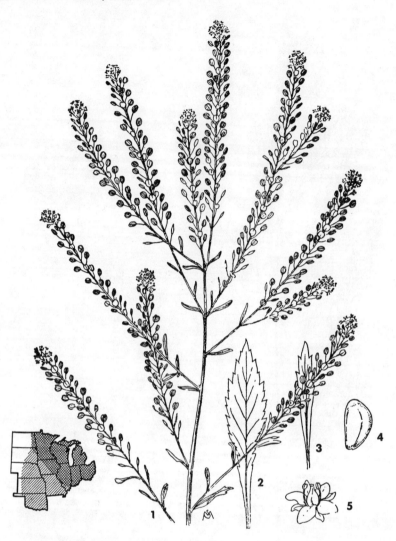

VIRGINIA PEPPERWEED, *Lepidium virginicum* L. **1**, top of plant; **2,3**, leaves; **4**, seed; **5**, flower. **Annual** or **winter annual**, reproducing by seed. **Stems** much branched, 6 to 18 inches (15 to 45 cm) high, not hairy, or with very fine hairs. **Leaves** on stem lanceolate to linear, coarsely toothed, usually without petioles; basal leaves obovate, with one large terminal lobe and several smaller dentate lateral ones, hairless. **Flowers** small, white, 4-petaled, borne in racemes which grow for considerable periods, so that there are often ripe seeds below and flowers at the tip of the raceme. **Seed pod** round, about ⅛ inch (3 mm) across, containing 2 reddish-yellow seeds. **Found** in fields, roadsides, waste areas. A common, but readily controlled, weed. Other similar but less common species are found in the region.

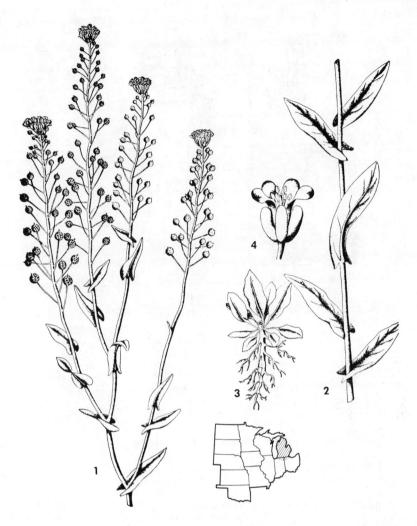

BALL MUSTARD, *Neslia paniculata* (L.) Desv. **1,** plant with flowers and fruit; **2,** stem and leaves; **3,** taproot and lower leaves; **4,** flower. **Annual** or **biennial,** reproducing by seed. **Stems** branched above, slender, hairy, yellow-green, erect, 1 to 2 feet (30 to 60 cm) tall. **Leaves** on stems alternate, 1 to 2½ inches (2.5 to 6.3 cm) long, hairy, arrow-shaped. The leaf base nearly encloses the stem and the tip is blunt to pointed. Lower leaves broad, narrowed at the base with a round tip. **Flowers** yellow, 4-petaled, produced on racemes 2 to 10 inches (5 to 25 cm) long. **Seed pods** round, about ⅛ inch (3 mm) in diameter, gray-brown with definite netlike surface markings. Each pod contains 1 seed, which is hard to separate from pod. **Seeds** yellow, about the size of white clover seeds. **Found** especially in grain fields and waste places.

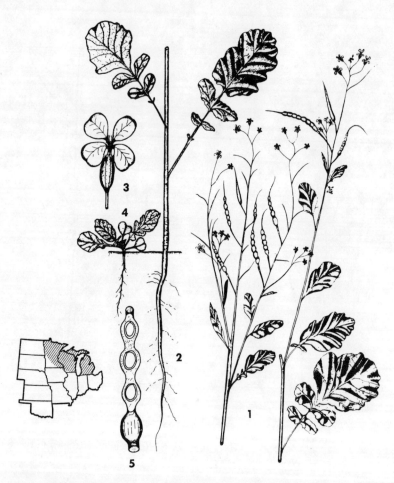

WILD RADISH, *Raphanus raphanistrum* L. **1,** upper part of plant with pods and flowers; **2,** lower part of plant; **3,** flower; **4,** seedling plant; **5,** pod with section. **Annual** or **winter annual**, reproducing by seeds. **Stems** erect, branching above, 1 to 3 feet (30 to 90 cm) tall, sparsely pubescent with stiff hairs, especially on lower parts. **Leaves** on lower stem with same type of pubescence, pinnately divided with a large rounded terminal segment. Upper leaves mostly undivided but with a few small segments. **Flowers** light yellow, shading into a whitish or purplish color, ½ inch (1.3 cm) in diameter, with 4 petals. **Seed pods** pithy and solid, 1½ to 3 inches (3.8 to 7.5 cm) long, ⅛ inch (3 mm) in diameter, at maturity breaking into segments containing seeds. Lower pods usually small and seedless. **Seeds** vary in size and shape but are usually oval, slightly flattened, light reddish-brown, and 3/16 inch (4.5 mm) in diameter. **Found** in small grain and flax crops, where it is serious; also common in wastelands. Pod segments containing seeds are hard to remove from seed grain.

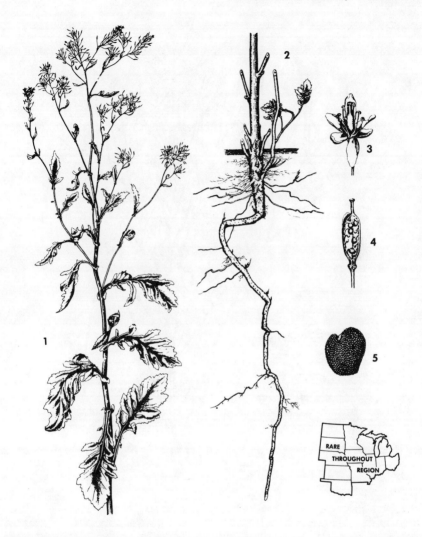

AUSTRIAN FIELDCRESS, *Rorippa austriaca* (Crantz) Bess. **1,** plant in bloom; **2,** root and base of plant; **3,** flower; **4,** seed pod; **5,** seed. **Perennial,** reproducing by rhizomes and occasionally by seeds. **Stems** erect or ascending, branching at the top, smooth, 1 to 3 feet (30 to 90 cm) tall. **Leaves** alternate. Upper leaves clasping the stem; lowermost leaves larger, with petioles, and more distinctly toothed than those on upper part of plant. **Flowers** with 4 small yellow petals, in loose clusters at tips of branches. **Seed pods** small, nearly spherical or oblong, with a distinct beak at the tip. **Seeds** small, brown to black, rough or warty, usually do not develop in northern regions. **Found** rarely in pastures, cropland, and waste areas, but regarded as a troublesome weed because it is very persistent. Spread chiefly by rhizome fragments.

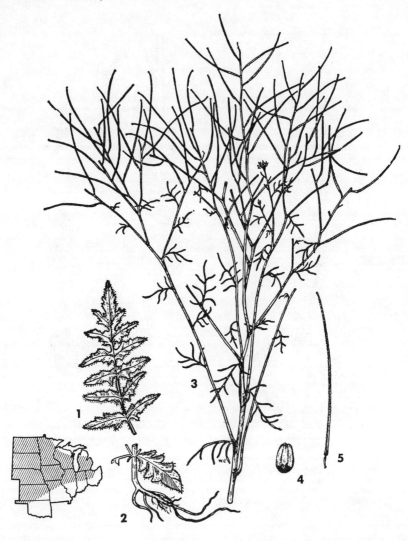

TUMBLE MUSTARD, *Sisymbrium altissimum* L. **1**, lower leaf; **2**, root; **3**, upper part of plant; **4**, seed; **5**, seed pod. **Annual** or **winter annual**, reproducing by seed, taprooted. **Stem** erect, 2 to 5 feet (0.6 to 1.5 m) tall, bushy, branching. Stem and branches smooth above, somewhat hairy below, pithy. **Leaves** pale green. Lower leaves are large and divided; upper leaves have smaller narrow segments. **Flowers** yellowish-white, ¼ to ½ inch (6 to 13 mm) in diameter, 4-petaled, growing in numerous but short racemes. **Seed pods** stiff, narrow, 2 to 4 inches (5 to 10 cm) long, divided into 2 parts; look like long stems rather than seed pods. **Seeds** oblong, about 1/16 inch (1.5 mm) long, dark reddish-brown. **Found** in small grains and waste places. Stem often breaks off at maturity causing plant to be blown about by wind.

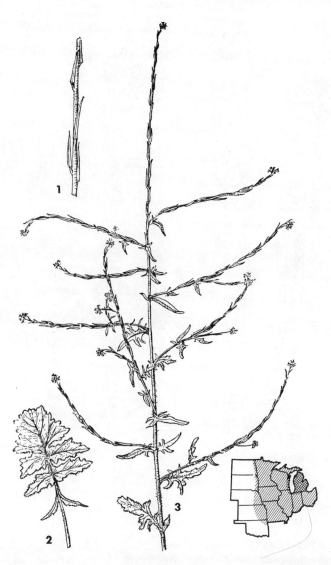

HEDGE MUSTARD, *Sisymbrium officinale* (L.) Scop. **1,** erect appressed pods; **2,** lower leaf; **3,** upper part of plant. **Annual** or **winter annual,** reproducing by seeds. **Stems** 1 to 4 feet (0.3 to 1.2 m) tall, erect, stiff, with a few branches above. **Leaves** divided, with coarse, pointed teeth. Lower leaves 4 to 10 inches (10 to 25 cm) long, often in form of a rosette; upper leaves much smaller. **Flowers** yellow, about ⅛ inch (3 mm) in diameter, 4-petaled, in small clusters at the tips of the elongated pod-bearing branches. **Pods** erect, following the stem, sharp pointed, about ½ inch (13 mm) long, somewhat hairy. **Seeds** greenish-brown, about 1/16 inch (1.5 mm) long, irregularly oval with a roughened surface. **Found** in grain fields and waste places.

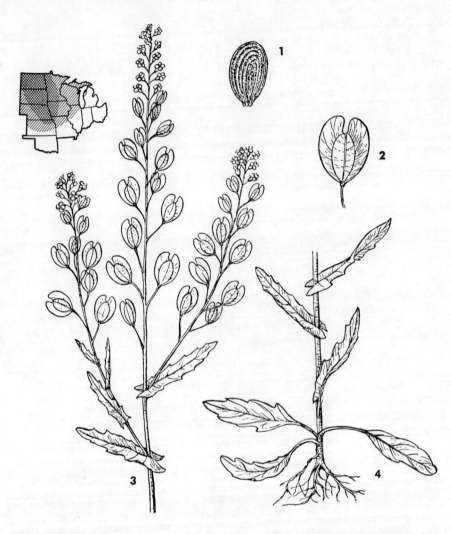

FIELD PENNYCRESS, *Thlaspi arvense* L. **1**, seed; **2**, seed pod; **3**, upper part of plant; **4**, lower part of plant. **Annual** or **winter annual**, reproducing by seed. **Stems** erect, 4 to 20 inches (10 to 50 cm) tall, simple or sometimes branched above, smooth throughout. **Leaves** alternate, simple, toothed, ½ to 2 inches (1.3 to 5 cm) long, clasping stem with earlike projections. **Flowers** white with 4 petals, in racemes which lengthen greatly at maturity. **Seed pod** flat, circular, about ½ inch (1.3 cm) in diameter, 2-valved, broadly winged, with a deep, blunt notch at the top. Each pod contains several seeds. **Seed** dark reddish-brown to black, ovate in outline, flattened, about 1/16 inch (1.5 mm) long with about 10 curved, granular ridges on each side. **Found** in small grains, legumes, and noncultivated areas. This weed imparts a bitter, garlicky flavor and odor to milk.

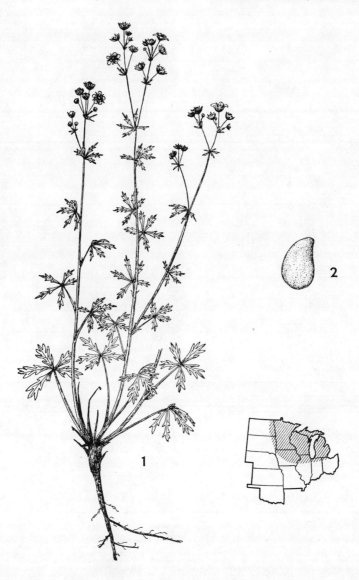

SILVERY CINQUEFOIL, *Potentilla argentea* L. **1**, entire plant; **2**, seed. **Perennial**, spreading by seed. **Stems** as long as 2 feet (60 cm), prostrate or with only the tips ascending. **Leaves** palmate, with 5 to 7 sharply toothed leaflets; lower surface densely covered with short hairs, giving a silvery color, petiole length variable. **Flowers** about ⅓ inch (1.3 cm) across; on short stalk, from the axils of the leaves, petals yellow. **Seeds** yellowish, kidney-shaped, numerous, 1/32 inch (0.8 mm) long. **Found** in lawns, pastures, and meadows, especially on sandy soils.

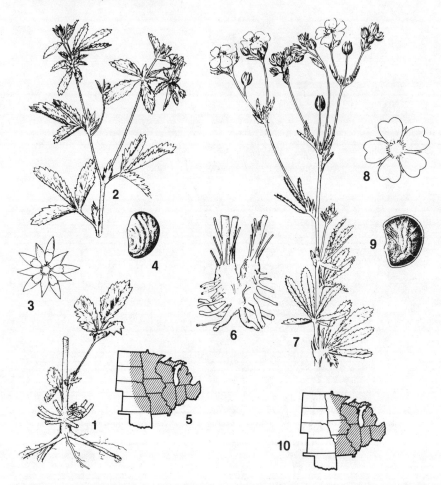

ROUGH CINQUEFOIL, *Potentilla norvegica* L. **1**, base of plant, with roots; **2**, top of plant, in bloom; **3**, flower; **4**, seed; **5**, distribution. **Annual, winter annual**, or **biennial**, reproducing by seed. **Stems** rough, hairy, semierect or spreading, 1 to 3 feet (30 to 90 cm) tall. **Leaves** palmately divided like strawberry, with 3 leaflets; alternate, usually hairy, coarsely toothed. **Flowers** small, inconspicuous, yellow, in clusters at tips of branches. **Seeds** 1/32 inch (0.8 mm) long, light brown, conspicuously marked. **Found** in fields, meadows, pastures, roadsides, and wasteland.

SULPHUR CINQUEFOIL, *Potentilla recta* L. **6**, lower part of plant; **7**, top of plant, in bloom; **8**, flower; **9**, seed; **10**, distribution. **Perennial**, reproducing by seed. **Stems** rough, stiffly erect, 1 to 3 feet (30 to 90 cm) tall, hairy. **Leaves** alternate, palmately divided with 5 to 7 coarsely toothed leaflets; hairy, pale beneath. **Flowers** conspicuous, sulphur yellow, 1 inch (2.5 cm) across, in terminal clusters. **Seeds** dark brown, with minute ridges. **Found** in same kinds of places as above.

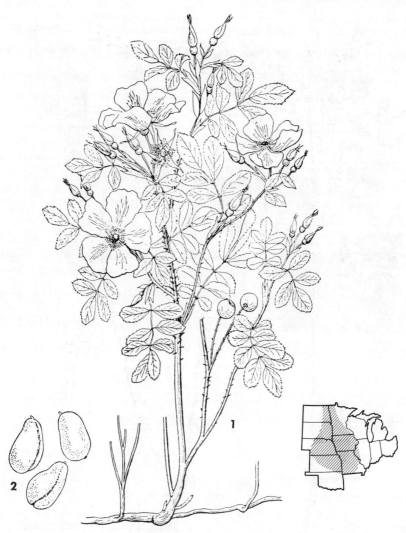

ARKANSAS ROSE, *Rosa arkansana* Porter. **1,** growth habit showing spiny stems, buds, flowers, and fruits; **2,** seeds. **Perennial,** reproducing by seed and deep underground rootstocks. **Stems** erect, 1 to 2½ feet (30 to 75 cm) high, densely prickly. **Leaves** compound with 7 to 11 oval leaflets seldom over 1 inch (2.5 cm) long, sharply serrated or toothed, smooth on both sides. **Flowers** about 2 inches (5 cm) broad, fragrant, light to dark pink, usually in groups at ends of branches. Fruit a round applelike structure about ⅓ to ½ inch (8 to 13 mm) in diameter, smooth or sometimes bristly. **Seeds** hard, hairy, brown, irregularly shaped, ⅛ to ¼ inch (3 to 6 mm) long. Seeds are often contained in oats, wheat, barley, rye, and sweet clover seed. **Found** in pastures, prairies, fields, roadsides, and fence rows. Many other species of *Rosa* similar to the above grow in the region.

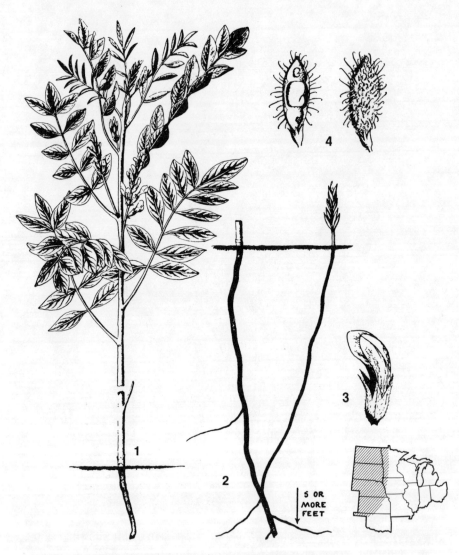

WILD LICORICE, *Glycyrrhiza lepidota* (Nutt.) Pursh. **1,** entire plant; **2,** roots; **3,** flower; **4,** seed pods with seed. **Perennial,** reproducing by underground rootstocks and by seeds. **Roots** deep and spreading, with a sweet taste. **Stems** 1 to 3 feet (30 to 90 cm) tall, smooth, erect, and branched. **Leaves** alternate, compound with 11 to 19 deeply veined leaflets, smooth-edged. **Flowers** yellowish-white, resembling those of alfalfa in shape, in a crowded terminal spike. **Seed pod** ½ to 1 inch (1.3 to 2.5 cm) long, brown, burlike, covered with hooked spines. **Seeds** green to reddish-brown, smooth, dull, bean-shaped. **Found** in pastures, meadows, and waste places. Plant does not persist in cultivated land.

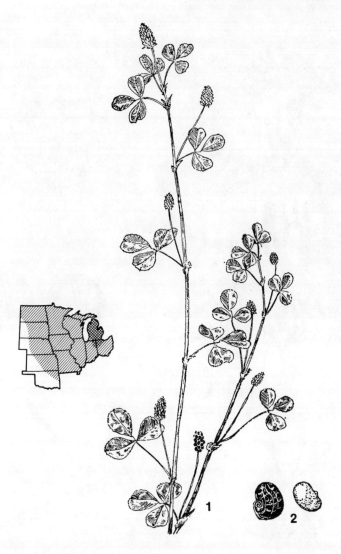

BLACK MEDIC, *Medicago lupulina* L. **1,** part of plant in bloom; **2,** pod and seed. **Annual, biennial,** or **perennial,** reproducing by seed, with shallow taproot. **Stems** slender, branched, spreading, 1 to 2 feet (30 to 60 cm) long. **Leaves** have 3 leaflets, the center one on a short stalk. **Flowers** are 1/16 inch (1.5 mm) long, yellow, in dense, globular spikes borne on short branches from the stem. **Seed pods** black, coiled, with thick walls, each pod containing 1 seed. **Seeds** yellowish-green, kidney-shaped. **Found** in lawns, pastures and meadows. Common and objectionable as an impurity in alsike clover seed, sometimes in other legume seeds. Grown for forage, but is small-yielding. Will inoculate soil for alfalfa.

109

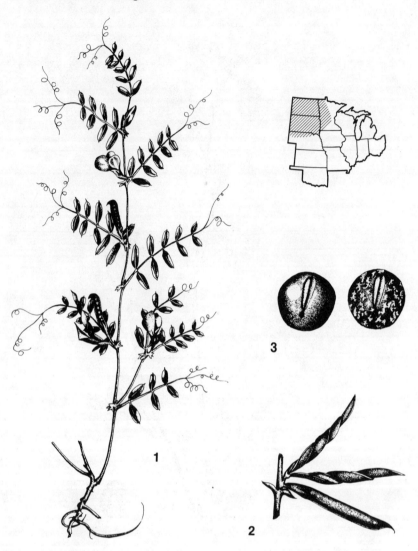

NARROWLEAF VETCH, *Vicia angustifolia* L. **1,** plant; **2,** seed pods; **3,** seed. **Annual,** reproducing by seed. **Stems** smooth, 1 to 3 feet (30 to 90 cm) long, upright but weak, clinging to support by means of tendrils at tips of leaves. **Leaves** pinnately compound with 8 to 12 leaflets. Leaflets on lower leaves oblong, on upper leaves linear, all with smooth margins. **Flowers** purple, in racemes containing 2 to 9 flowers. **Pods** smooth, 1 to 1½ inches (2.5 to 3.8 cm) long, with 4 to 7 seeds. **Seeds** spherical, brown-black or olive brown, mottled with fine black spots. **Found** in fields and waste places. Has forage value but is objectionable in wheat fields because the vetch seed contaminates the threshed grain.

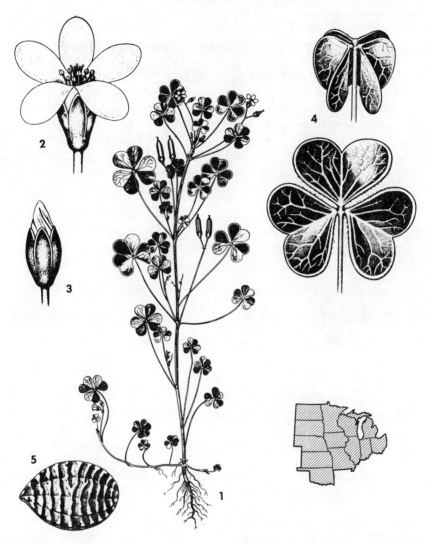

COMMON YELLOW WOODSORREL, *Oxalis stricta* L. **1,** plant in flower; **2,** flower; **3,** flower bud; **4,** leaves; **5,** seed. **Perennial** or **annual,** reproducing by seed. Plants low, bushy, 4 to 18 inches (10 to 45 cm) tall. **Stems** weak, branched at the base, hairy; may root at the joints. **Leaves** with long petioles, sour-tasting, divided into 3 heart-shaped leaflets. **Flowers** yellow, 5-petaled, occurring in clusters. **Seed pods** ½ to 1 inch (1.3 to 2.5 cm) long, slender, 5-ridged, pointed. **Seeds** small, flat, brown, thrown from the parent plant when seed pods burst. **Found** in pastures, lawns, and waste places, often becoming a troublesome lawn and garden pest. Several other species of *Oxalis*, differing in detail from this, are readily recognized as woodsorrels from this figure.

111

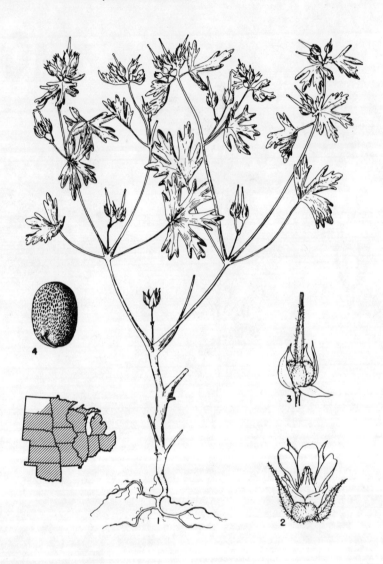

CAROLINA GERANIUM, *Geranium carolinianum* L. **1**, part of plant showing habit; **2**, flower; **3**, seed pod enclosed by calyx; **4**, seed. **Annual** or **biennial**, reproducing by seeds. **Root** system fibrous. **Stems** erect, branching near base, 4 to 20 inches (10 to 50 cm) high. **Leaves** 1 to 3 inches (2.5 to 7.5 cm) broad, alternate, deeply cut into 5 to 8 fingerlike, toothed divisions. **Flowers** small, 5-petaled, pale pink to lavender, found singly or in loose clusters at tips of stems and branches. **Seed pod** long, pointed, splitting at maturity into 5 curled sections. **Seeds** dark brown, 1/16 inch (1.5 mm) long, oval to slightly oblong, surface pitted. **Found** in woods, pastures, lawns, waste places, and along highways. Usually not troublesome in cultivated fields.

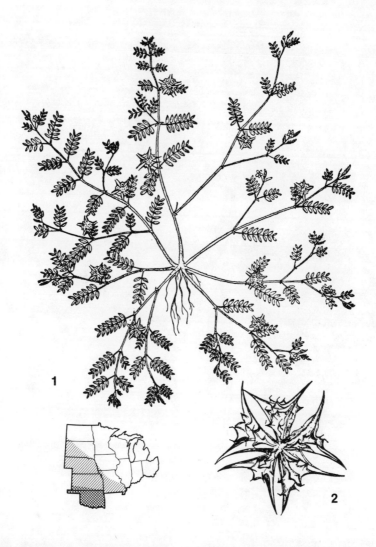

PUNCTUREVINE, *Tribulus terrestris* L. **1,** plant; **2,** seed pod showing burs. **Annual,** reproducing by seeds. **Root system** simple taproot. **Stems** hairy, prostrate, branching from base to form dense mats of slender trailing branches 6 to 8 feet (1.8 to 2.4 m) long. **Leaves** oblong, opposite, hairy, divided into pinnate leaflets. **Flowers** small, yellow, 5-petaled, produced in axils of leaves. **Seed pods** contain 5 burs, each having 2 sharp, long, stout, rough spines, strong enough to penetrate shoe soles or bicycle tires. **Burs** separate as they mature and often lie in the soil for years before germinating. **Found** in pastures, roadsides, and waste places, along railroad tracks, and sometimes in cultivated fields. A serious weed, listed as noxious in some states. Cattle do not graze areas infested with puncturevine.

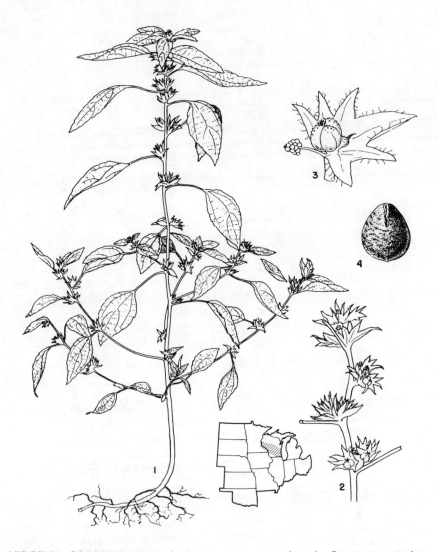

VIRGINIA COPPERLEAF, *Acalypha virginica* L. **1**, plant in flower; **2**, section of stem with flowers; **3**, flower surrounded at base by deeply notched leaf-like structure; **4**, seed. **Annual**, reproducing by seed. **Taproot** shallow. **Stems** hairy, 1 to 2 feet (30 to 60 cm) tall, frequently branched at base and spreading over the ground. **Leaves** egg-shaped, on long petioles; the lower leaves arranged in pairs on stems, the upper ones alternate. **Flowers** in clusters, small, borne in leaf axils in upper portion of stems and branches. Male and female flowers separate but borne together. **Seed pod** containing 3 seeds, surrounded with deeply cut leaflike structure. **Seeds** egg-shaped, small, dull reddish-brown to gray with reddish-brown spots. **Found** in wasteland, grassland, and cultivated fields. Seed occasionally mixed in crop seeds.

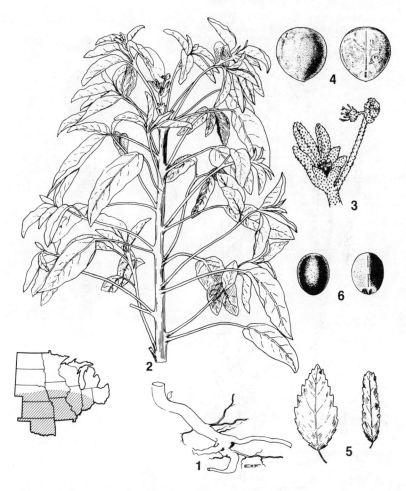

WOOLLY CROTON, *Croton capitatus* Michx. **1,** part of lower stem and roots; **2,** upper portion of plant; **3,** flower clusters with deeply cut, hairy, leaf-like structure; **4,** seeds. **Annual,** reproducing by seeds. **Taproot** shallow. **Stems** 1 to 2 feet (30 to 60 cm) tall, extensively branched, densely hairy. **Leaves** narrow, woolly with short hairs, smooth-edged, borne on long petioles, usually alternate. **Flowers** in small, dense clusters at ends of stems and branches, surrounded by leafy bract. **Seed pod** densely hairy, 3-sided, containing 3 seeds. **Seeds** grayish, broadly egg-shaped, about 3/16 inch (4.5 mm) long. **Found** commonly in old overgrazed pastures.

TROPIC CROTON, *Croton glandulosus* L. **5,** lower and upper leaves; **6,** seeds. Similar to the above species. **Annual,** reproducing by seeds. **Stems** greenish, rough-hairy but not woolly. **Leaves** oblong to egg-shaped, with sharply toothed edges, borne on relatively short petioles. **Seed** ovate, nearly elliptical, about ⅛ inch (3 mm) long. **Found** in sandy soils, waste areas, and overgrazed pastures.

115

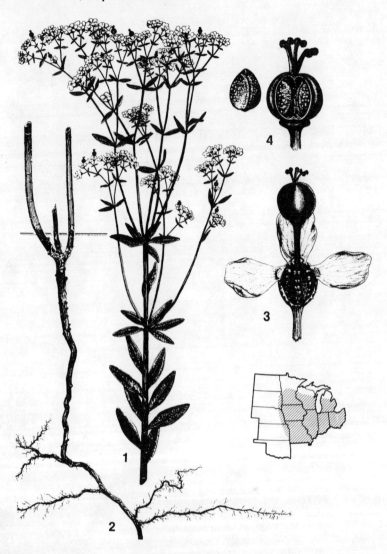

FLOWERING SPURGE, *Euphorbia corollata* L. **1,** top of plant; **2,** roots; **3,** immature seed pod and flower; **4,** seed and seed pod. **Perennial,** reproducing by seed and by short rootstocks. **Stems** 1 to 3 feet (30 to 90 cm) tall, erect, light green, smooth, branched near the top, with a milky juice. **Leaves** oblong, narrow, light green; lower ones alternate, upper leaves in whorls on the branches. **Flowers** small, surrounded by 5 white petallike bracts in the form of a cup. Flowers borne in terminal clusters and in the axils of the upper leaves. **Seed pods** on short stalks from the cuplike base, smooth, 3-lobed with 3 seeds. **Seeds** egg-shaped, gray or light brown, mottled, shallowly pitted, with a dark line on one side. **Found** in pastures, roadsides, and waste places, especially in dry or sandy areas.

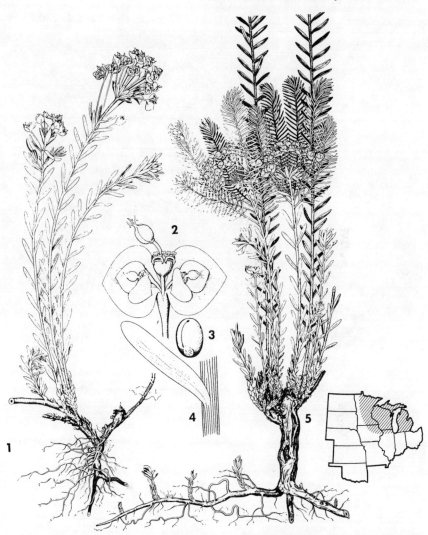

CYPRESS SPURGE, *Euphorbia cyparissias* L. **1,** plants arising from old stems and creeping rootstocks; **2,** inflorescence; **3,** seed; **4,** leaf and portion of stem; **5,** entire plant. **Perennial,** usually reproducing by creeping rootstocks but occasionally by seeds. **Stems** in tufts, forming dense mats if not disturbed, usually not exceeding 1 foot (30 cm) in height, somewhat branched, smooth, very leafy, with milky juice. **Leaves** oblong, narrow, smooth, alternate, pale green. **Flowers** small, greenish, having petals fused in the form of a cup; growing in axils of a terminal whorl of yellowish floral bracts that turn purplish at maturity. **Seed pods** on short stalk from the cuplike base, smooth, waxy, 3-lobed with 3 seeds. **Seeds** brownish-gray, smooth. **Found** in pastures, roadsides, and waste places. Often spreads from gardens where it is used as an ornamental.

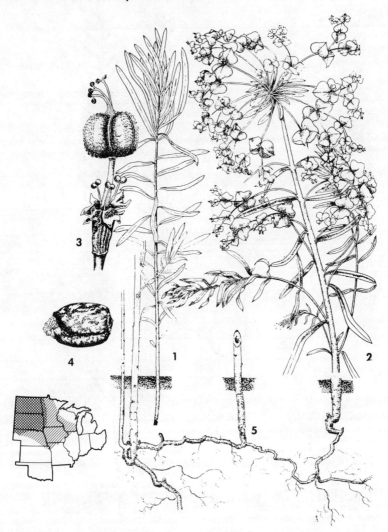

LEAFY SPURGE, *Euphorbia esula* L. **1,** leafy stem; **2,** top of stem with flowers; **3,** flower with seed pod; **4,** seed; **5,** root system. **Perennial,** reproducing from extensive rootstocks and seeds. **Roots** deep and spreading, woody, very persistent. **Stems** erect, smooth, branched at top, 1 to 2 feet (30 to 60 cm) tall, with milky juice. **Leaves** alternate on stems, narrowly strap-shaped, ¼ inch (6 mm) wide, usually drooping. **Flowers** small, greenish, petals fused into a cuplike structure, borne just above the greenish-yellow heart-shaped floral bracts on top of stem. **Seed pods** on short stalks from the cuplike base, 3-lobed, with 3 seeds. **Seeds** smooth, light gray, with yellowish or white appendage attached to the tip. **Found** in pastures, waste areas, along roadsides, and in cultivated fields. A troublesome weed because of its spreading nature and persistence.

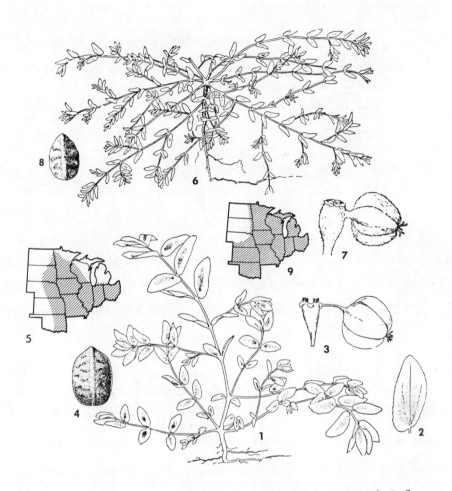

SPOTTED SPURGE, *Euphorbia preslii* Guss. **1,** whole plant; **2,** leaf; **3,** flower and seed pod; **4,** seed; **5,** distribution. **Annual,** with shallow taproot, germinating late in the spring or early summer. **Stems** erect and spreading, 6 inches to 3 feet (15 to 90 cm) in height, with milky juice. **Leaves** ovate, edges slightly toothed, borne on a short petiole, with a conspicuous reddish spot or blotch. **Flowers** small, with minute petals in the form of a cup. **Seed pods** on short stalks from the cuplike base, smooth, 3-lobed, ribbed, with 3 seeds. **Seeds** 3-sided, oblong, dark brown or black, pitted with ridged surfaces. **Found** in gardens, fields, and waste areas. Also commonly known as nodding spurge.

PROSTRATE SPURGE, *Euphorbia maculata* L. **6,** whole plant; **7,** flower and seed pod; **8,** seed; **9,** distribution. **Stems** prostrate, forming a mat. **Leaves** and seed pods are hairy and much smaller than the above. Leaves spotted like those of spotted spurge. **Found** chiefly in gardens and open areas; also in lawns and turf. Also commonly known as milk purslane.

119

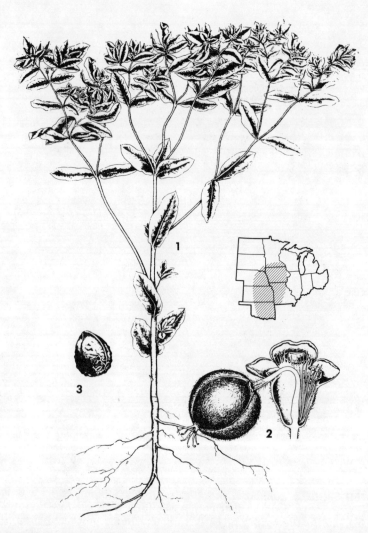

SNOW-ON-THE-MOUNTAIN, *Euphorbia marginata* Pursh. **1,** entire plant; **2,** flower, seed pod at left; **3,** seed. **Annual** with milky, sticky sap. **Taproot** slender. **Stems** 1 to 3 feet (30 to 90 cm) tall, erect, branched, usually with fine hairs, at least on upper part. **Leaves** alternate except just below the flower clusters, where they are whorled; ovate or oblong-ovate, edges smooth, bright green except for conspicuous white marginal areas. **Flowers** small, white, in small clusters, without true petals but with 5 white appendages on the cuplike structure in which the ovary and stamens are produced. **Seed pods** hairy, 3-lobed and 3-seeded, elevated above the cup on a slender stalk. **Found** in dry soil and waste places, sometimes grown as an ornamental. The plant is poisonous to livestock, and the milky sap causes skin irritation on many persons.

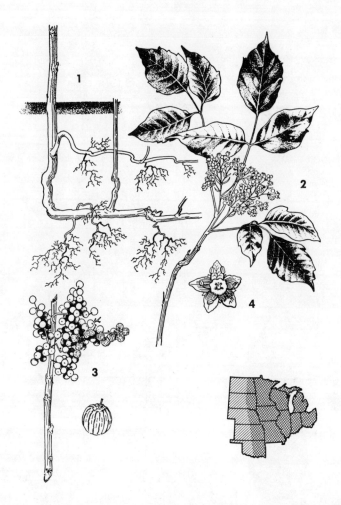

POISON IVY, *Rhus radicans* L. **1**, root and base of plant; **2**, flowering branch; **3**, cluster of berries, and single berry; **4**, flower. **Woody perennial**, reproducing by seed and rootstocks. The plant may be either a low shrub or a vine climbing high into trees. In climbing it is supported by aerial roots along the stem. **Leaves** consist of 3 large shiny leaflets each 2 to 4 inches (5 to 10 cm) long, pointed at tip. Leaflet edges either smooth or irregularly toothed. **Flowers** small, green, 5-petaled, borne in a head 1 to 3 inches (2.5 to 7.5 cm) long. Berries small, white, round, and hard. **Found** in open woods, fence rows, thickets, orchards, and wasteland. All parts of this plant contain a poisonous material which may cause blistering of the skin. The plant changes from a bright green to a very attractive red or reddish-yellow in the fall, tempting unwary collectors. This is a variable species, not only in habit of growth, but in leaflet shape, rooting habit, pubescence on leaves, petioles, and fruit.

121

MALLOW FAMILY, *Malvaceae*

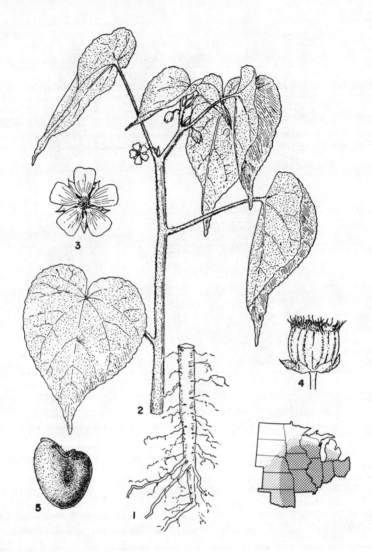

VELVETLEAF, *Abutilon theophrasti* Medic. **1**, root; **2**, upper part of stem with flowers; **3**, flower; **4**, seed pod; **5**, seed. **Annual**, with strongly developed taproot and stem. **Stem** smooth, covered with short velvety hairs, often 6 to 8 feet (1.8 to 2.4 m) tall. **Leaves** large, heart-shaped, pointed, alternate, petioled, and with a soft, velvety, hairy surface. **Flowers** about ¾ inch (1.9 cm) in diameter with 5 yellow petals; borne on short stalks attached to leaf axils on upper part of stem. **Seed pod** cup-shaped, about 1 inch (2.5 cm) in diameter, with ring of prickles about upper edge; contains 5 to 15 seeds. **Seeds** grayish-brown, flattened, notched, about ⅛ inch (3 mm) long. **Found** principally in soybean and corn fields but occasionally in gardens, along fence rows, and in waste places. Also commonly known as buttonweed.

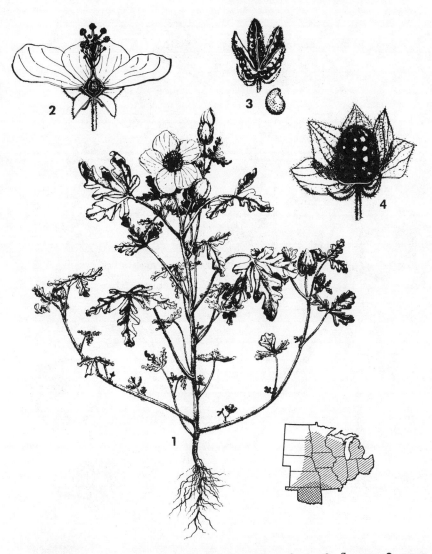

VENICE MALLOW, *Hibiscus trionum* L. **1**, entire plant; **2**, flower; **3**, open seed pod with a seed; **4**, mature seed pod with sepals. **Annual,** reproducing by seed. **Stems** erect or spreading, hairy, 8 to 20 inches (20 to 50 cm) tall. **Root** system fibrous. **Leaves** alternate, irregularly shaped, with 3 to 7 parts. **Flowers** 1 to 2 inches (2.5 to 5 cm) in diameter, with 5 petals, pale yellow or whitish with a purplish-black center. Petals often have a purple margin. Each flower remains open for only a few hours. **Seed pod** hairy, containing many seeds. **Seeds** grayish-black, kidney-shaped, rough, about 1/16 inch (1.5 mm) long. Found in gardens, cultivated fields, and waste places. Especially serious in cultivated crops after the last cultivation. Also commonly known as flower-of-an-hour.

123

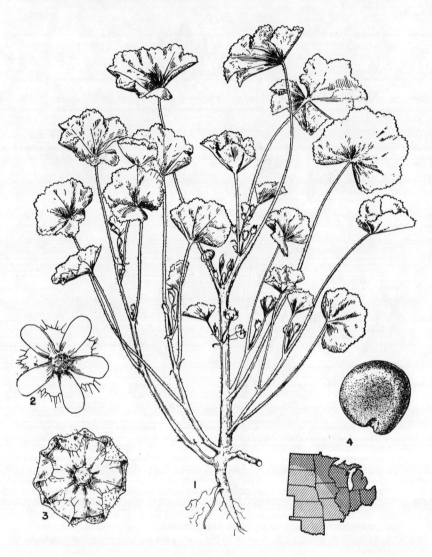

COMMON MALLOW, *Malva neglecta* Wallr. **1,** young plant; **2,** flower; **3,** seed pod; **4,** seed. **Annual** or **biennial** with a short straight taproot, reproducing by seeds. **Stems** branching, nearly erect, or spreading on the surface of the ground with tip generally turning up. **Leaves** large, circular in outline, simple, toothed or slightly lobed, mostly hairy, on very long slender petioles. **Flowers** small, with 5 whitish petals, borne singly or in clusters at bases of petioles. **Seed pod** a flattened disk, when ripe breaking up into 10 to 20 small, hairy, 1-seeded sections. **Seed** nearly round, flattened, reddish-brown, about 1/16 inch (1.5 mm) in diameter, notched. **Found** in cultivated fields, waste places, gardens, yards, lawns, and roadsides.

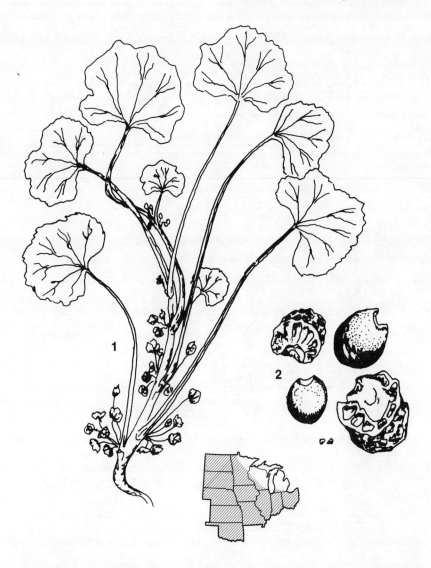

DWARF MALLOW, *Malva rotundifolia* L. **1,** entire plant; **2,** seeds. **Annual,** reproducing by seed. **Root** a short, straight taproot. **Stems** branching, nearly erect or spreading on surface of ground with tips generally turning up. **Leaves** rounded, often wider than long, 1 to 3 inches (2.5 to 7.5 cm) long, with 5 to 7 broad, rounded lobes. **Flowers** pale blue or nearly white, ⅓ to ½ inch (8 to 13 mm) wide, borne singly or in clusters at bases of petioles. **Seed pod** a flattened disk, usually breaking into 10 segments, 1 seed per section. **Seed** segments generally pie-shaped, dark brown, enclosing a black seed. **Found** frequently in yards, gardens, and roadsides; occasionally in cultivated fields.

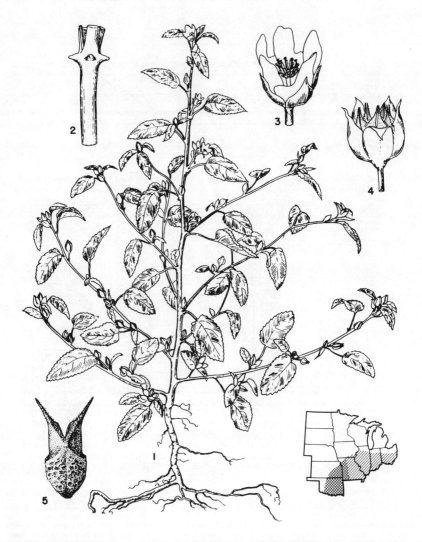

PRICKLY SIDA, *Sida spinosa* L. **1**, plant; **2**, section of stem showing spines; **3**, flower; **4**, seed pod enclosed by calyx; **5**, single section of pod containing seed. **Annual**, reproducing by seeds. **Taproot** slender, branching, rather long. **Stems** erect, branching widely, softly hairy, bearing 2 to 3 short, blunt, spiny projections below each node. **Leaves** alternate, simple, oblong, with toothed edges. **Flowers** with 5 pale yellow petals, solitary or clustered in axils of leaves. **Seed pod** splitting when ripe into 5 one-seeded sections, each with 2 sharp, spreading spines at the top. **Seeds** about 1/16 inch (1.5 mm) long, 3-angled, egg-shaped, dull dark reddish-brown. **Found** late in the season in waste places, cultivated fields, gardens, and pastures.

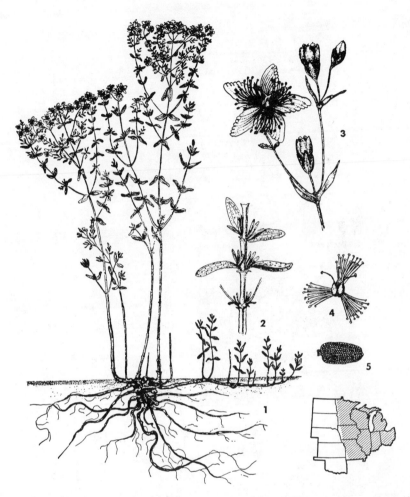

ST. JOHNSWORT, *Hypericum perforatum* L. **1**, plant in flower; **2**, portion of stem with leaves; **3**, flower and buds; **4**, stamens and ovaries; **5**, seed. **Perennial**, reproducing by seeds and rootstocks. **Root** system branched and extending to considerable depth. Shallow, short rootstocks extend out several inches from crown. **Stems** smooth, branched, erect, somewhat 2-edged, 1 to 2 feet (30 to 60 cm) tall, woody at base. **Leaves** opposite, elliptic to oblong, covered with small clear dots. **Flowers** about ¾ inch (1.9 cm) in diameter, 5-petaled, orange-yellow with occasional black dots along edges of petals. **Seed pods** rounded, pointed, with 3 parts and many seeds. **Seeds** about 1/16 inch (1.5 mm) long, cylindrical, blackish, shiny with a rough, pitted, resinous surface. **Found** in pastures, meadows, rangelands and along roadsides. Not relished by grazing animals, may cause skin irritation and loss of condition in livestock, especially white animals. Also commonly known as Klamath weed.

127

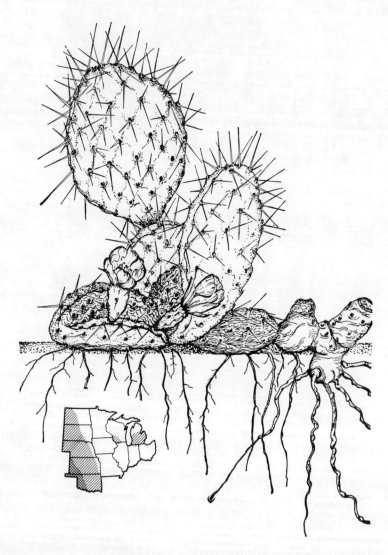

PRICKLYPEAR, *Opuntia* spp. Mill. **Perennial,** reproducing by stems and seeds. **Stems** flat, fleshy, covered with spines several inches in length, rooting freely at the joints. May be prostrate to erect and 3 feet (90 cm) or more tall. **Flowers** are several inches across, bright yellow, sometimes with red centers. **Fruits** somewhat pear-shaped, fleshy to dry and spiny, filled with many hard seeds. **Seeds** about 3/16 inch (4.5 mm) in diameter, flattened. **Found** in the drier sandier soils but not generally troublesome except on overgrazed rangelands or pastures. Variable in form; several similar species are found in the area.

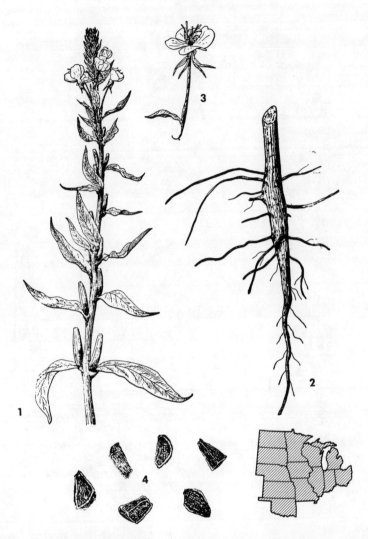

COMMON EVENINGPRIMROSE, *Oenothera biennis* L. **1**, upper portion of stem showing seed pods, flowers and buds; **2**, root; **3**, single flower; **4**, seeds. **Biennial**, reproducing by seeds. Produces large rosette of leaves and a fleshy root the first year. **Stem** the second year erect, leafy, 1 to 5 feet (0.3 to 1.5 m) tall, branching only in upper portion if at all; lower stem often tinged with purple and somewhat hairy. **Leaves** variable, but usually lanceolate and without petioles, lower leaves often purplish and hairy like lower stem. **Flowers** about 1 inch (2.5 cm) across, with 4 yellow petals, opening over a period of several weeks. **Seed pods** woody, cylindrical, containing many seeds. **Seeds** 1/16 inch (1.5 mm) long, irregular, angular, brown. **Found** in wasteland and fields, especially in dry or sandy soil.

129

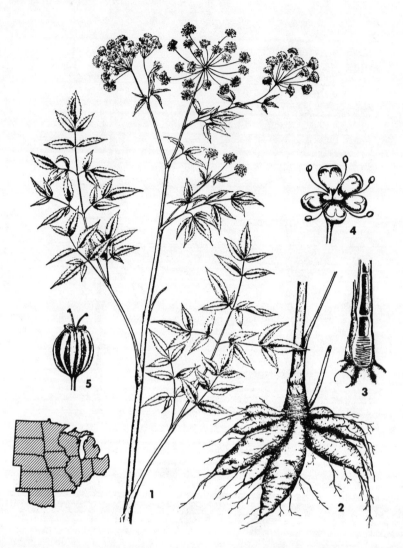

SPOTTED WATERHEMLOCK, *Cicuta maculata* L. **1,** stems, leaves, and flowers; **2,** roots; **3,** hollow base of stem; **4,** flower; **5,** seed. **Perennial,** reproducing by seeds and tuberous roots. **Stem** smooth, 3 to 5 feet (0.9 to 1.5 m) tall, branched at top only, frequently streaked with purplish spots. **Leaves** compound, 8 to 12 inches (20 to 30 cm) long, alternate, smooth with toothed edges, often spotted; base of petioles clasping stem. **Flowers** very small, with 5 white petals, borne in compound umbels. **Seed** flat on one side and rounded on the other, ridged lengthwise with light and dark lines. **Found** in swamps and lowlands, usually in water or at its edge. Both seed and tubers have a distinct aromatic odor. All parts of the plant, but especially the roots, are poisonous if eaten.

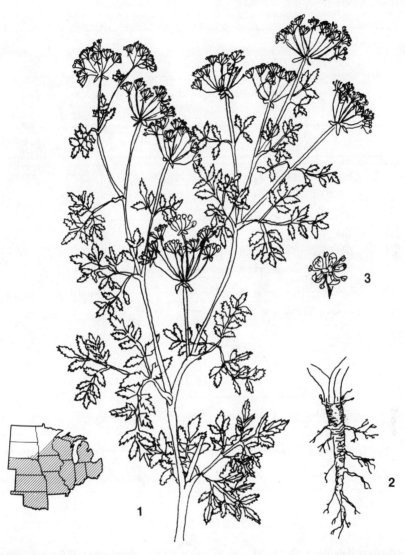

POISON HEMLOCK, *Conium maculatum* L. **1,** upper part of plant in bloom; **2,** root; **3,** flower. **Biennial,** forming a rosette the first year, reproducing by seed the second year. **Root** is fleshy, parsniplike taproot. **Leaves** alternate, large, 4 to 5 times compound, finely divided, and toothed, giving a lacy appearance. **Stems** smooth, erect, 2 to 7 feet (0.6 to 2 m) tall, much branched, with purplish spots and blotches; hollow between the nodes. **Flowers** white, produced in large terminal compound umbels that are flattish to slightly convex. **Seeds** borne in pairs, ovoid, flattened, smooth, prominently ribbed, pale brown. **Found** in wet sites along streams, in gardens, roadsides, waste areas. Sometimes grown as an ornamental. The entire plant is very poisonous.

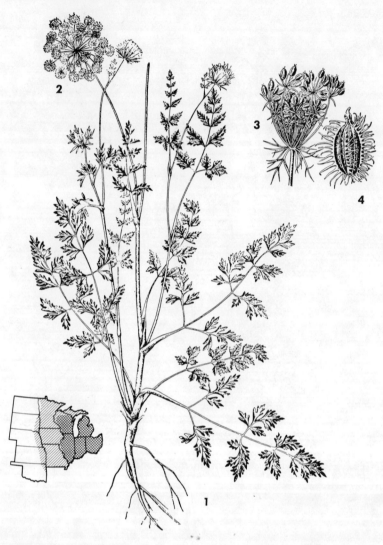

WILD CARROT, *Daucus carota* L. **1**, entire plant; **2**, flower head; **3**, head in seed; **4**, seed. **Biennial**, reproducing by seeds. In first year, produces rosette of finely divided leaves and fleshy taproot; in second year blooms and dies. **Stem** (second year) erect, 1 to 3 feet (30 to 90 cm) tall, hairy, stout, and branched at top. **Leaves** alternate, finely pinnately divided, hairy, with distinct carrotlike odor. **Flowers** small, with 5 white petals, borne in umbels at ends of branches. **Seeds** ⅛ inch (3 mm) or less long, one side flattened, the other rounded and showing 4 heavy long-bristled ridges with smaller ones between. The outside seed-bearing stalks curve in sharply as they mature. **Found** in meadows, pastures, and roadsides; not in cultivated fields. Also known as Queen Anne's lace.

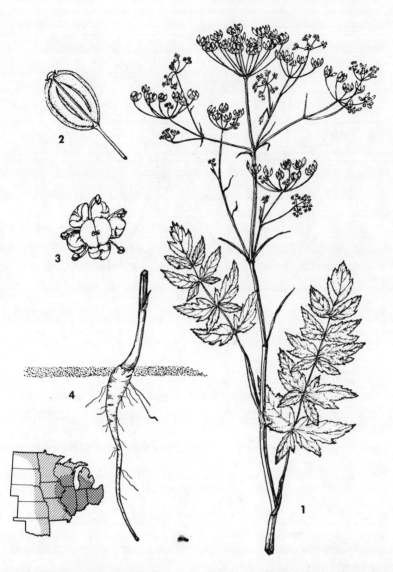

WILD PARSNIP, *Pastinaca sativa* L. **1**, top of plant showing leaves, seeds, and flowers; **2**, seed; **3**, flower; **4**, root. **Biennial**, reproducing by seeds. Produces a rosette of large upright leaves and a large fleshy root the first year. **Stem** (second year) usually somewhat hairy, grooved, erect, 2 to 5 feet (0.6 to 1.5 m) tall. **Leaves** alternate, pinnately compound, with coarsely sawtoothed edges, not hairy. **Flowers** small, with 5 yellow petals, in umbels at the top of stems and branches. **Seeds** flat, rounded, smooth, straw-colored, with low ribs across them. **Found** in wastelands and pastures. This is not poisonous but sometimes has been thought to be.

133

DOGBANE FAMILY, *Apocynaceae*

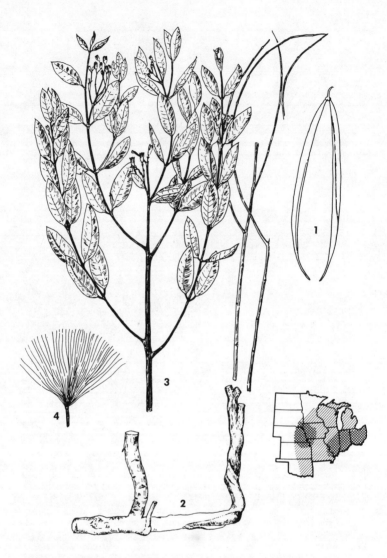

HEMP DOGBANE, *Apocynum cannabinum* L. **1,** seed pods; **2,** section of stems and rootstock; **3,** upper part of stem with leaves and flowers; **4,** seed. **Perennial**, reproducing by seed and long, horizontal rootstocks. **Stems** erect, 1 to 2 feet (30 to 60 cm) tall from a woody base, exuding milky juice when broken. **Leaves** erect, elliptical, narrow, and smooth-edged. **Flowers** with 5 greenish-white petals which are slightly longer than the green sepals. **Seed pod** long and slender. **Seed** thin and flat, with a tuft of soft silky hairs at one end. **Found** in wasteland and cultivated fields. Another species of dogbane, *Apocynum sibericum* Jacq., is very similar to this one and is found in abundance in much of the same area.

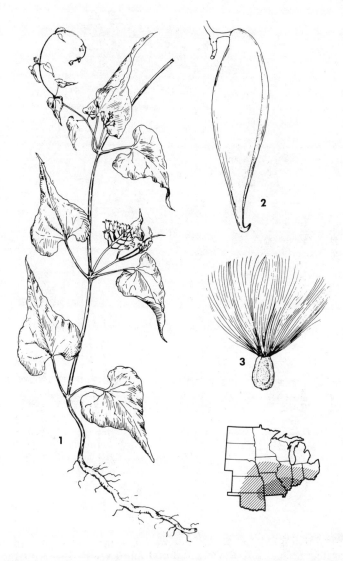

HONEYVINE MILKWEED, *Ampelamus albidus* (Nutt.) Britt. **1,** portion of plant; **2,** seed pod; **3,** seed. **Perennial,** reproducing by seeds and by long spreading roots. **Stems** smooth, slender, twining, without milky juice. **Leaves** smooth, heart-shaped, pointed, with long petioles, in pairs at the nodes on the stem. **Flowers** small, whitish, borne in clusters on stalks from the axils of the leaves. **Seed pod** similar to that of common milkweed but smooth and green. **Seeds** brown, flattened, oval, with a tuft of silky, white hairs at tip. **Found** in cultivated fields and fence rows, especially in areas with fertile, moist soil.

135

MILKWEED FAMILY, *Asclepiadaceae*

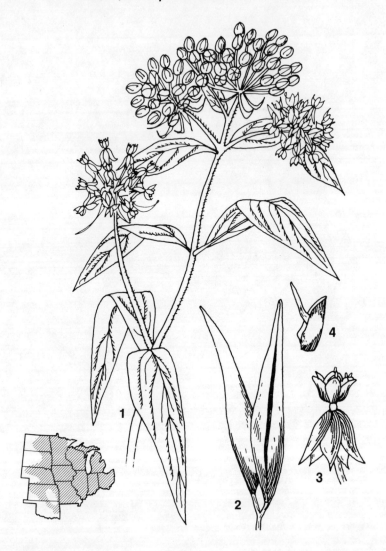

SWAMP MILKWEED, *Asclepias incarnata* L. **1,** upper part of plant in flower; **2,** seed pods; **3,** single flower; **4,** hood (5 of which make up the corona). **Perennial,** reproducing by seeds and weakly creeping rootstocks. **Stems** single or clustered, 1 to 4 feet (0.3 to 1.2 m) tall, very leafy, branched toward top, with milky juice. **Leaves** opposite, long, narrow, oblong but tapering toward tip, smooth or hairy, 4 to 7 inches (10 to 17.5 cm) long. **Flowers** pink to rose-purple or whitish, clustered into several ball-like groups (umbels). **Seed pod** erect on short stems, about 3 inches (7.5 cm) long, smooth or slightly hairy. **Seeds** oval, about 3/8 inch (9 mm) long, with tuft of hairs at tip. **Found** in swamps, ditches, and wet prairies, seldom in cultivated fields. Poisonous to livestock.

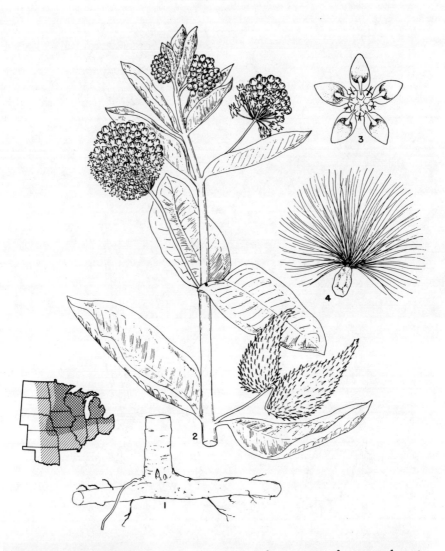

COMMON MILKWEED, *Asclepias syriaca* L. **1**, lower part of stem and root-stock; **2**, upper part of stem with flower clusters and seed pods; **3**, single flower; **4**, seed. **Perennial**, reproducing by seed and from rootstocks. **Stems** stout and erect, 2 to 5 feet (0.6 to 1.5 m) tall, covered with short downy hairs, with milky juice. **Leaves** opposite, oblong, rounded, 4 to 8 inches (10 to 20 cm) long with prominent veins. Upper surface smooth, lower surfaces covered with short white hairs. **Flowers** sweet-smelling, pink to white, in large, many-flowered, ball-like clusters at the tips of stems and in the axils of upper leaves. **Seed pod** grayish, hairy, covered with soft spiny projections. **Seed** brown, flat, oval, with a tuft of silky, white hairs attached to tip. **Found** in cultivated fields, pastures, open woods and roadsides.

137

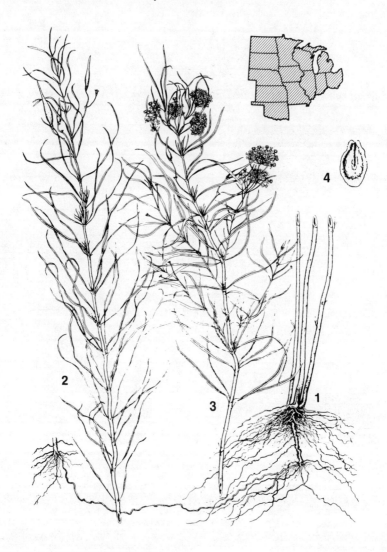

EASTERN WHORLED MILKWEED, *Asclepias verticillata* L. **1**, base of plant with roots and rootstock; **2**, shoot; **3**, upper portion of plant with flower clusters; **4**, seed. **Perennial**, reproducing from seed and creeping rootstocks. **Stems** 1 to 2 feet (0.3 to 0.6 m) tall, slender, smooth, branching at top of plant only, with milky juice. Each crown may produce several stems. **Leaves** light green, narrow, arranged in groups of 3 to 7 in whorls around stem. **Flowers** greenish-white, with 5 petals, borne in clusters at top of stem or in the axils of upper leaves. **Seed pod** 2 to 4 inches (5 to 10 cm) long, slender, smooth, containing numerous seeds. **Seeds** flat, brown, with a tuft of fine hairs at tip. **Found** in meadows, pastures, and waste places. Seldom found in cultivated fields. This plant is poisonous to livestock.

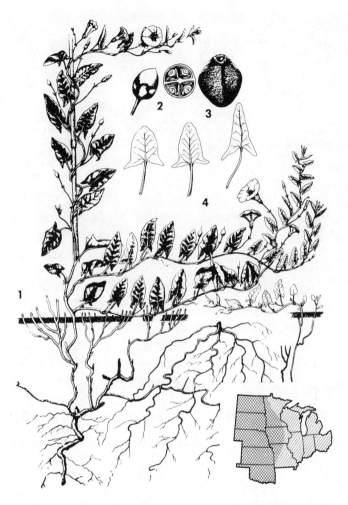

FIELD BINDWEED, *Convolvulus arvensis* L. **1**, plant in flower; **2**, seed pod, entire and in cross section; **3**, seed; **4**, variations in leaf shape. **Perennial**, reproducing by seeds and rootstocks. **Root** system extensive; may go down 20 to 30 feet (6 to 9 m). **Stems** smooth, slender, 2 to 7 feet (0.6 to 2 m) long, twining or spreading over surface of ground. **Leaves** ovate with spreading basal lobes. **Flowers** white or pink, funnel-shaped, about 1 inch (2.5 cm) across, usually borne singly in the axils of leaves. Flower stalk has 2 bracts ½ to 2 inches (1.3 to 5 cm) below the flower, which distinguish this weed from hedge bindweed. **Seed pod** egg-shaped, usually containing 4 seeds. **Seeds** dark brownish-gray, roughened, about ⅛ inch (3 mm) long, with 1 rounded and 2 flattened sides. **Found** in and able to persist and spread in all noncultivated areas and under most cropping systems. One of the most troublesome weeds in the region. Also known as creeping jenny.

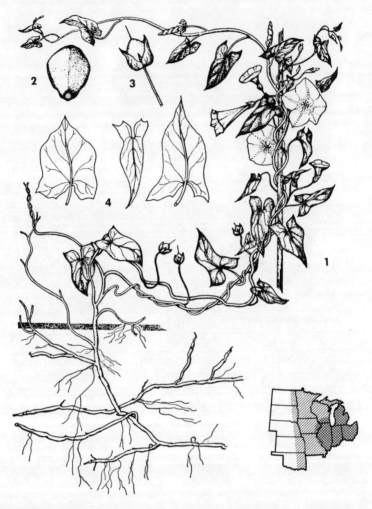

HEDGE BINDWEED, *Convolvulus sepium* L. **1**, plant in flower; **2**, seed; **3**, seed pod; **4**, variations in leaf shape. **Perennial**, reproducing by seed and fleshy creeping rootstocks. **Roots** extensive but relatively shallow. **Stems** smooth, 3 to 10 feet (0.9 to 3 m) long, twining on plants or trailing on surface of ground. **Leaves** large, alternate, usually sharp-pointed at tip, basal lobes large. **Flowers** large, 1½ to 2 inches (3.8 to 5 cm) across, white or pinkish. The flower bud and later the lower part of the flower and seed pod are enclosed in 2 leafy bracts. **Seed pod** about ⅜ inch (9 mm) in diameter, egg-shaped, containing 2 to 4 seeds. **Seeds** slate-colored to black, dull, usually with 1 rounded and 2 flattened sides. **Found** in cultivated fields, fence rows and waste areas, especially on bottomlands. Less drouth-enduring than field bindweed, but under humid conditions usually a more serious problem.

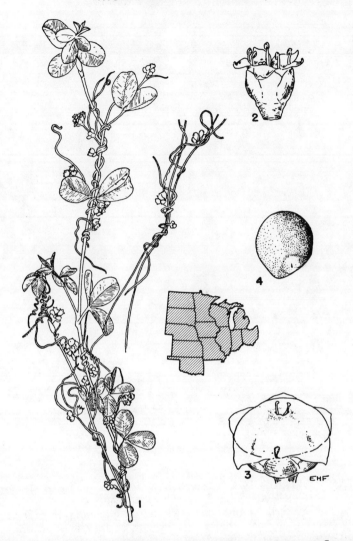

DODDER, *Cuscuta* spp. L. **1**, dodder twined on legume plant; **2**, flower; **3**, seed pod; **4**, seed. **Annual,** reproducing by seed. Dodder is a parasitic plant without chlorophyll. It obtains its food by twining around a host plant and sending rootlike projections into its stem. **Stems** are stringlike, smooth, yellow or orange, branching extensively, forming dense masses. **Leaves** absent or reduced to small bracts. **Flowers** numerous, small, white with 5 lobes, borne in clusters. **Seed pod** about ⅛ inch (3 mm) in diameter, with thin papery walls, containing 4 seeds. **Seeds** triangular in cross section, brown, with a roughened seed coat. **Found** principally on clovers, alfalfa, and lespedeza, although it can grow on many broad-leaved plants. It is difficult to remove the seeds from clover and alfalfa seeds. A number of similar species growing on various host plants are found in the region.

141

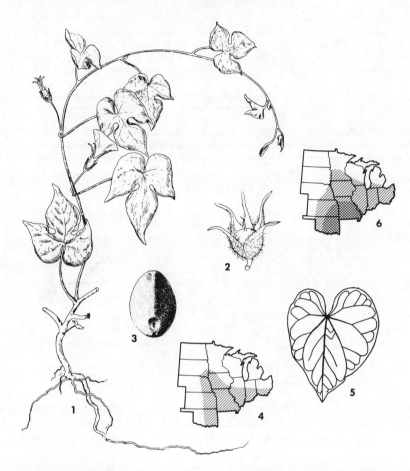

IVYLEAF MORNINGGLORY, *Ipomoea hederacea* (L.) Jacq. **1**, portion of plant; **2**, seed pod surrounded by calyx; **3**, seed; **4**, distribution. **Annual**, reproducing by seed. **Stems** hairy, twining or spreading on ground. **Leaves** usually 3-lobed, alternate, hairy. Plants with entire leaves occur rarely, becoming more common toward southern part of region. **Flowers** funnel-shaped, purple or blue varying to white, borne singly on long stalks. **Seed pods** egg-shaped, partly covered by bristly calyx, usually with 4 to 6 seeds. Sepals lanceolate, narrowed from below the middle into a slender, recurved tip. **Seeds** about ¼ inch (6 mm) long, dark brown to black, with 1 round and 2 flattened sides. **Found** in gardens, fields, and waste places. A troublesome weed in cultivated fields, especially corn and soybeans, where it ties plants together before harvest.

TALL MORNINGGLORY, *Ipomoea purpurea* (L.) Roth. **5**, leaf; **6**, distribution. Very similar to the above species. **Leaves** are larger, heart-shaped, very rarely lobed. **Flowers** blue, purple, white, or variegated. Sepals lanceolate to oblong, acute to acuminate.

142

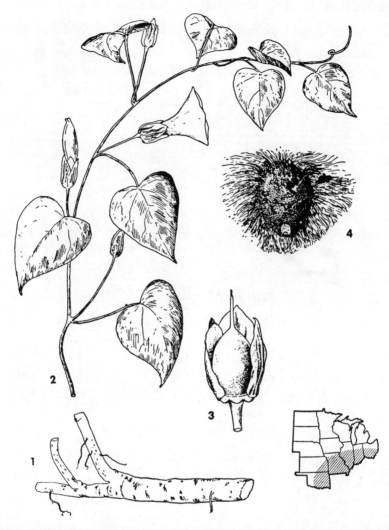

BIGROOT MORNINGGLORY, *Ipomoea pandurata* (L.) G. F. W. Mey. **1,** portion of root; **2,** portion of vine with flowers; **3,** seed pod; **4,** seed. **Perennial,** reproducing by seed and from roots. **Roots** yellowish white, enlarging greatly so that they may weigh many pounds, buried in the soil below the plow line. **Stems** trailing or twining on plants, 2 to 10 feet (0.6 to 3 m) long, smooth, often purplish. **Leaves** alternate, heart-shaped, 2 to 6 inches (5 to 15 cm) long, smooth, with long petioles. **Flowers** funnel-shaped, 2 to 3 inches (5 to 7.5 cm) in diameter, white with dark purple center. **Seed pod** egg-shaped, enclosed by several leaflike sepals, containing 2 to 4 seeds. **Seeds** dark brown, fringed with soft hairs. **Found** in cultivated fields, along fences and roadsides, especially on sandy soils. Most troublesome in corn, soybeans, and small grain crops. Also commonly known as wild sweet potato.

143

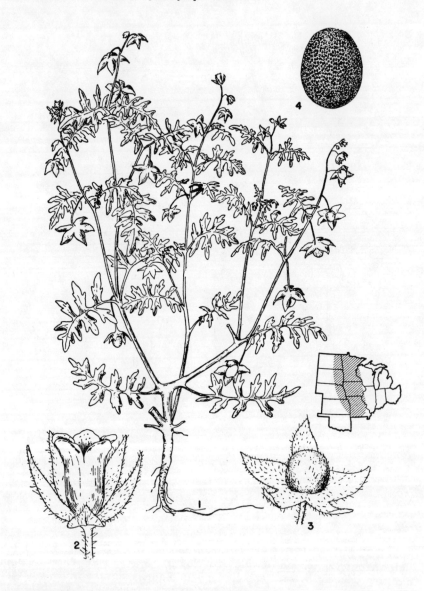

WATERPOD, *Ellisia nyctelea* L. **1,** entire plant; **2,** flower; **3,** seed pod with enlarged calyx at base; **4,** seed. **Annual,** reproducing by seed. **Stems** branching widely at base, 6 to 18 inches (15 to 45 cm) tall. **Leaves** deeply cut into numerous divisions which are 1- to 3-toothed, alternate or opposite. **Flowers** small, 5-lobed, whitish to pale blue, borne singly on long hairy stalks. **Seed pod** green, hairy, drooping, 2-celled, containing 4 seeds, surrounded at base by 5 green, enlarged sepals. **Seeds** oval, brown, with pitted surface. **Found** chiefly in moist areas on wasteland and along ditches.

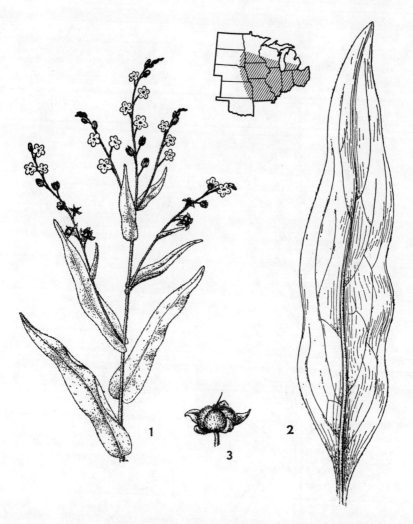

HOUNDSTONGUE, *Cynoglossum officinale* L. **1,** upper part of plant; **2,** leaf from lower part of stem; **3,** seed pod. **Biennial,** with mousy odor, reproducing by seeds and from thick, black roots. **Stems** erect, ridged, leafy; covered with short, soft hairs. **Leaves** in a rosette the first year, narrow and tapered (especially the upper ones) in the second year; petioles absent, leaves rounded at base, sometimes clasping, softly hairy. **Flowers** in racemes, nearly without bracts, with 5 dull red petals. **Fruits** grouped into 4 nutlets about ¼ inch (6 mm) long, that separate when ripe. The flat outer surfaces of the nutlets are bristly, and they cling to clothing and the fleece of sheep. The top of each nutlet is flat with a scar on one side near base. **Found** in pastures and wasteland, frequently on gravelly, somewhat alkaline soils.

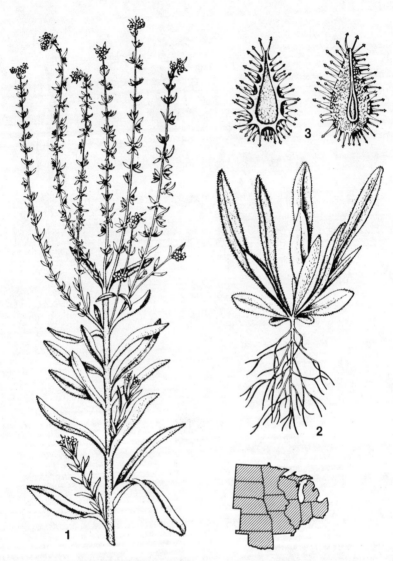

EUROPEAN STICKTIGHT, *Lappula echinata* Gilib. **1**, upper part of plant; **2**, young plant with roots; **3**, seeds. **Annual** or **winter annual**, reproducing by seeds. **Stem** slender, widely branched above, 1 to 2 feet (30 to 60 cm) tall, entire plant covered with rough hairs. **Leaves** hairy, narrowly oblong, 1 to 2 inches (2.5 to 5 cm) long, at first forming a rosette at base of plant. **Flowers** small, with 5 blue petals, borne in the axils of small leafy bracts along upper branches. **Seed pods** rough with hooked spines, at maturity splitting into 4 segments, each containing 1 seed. **Found** in dry soils along roadsides and in wooded areas and waste places.

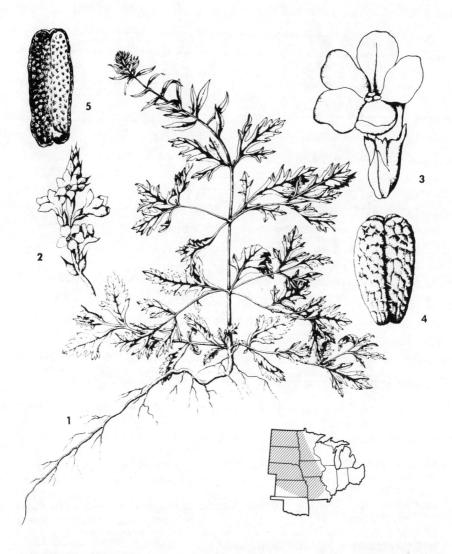

PROSTRATE VERVAIN, *Verbena bracteata* Lag. and Rodr. **1,** entire plant; **2,** flowering stem; **3,** single flower; **4,** seed pod or fruit; **5,** single seed. **Annual,** reproducing by seed. **Stems** mostly prostrate, a few inches to more than a foot long, hairy, freely branching at base. **Leaves** numerous, small, rough, opposite, lobed and toothed, hairy. **Flowers** blue or purplish, small, in dense spikes, almost hidden by the conspicuous bracts. **Seeds** result from pod splitting into 4 segments, each with 2 flattened sides and 1 rounded side, oblong, about ⅛ inch (3 mm) long, dark brown. **Found** in barnyards, lawns, pastures, meadows, and waste places. Rarely found in cultivated fields.

147

VERVAIN FAMILY, *Verbenaceae*

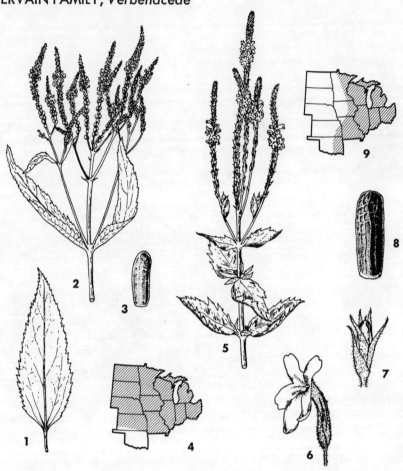

BLUE VERVAIN, *Verbena hastata* L. **1,** leaf from middle of stem; **2,** upper part of stem; **3,** seed; **4,** distribution. **Perennial,** reproducing by seed and short rhizomes. **Stems** erect, branched above, 2 to 4 feet (0.6 to 1.2 m) tall, somewhat rough. **Leaves** opposite, simple, toothed, lanceolate, with short petioles. **Flowers** small, blue, in short compact spikes. **Seeds** borne 4 in a pod; brown, oblong. **Found** mostly in pastures, roadsides, fence rows, and waste places, especially on low ground.

HOARY VERVAIN, *Verbena stricta* Vent. **4,** distribution; **5,** upper part of stem in flower; **6,** single flower; **7,** pod enclosed by calyx; **8,** seed. Similar to the above species but hairy all over. **Leaves** shorter, less pointed, without petioles. **Flowers** purplish, borne in long spikes. Usually found in upland pastures.

WHITE VERVAIN, *Verbena urticifolia* L. **9,** distribution. Similar to blue verbain. **Leaves** ovate with scattered hairs. **Flowers** white on long slender spikes. Frequently found in or near wooded areas, pastures, and waste areas.

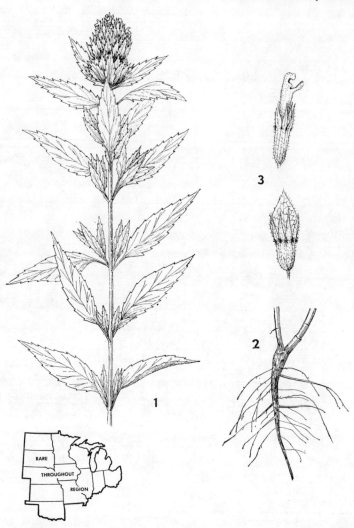

DRAGONHEAD, *Dracocephalum parviflorum* Nutt. **1,** upper part of plant; **2,** lower part of plant; **3,** flowers. **Annual** or **biennial,** reproducing by seeds. **Stems** square, erect, 8 to 40 inches (20 to 100 cm) tall, either single or in clumps, and either simple or branched. **Leaves** opposite, narrow to somewhat oval-shaped, pinnately veined, with petioles, and with small sharp teeth on margins. **Flowers** clustered in globelike spikes subtended by sharp-toothed overlapping bracts. Petals light blue to violet, tubular, strongly 2-lipped with notch in upper lip and 3 lobes in lower lip. **Fruits** are 4 nutlets that separate when ripe; each nutlet is about 1/16 inch (1.5 mm) long, brownish-black and granular in appearance, with a crescent-shaped scar on angular side at base. **Found** in meadows, fields, garden clearings, new woods, and wasteland, often on rocky or gravelly limy soils.

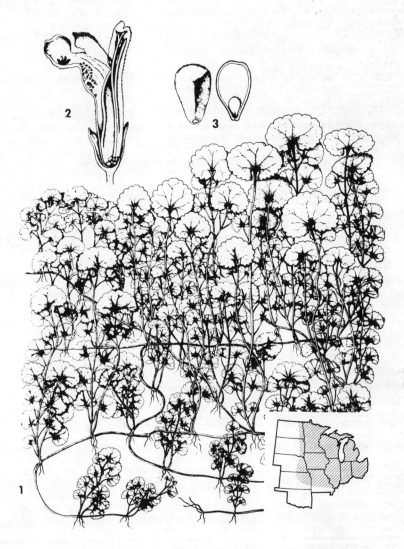

GROUND IVY, *Glechoma hederacea* L. **1**, vegetative growth of stems and leaves; **2**, flower section; **3**, seeds. **Perennial**, with shallow roots, spreading by seeds and by creeping stems. **Stems** 15 to 30 inches (38 to 75 cm) long, prostrate, 4-sided, rooting at the nodes. **Leaves** almost round or kidney-shaped, with round-toothed edges, bright green, ½ to 1½ inches (13 to 39 mm) in diameter, hairy, opposite, borne on long petioles, with a minty odor. **Flowers** small, bluish-purple, funnel-shaped but 2-lipped, borne in small clusters in the axils of the leaves. **Seeds** rough, dark brown, in groups of 4, flat on 2 sides and round on the third side, with a white scar at tip. **Found** in lawns, orchards, and waste places, especially shady areas with damp, rich soil. Also commonly known as creeping charlie.

150

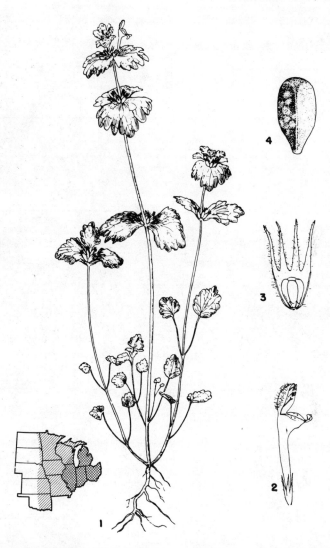

HENBIT, *Lamium amplexicaule* L. **1**, entire plant; **2**, flower; **3**, seeds with part of calyx; **4**, single seed. **Annual**, reproducing by seeds. **Roots** fibrous. **Stems** 4 to 16 inches (10 to 40 cm) tall, slender, smooth, 4-angled, with many branches that are more or less prostrate with ascending tips; frequently rooting where the nodes are in contact with ground. **Leaves** opposite, hairy, with rounded teeth. Lower leaves with petioles; the upper without petioles and clasping stem. **Flowers** in whorls in the axils of upper leaves, tubular but 2-lipped, about ⅜ inch (9 mm) long, pinkish to purple, surrounded at base by calyx with 5 sharp teeth. **Seeds** borne 4 in a pod, sharply 3-angled, grayish-brown, about 1/16 inch (1.5 mm) long. **Found** in gardens, cultivated fields, and waste places, especially those with rich soil.

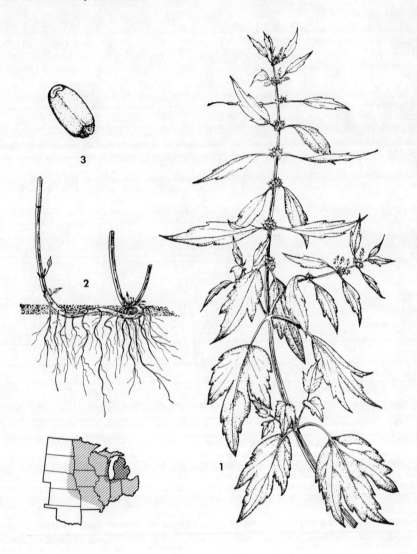

MOTHERWORT, *Leonurus cardiaca* L. **1,** upper portion of plant; **2,** base of plant; **3,** seed. **Perennial,** reproducing by seed and rhizomes. **Roots** extensive but shallow. **Stems** 2 to 5 feet (0.6 to 1.5 m) tall, 4-sided, erect, coarse, stiff, nearly smooth, branched near top. **Leaves** opposite; lower leaves toothed and 3-lobed; upper leaves narrow, notched. **Flowers** in tight clusters in axils of leaves, spiny and burlike when dry, petals formed into 2-lipped purple or white tube. **Seeds** borne 4 in a pod, oval, 3-sided, dark red to brown. **Found** mostly in waste places and noncultivated fields. Usually not troublesome except in low, rich soils.

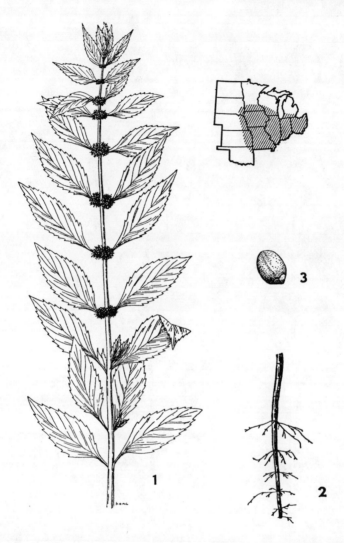

FIELD MINT, *Mentha arvensis* L. **1,** upper part of plant; **2,** lower part of plant; **3,** seed. **Perennial**, reproducing by seeds and rhizomes, aromatic. **Stems** square, usually branching, up to 2½ feet (75 cm) tall; barbed hairs on angles and sometimes on sides of stem. **Leaves** opposite, with petioles, strongly scented, pinnately veined, narrow to oval, with small teeth on margins and with minute glandular hairs on leaf surface. **Flowers** clustered in axils of upper leaves. Petals pink, lavender, or occasionally white; ⅛ to ¼ inch (3 to 6 mm) long, with 5 teeth and prominent nerves in the tube. **Fruits** are nutlets less than 1/16 inch (1.5 mm) long, smooth, light brown, each with an irregular dark line on the convex side. **Found** in meadows, in pastures, along ditches and shores, mostly on damp, open gravel.

153

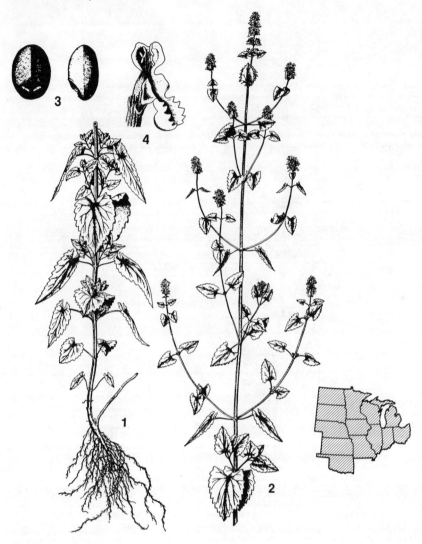

CATNIP, *Nepeta cataria* L. **1**, lower portion of plant; **2**, upper part of plant in bloom; **3**, seeds; **4**, single flower. **Perennial**, reproducing by seed and from short rhizomes. **Stems** covered with fine short hair, erect, 2 to 3 feet (60 to 90 cm) tall, 4-sided, light green. **Leaves** opposite, pointed, heart-shaped with saw-toothed margins, green above, light green or whitish underneath, covered with fine hairs, with a characteristic minty odor. **Flowers** in dense clusters at ends of stems and branches, petals formed into a 2-lipped tube, pale purple, dark-dotted. **Seeds** borne 4 in a pod, oval, with 2 flattened sides and 1 rounded side, dark reddish-brown with 2 white spots at one end. **Found** in waste places, in yards, and along roadsides. Sometimes cultivated.

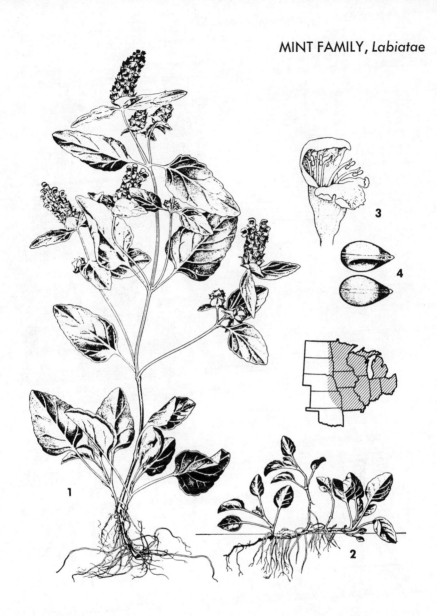

HEAL-ALL, *Prunella vulgaris* L. **1**, plant in flower; **2**, prostrate stem; **3**, single flower; **4**, seed. **Perennial**, reproducing by seed and by runners which root freely at the nodes. **Stems** 2 to 24 inches (5 to 60 cm) long, erect or prostrate, branched, 4-sided, hairy when young, becoming smooth when older. **Leaves** oval, opposite, margins smooth or slightly notched, 1 to 4 inches (2.5 to 10 cm) long, hairy to smooth, with moderately long petioles. **Flowers** 2-lipped tubes, violet or purple, borne in the axils of short bracts in a dense spike. **Seeds** borne 4 in a pod, each somewhat pear-shaped, slightly flattened on 2 sides, brown with dark lines, slightly rough. **Found** in lawns, fields, and waste places where there is considerable moisture.

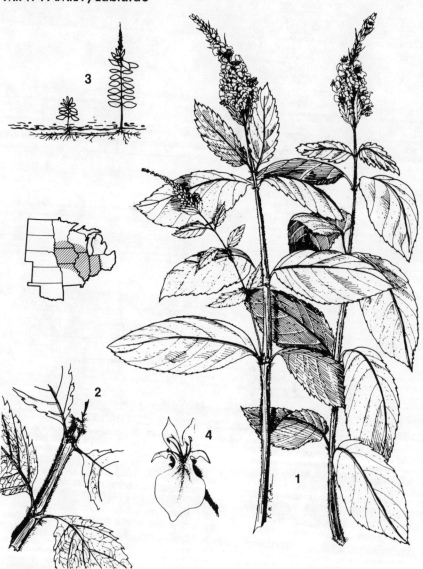

AMERICAN GERMANDER, *Teucrium canadense* L. **1**, upper part of plant; **2**, portion of stem and leaves; **3**, diagram of growth habit showing underground rhizome; **4**, flower. **Perennial**, reproducing from long slender rhizomes. **Stems** square, pubescent, especially on the angles, 1 to 2 feet (30 to 60 cm) tall, often branching. **Leaves** opposite, ovate, acute or acuminate at tip, rounded at base, finely toothed, pubescent, and short-petioled. **Inflorescence** spike-like, with several pink-purple, irregularly lobed flowers at each node. **Seeds** borne 4 in a nutlet, light to dark brown, surface covered with network of veins or ridges. **Found** on moist soils mostly in cultivated crops.

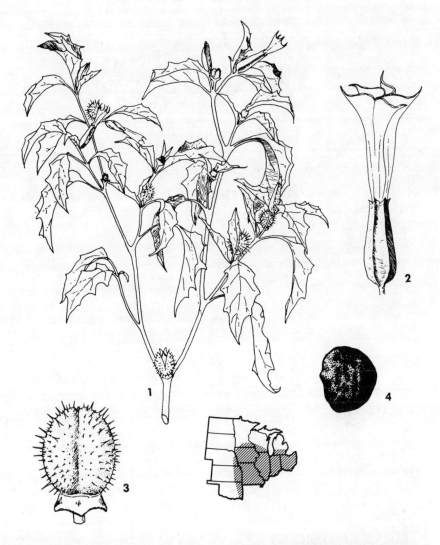

JIMSONWEED, *Datura stramonium* L. **1,** upper portion of plant; **2,** flower; **3,** seed pod; **4,** seed. **Annual,** reproducing by seed. **Roots** thick, shallow, extensively branched. **Stems** smooth, thick, erect, branching widely in upper part, 2 to 4 feet (0.6 to 1.2 m) tall. **Leaves** alternate, large, coarse, smooth, ovate, with irregularly toothed edges and a distinctive rank odor. **Flowers** large, funnel-shaped, white to pinkish, 2 to 5 inches (5 to 12.5 cm) long, borne singly on short stalks in the axils of the branches. **Seed pod** about 1 inch (2.5 cm) in diameter, egg-shaped, covered with short, sharp spines. **Seed** dark brown to black, kidney-shaped, flattened, surface irregular and pitted. **Found** in cultivated crops on rich land and especially in old feedlots. This plant contains poisonous materials.

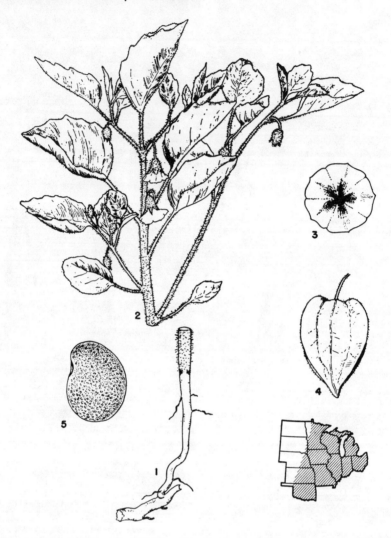

CLAMMY GROUNDCHERRY, *Physalis heterophylla* Nees. **1**, lower portion of plant; **2**, upper portion of plant; **3**, flower; **4**, inflated calyx surrounding fruit; **5**, seed. **Perennial**, reproducing by seeds and rootstocks. **Stems** hairy, erect at first but later branching to form a dense bush 1 to 3 feet (30 to 90 cm) tall. **Leaves** alternate, 2 to 3 inches (5 to 7.5 cm) long, oval with round-toothed edges, hairy. **Flowers** bell-shaped, 5-lobed, drooping, greenish-yellow with brown or purplish center, about ¾ inch (19 mm) in diameter. **Fruit** round, berrylike, yellow, enclosed by inflated papery calyx. **Seeds** numerous, small, yellow, flattened, oval, about 1/16 inch (1.5 mm) in diameter. **Found** in cultivated fields, gardens, pastures, and meadows. Several similar species differing chiefly in growth habit, growth period, and degree of hairiness are found in the region.

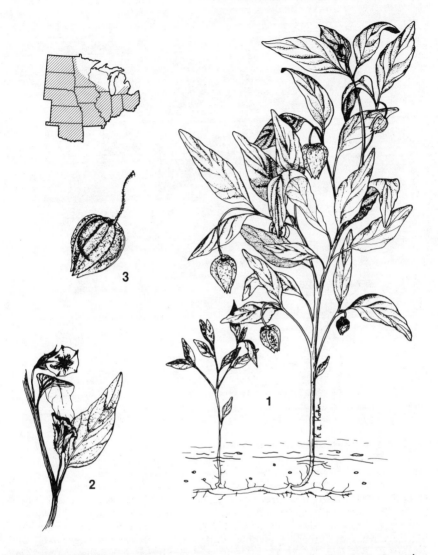

SMOOTH GROUNDCHERRY, *Physalis subglabrata* Mack. and Bush. **1,** entire plant with perennial horizontal rootstock and young plant; **2,** portion of stem with leaves and flowers; **3,** fruit. **Perennial,** reproducing by seeds and rootstocks. **Stems** erect but may be widely branching; hairy on young growth, smooth later; 1 to 3 feet (30 to 90 cm) tall. **Leaves** alternate, thin, ovate to lanceolate, entire to slightly toothed, long-petioled, smooth or slightly hairy. **Flowers** bell-like, yellow to yellowish-green with purple center, calyx sharply 5-toothed. **Fruit** round, berrylike, reddish to purplish, enclosed by inflated papery calyx. **Seeds** numerous, small, yellowish-brown, flattened, and wrinkled. **Found** in cultivated fields, gardens, and noncultivated areas.

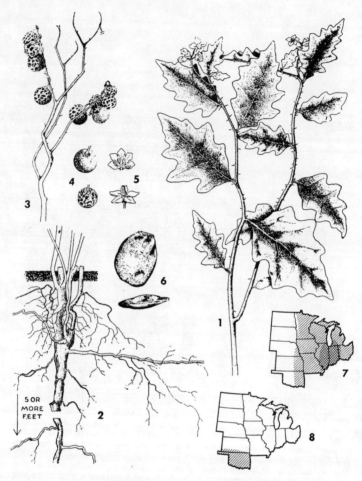

HORSENETTLE, *Solanum carolinense* L. **1**, top of plant; **2**, lower portion of plant; **3**, stem with mature berries; **4**, mature and immature berries; **5**, flower; **6**, top and edge view of seeds; **7**, distribution. **Perennial**, reproducing by seeds from creeping rootstocks. **Stems** simple or branched, hairy and prickly, 1 to 4 feet (0.3 to 1.2 m) tall. **Leaves** alternate, oblong, wavy-edged or lobed, with yellow prickles on petioles, midrib, and veins. **Flowers** white or bluish, 5-lobed, about 1 inch (2.5 cm) across, borne in clusters. **Berries** yellow, juicy, ⅜ to ⅝ inch (9 to 15 mm) in diameter, containing numerous seeds, borne in clusters, smooth at first but becoming wrinkled late in the season. **Seeds** about 1/16 inch (1.5 mm) in diameter, round, flattened, yellowish. **Found** in fields, gardens, and waste areas, especially those with sandy soil.

SILVERLEAF NIGHTSHADE, *Solanum elaeagnifolium* Cav. **8**, distribution. Similar to the above species. **Leaves** somewhat narrower, less prickly, and with a silvery appearance due to numerous fine hairs.

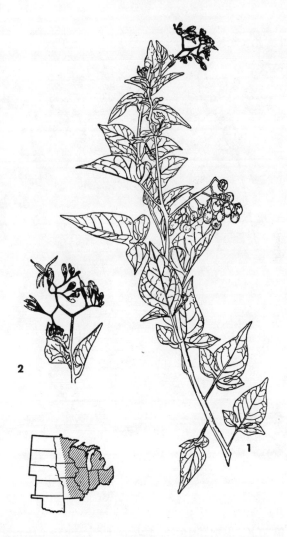

BITTER NIGHTSHADE, *Solanum dulcamara* L. **1,** fruiting branch; **2,** cluster of flowers. **Perennial,** reproducing by seeds and by rooting of prostrate stems. **Stems** slender, vinelike, somewhat woody, 2 to 10 feet (0.6 to 3 m) long, twining on low vegetation or prostrate on ground. **Leaves** dark green, 2 to 5 inches (5 to 12.5 cm) long, variously lobed at base, alternate, petioled, with a disagreeable odor. **Flowers** purplish or white, 5-lobed, about ½ inch (1.3 cm) across, in loose clusters from the axils of the leaves. **Berries** oval, about ⅜ inch (9 mm) long, light green turning bright red at maturity, containing many seeds. **Seeds** about 1/16 inch (1.5 mm) in diameter, round, flattened, light yellow. **Found** in thickets, fence rows, edges of clearings, usually in moist soil. A mildly poisonous plant. Should not be confused with bittersweet, which is woody and has orange fruits and a more viny growth.

161

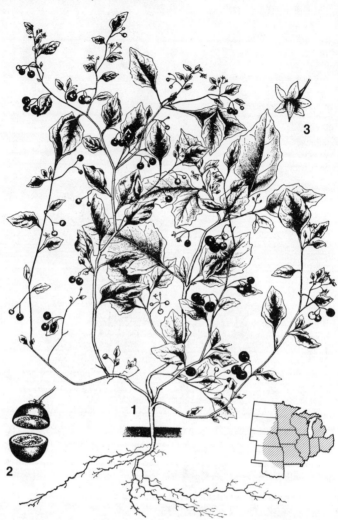

EASTERN BLACK NIGHTSHADE, *Solanum ptycanthum* Dun. **1**, entire plant; **2**, berry; **3**, flower. **Annual,** reproducing by seed. **Stem** erect or spreading, becoming widely branched, 1 to 2 feet (30 to 60 cm) tall. **Leaves** ovate, 1 to 3 inches (2.5 to 7.5 cm) long, alternate, edges wavy. **Flowers** white, 5-lobed, about ¼ inch (6 mm) across, in small clusters. **Berries** green, turning black at maturity, smooth, about ⅜ inch (9 mm) in diameter, containing numerous seeds. **Seeds** flattened, about 1/16 inch (1.5 mm) in diameter, dull, pitted, yellow to dark brown. **Found** in cultivated fields, garden areas, and waste places. Unripe berries may be poisonous. This species was formerly known as black nightshade (*Solanum nigrum* L.). According to recent taxonomic studies, *S. nigrum* occurs in the U.S. only in the western states. *S. ptycanthum*, which differs slightly from *S. nigrum*, is the species found east of the Rocky Mountains.

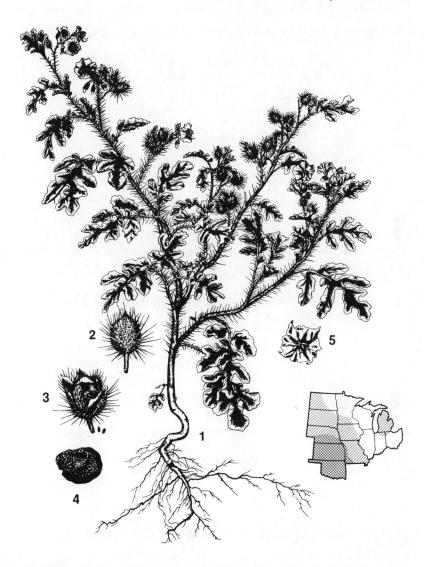

BUFFALOBUR, *Solanum rostratum* Dunal. **1,** entire plant; **2, 3,** seed pods; **4,** seed; **5,** flower. **Annual,** reproducing by seeds. **Stem** erect, branched in upper portion, 6 to 24 inches (15 to 60 cm) tall, hairy, densely covered with long stiff yellow prickles. **Leaves** 2 to 5 inches (5 to 12.5 cm) long, alternate, petioled, densely hairy, cut into deep rounded lobes; veins, midribs, and petioles very prickly. **Flowers** yellow with 5 lobes, 1 to 1½ inches (2.5 to 3.8 cm) across, in clusters from stalks on upper branches. **Fruit** a berry enclosed in a rough-spiny bur. **Seeds** numerous, round, flattened, dull brownish-black. **Found** in fields, overgrazed pastures, yards, roadsides, and waste areas.

FIGWORT FAMILY, *Scrophulariaceae*

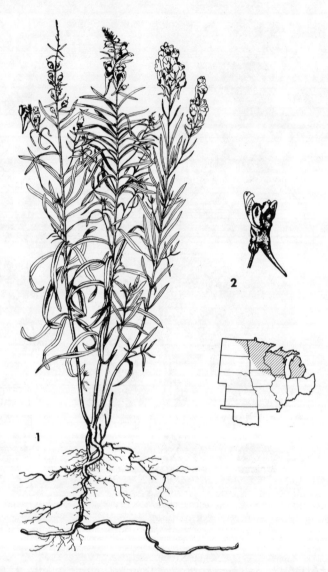

YELLOW TOADFLAX, *Linaria vulgaris* Hill. **1,** entire plant; **2,** single flower. **Perennial,** reproducing by seeds and rootstocks. **Stems** leafy, with very few branches, smooth, 1 to 2 feet (30 to 60 cm) tall, often in clumps, pale green. **Leaves** mostly alternate, narrow, smooth, pale green. **Flowers** snapdragon-like, about 1 inch (2.5 cm) long, bright yellow with deep orange center, in racemes at top of stems. **Seeds** dark brown or black, round, flattened, warty, numerous, in a 2-celled pod. **Found** in circular patches in native pastures, roadsides, and waste places, and along railroads. Sometimes cultivated in gardens, from which it escapes. Rather persistent under cultivation.

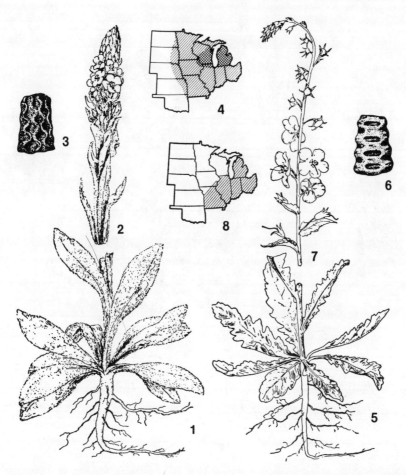

COMMON MULLEIN, *Verbascum thapsus* L. **1**, lower portion of plant; **2**, upper portion of plant; **3**, seed; **4**, distribution. **Biennial**, reproducing by seed. **Stems** 3 to 6 feet (0.9 to 1.8 m) tall, stout, usually unbranched, covered with woolly hairs. **Leaves** at base of plant a rosette, each leaf 6 to 18 inches (15 to 45 cm) long, oblong, densely woolly; upper leaves woolly, smaller, and more pointed, the bases attached to stem and continuing down it to the next leaf. **Flowers** 5-lobed, sulfur-yellow, about 1 inch (2.5 cm) in diameter, in dense spikes. **Seeds** about 1/32 inch (0.8 mm) across, angular, brown, roughened, numerous, contained in an egg-shaped pod. **Found** in pastures, fence rows, and roadsides.

MOTH MULLEIN, *Verbascum blattaria* L. **5**, lower part of plant; **6**, seed; **7**, upper part of plant; **8**, distribution. Similar in some respects to the above species. **Stem** slender and smooth, 2 to 4 feet (0.6 to 1.2 m) tall. **Leaves** on lower part of stem a rosette, dark green, smooth or only slightly hairy, oblong, toothed or lobed; upper leaves alternate, sharp-pointed. **Flowers** yellowish or whitish, on a long, loose spike.

FIGWORT FAMILY, *Scrophulariaceae*

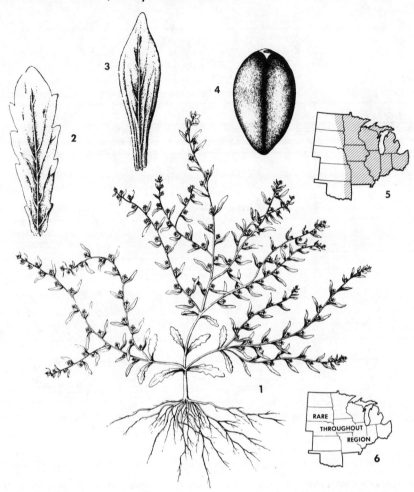

PURSLANE SPEEDWELL, *Veronica peregrina* L. **1**, entire plant; **2**, leaf from lower stem; **3**, leaf from upper stem; **4**, seed; **5**, distribution. **Annual** or **winter annual**, reproducing by seeds. **Root** system fibrous. **Stems** numerous, erect, branching from base, smooth, seldom over 8 inches (20 cm) tall. **Leaves** simple, narrow; those at base opposite and slightly toothed, those on upper stem alternate, with smooth margins. **Flowers** small, white, in axils of upper leaves. **Seed pod** flattened, heart-shaped, about ⅛ inch (3 mm) wide. **Seeds** a long oval, flattened, translucent, glossy, orange-yellow, with a scar on one side. **Found** in lawns, waste places, fertile fields, and gardens.

THYMELEAF SPEEDWELL, *Veronica serpyllifolia* L. **6**, distribution. Similar to the above species. **Stems** almost entirely creeping. **Leaves** opposite, ovate. **Flowers** blue. **Found** in lawns in some areas. A number of other similar species are found locally in the region.

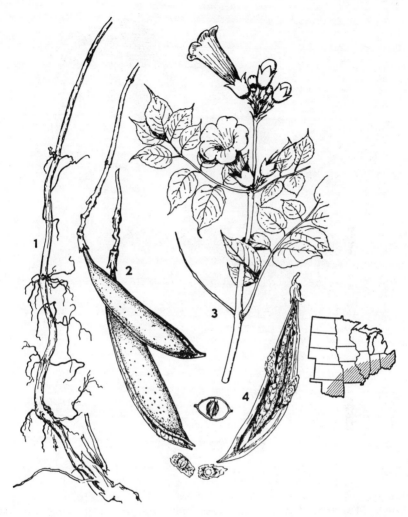

TRUMPETCREEPER, *Campis radicans* (L.) Seem. **1**, root; **2**, seed pods; **3**, upper part of plant with flowers; **4**, lengthwise and crosswise section of seed pod. **Perennial**, reproducing by seeds and vigorous running roots. **Stems** smooth, woody, vining, 20 to 40 feet (6 to 12 m) long if undisturbed. In cultivated fields plant can maintain itself and produce stems 2 to 10 feet (0.6 to 3 m) long. **Leaves** opposite, 8 to 15 inches (20 to 37.5 cm) long, petioled, pinnately compound, with 7 to 11 leaflets. **Flowers** showy, orange and scarlet, 2½ inches (6.3 cm) long, funnel-shaped, in short-stemmed clusters. **Seed pod** 4 to 6 inches (10 to 15 cm) long, rather cigar-shaped, smooth, ridged at the edges of the two lengthwise halves of the pod. **Seeds** broadly winged, in several rows on inside of pod. **Found** in fields, fence rows, yards. Originally cultivated as an ornamental, but has become an aggressive, widely distributed weed.

167

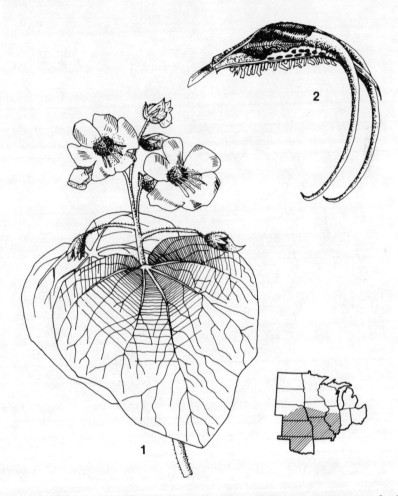

DEVILSCLAW, *Proboscidea louisianica* (Mill.) Thell. **1,** upper part of plant showing leaves and flowers; **2,** seed pod. **Annual,** reproducing by seeds. Often possessing a pronounced odor. **Stems** thick, soft, widely branching, producing a bushy plant up to 3 feet (0.9 m) high and 4 feet (1.2 m) across. **Leaves** opposite, or the upper ones alternate, simple, rounded or kidney-shaped, up to 12 inches (30 cm) across in well-developed plants, densely covered with glandular hairs giving the plant a "clammy" feel. **Flowers** dull white or yellow, with purplish spots, petals united into an irregular tube, 1 to 2 inches (2.5-5 cm) across. **Seed pod** woody at maturity, consisting of a rough-surfaced body about 2 inches (5 cm) long, with 2 up-curved spines, 3 to 5 inches (7.5-12 cm) long, projecting from one end. **Seeds** numerous, egg-shaped, ¼ inch (6 mm) long, dull gray or silvery gray and conspicuously wrinkled. **Found** in dry open prairies and pastures; more abundant in western part of the range. Sometimes cultivated as an ornamental. Seldom an aggressive weed, but the seed pods show up in baled hay.

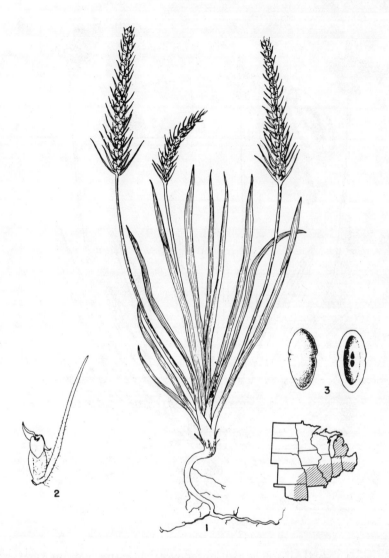

BRACTED PLANTAIN, *Plantago aristata* Michx. **1,** entire plant; **2,** single flower with bract; **3,** two views of seed. **Annual** or **winter annual,** reproducing by seeds. **Stems** erect, simple, leafless, hairy, 6 to 18 inches (15 to 45 cm) tall, terminating in flower spike. **Leaves** at ground level in basal rosette, long, loosely hairy, becoming smooth. **Flowers** numerous, petals inconspicuous, in axils of long bracts, in spikes at top of stem. **Seed pods** 2-seeded. **Seeds** boat-shaped with groove across oval side of seed, 2 white scars in indentation on inner surface, rough-surfaced, dull light brown in color, about ⅛ inch (3 mm) long. **Found** in meadows, pastures, and waste places, usually on rather dry soil of low fertility.

169

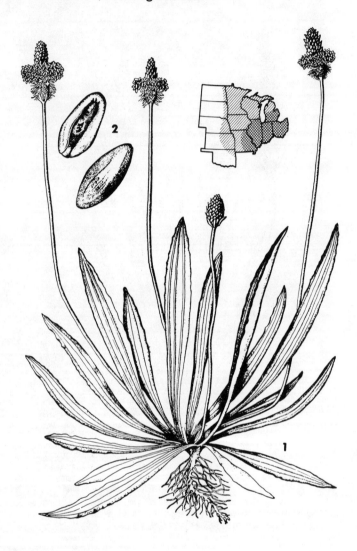

BUCKHORN PLANTAIN, *Plantago lanceolata* L. **1**, entire plant in bloom; **2**, two views of seed. **Perennial**, reproducing by seed. **Stems** erect, leafless, 4 to 12 inches (10 to 30 cm) long, terminating with flower spike. **Leaves** at ground level in a basal rosette, hairy, 2 to 10 inches (5 to 25 cm) long, ¼ to 1 inch (0.6 to 2.5 cm) wide, with 3 to 5 prominent veins running lengthwise. **Flowers** numerous, petals inconspicuous, in short cylindrical spikes at ends of stems. **Seed pods** 2-seeded, splitting across the middle. **Seeds** small, brown, shiny, smooth, boat-shaped, with an indentation in the middle of one side, sticky when damp. **Found** in lawns, meadows, pastures, and waste places. The seeds are difficult to separate from those of small-seeded grasses and legumes.

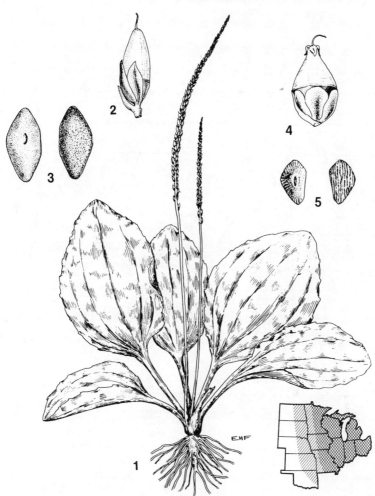

BLACKSEED PLANTAIN, *Plantago rugelii* Dcne. **1**, whole plant; **2**, mature seed pod; **3**, seeds. **Perennial**, reproducing by seeds. **Roots** mostly fibrous. **Stems** erect, leafless, 6 to 12 inches (15 to 30 cm) tall, terminating in the flower spike. **Leaves** simple, broad, egg-shaped, usually wavy-edged, veins conspicuous, base of petiole purplish. **Flowers** numerous, petals inconspicuous, in spikes on the ends of the stems. **Seed pods** nearly cylindrical, about 3/16 inch (4.5 mm) long, splitting across the lower half, containing numerous seeds. **Seeds** dark brown or black, angular, with a scar near center on one side. **Found** on damp, rich soils, especially where shaded. Common in lawns.

BROADLEAF PLANTAIN, *Plantago major* L. **4**, mature seed pod; **5**, seeds. Similar to the above species. **Stems** shorter. **Leaves** smaller and without purplish coloration at base of petiole. **Seed pod** nearly spherical, splitting across upper half. **Seeds** light to dark brown, covered with fine ridges.

171

PLANTAIN FAMILY, *Plantaginaceae*

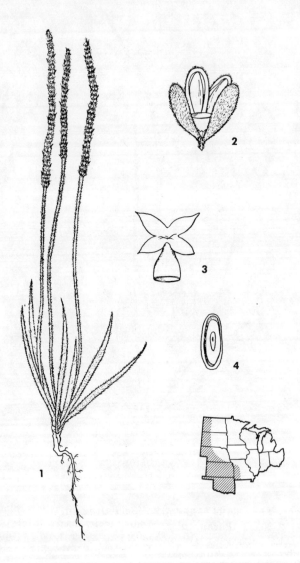

WOOLLY PLANTAIN, *Plantago purshii* Roem. and Schult. **1,** entire plant with taproot; **2,** lower half of seed pod; **3,** upper half of seed pod; **4,** seed. **Annual,** reproducing by seeds. **Stems** erect, without leaves, 3 to 10 inches (7.5 to 25 cm) tall, woolly-haired. **Leaves** narrow, ascending, linear, narrowing to a petiole at the base, 3-nerved, 1 to 5 inches (2.5 to 12.5 cm) long, covered with silky, white hairs. **Flowers** numerous, petals inconspicuous, surrounded by bracts, in dense cylindrical spikes. **Seed pod** containing 2 seeds, splitting across middle. **Seeds** reddish-brown, with convex side and hollow inner face giving a boat-shaped appearance. **Found** in dry overgrazed pastures and wasteland.

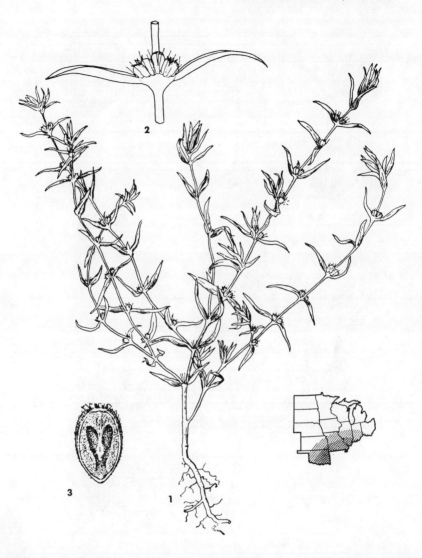

POORJOE, *Diodia teres* Walt. **1**, plant; **2**, section of stem showing flower, leaves, and young pods; **3**, seed. **Annual. Roots** shallow, slender, taprooted. **Stems** hairy, branching, moderately erect, 8 to 24 inches (20 to 60 cm) long. **Leaves** narrow, tapering to long point, edges smooth, opposite, without petioles; fastened in pairs directly to joints of stem, together with long bristles. **Flowers** small, whitish-pink to lavender, at base of leaves. **Seed pods** hairy, with 4 short, green calyx teeth at the top; splitting, when ripe, into 2 parts. **Seeds** hairy, oval, light brown, ⅛ inch (3 mm) long, inner surface indented with a forked groove. **Found** in abandoned fields and along roadsides. Also known as rough buttonweed.

173

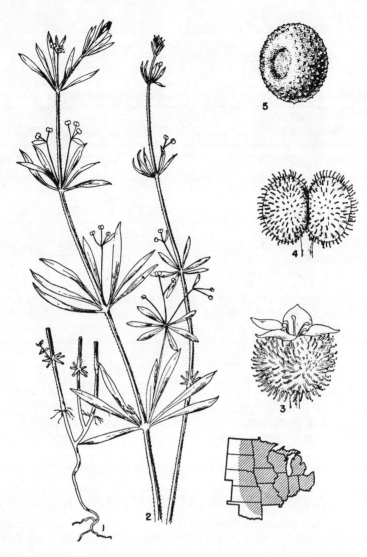

CATCHWEED BEDSTRAW, *Galium aparine* L. **1**, lower section of plant; **2**, upper portion of stems; **3**, flower; **4**, seed pod; **5**, seed. **Annual. Roots** branching, short, shallow. **Stems** 1 to 3 feet (0.3 to 0.9 m) long, weak, sprawling, 4-sided with each edge bearing a row of downward-pointing stiff bristles. **Leaves** narrow, rough, bristle-pointed, 6 to 8 borne in a circle at each joint of stem. **Flowers** very small, white, with 4 petals, borne on slender branches attached at the joints of the stems. **Seed pod** in 2 nearly spherical halves, covered with stiff bristles. **Seed** ball-shaped with deep pit in one side and short, sharp spines, ⅛ inch (3 mm) long, on outer surface. **Found** on moist land in meadows, pastures, woodlands, and fence rows.

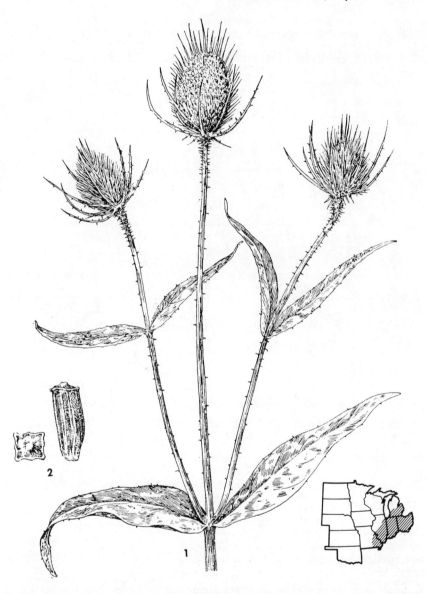

TEASEL, *Dipsacus sylvestris* Huds. **1**, portion of stem with flowers; **2**, seed. **Biennial**, reproducing by seed. **Stem** the second year, coarse, upright, prickly, 2 to 5 feet (0.6 to 1.5 m) tall. **Leaves** lance-oblong, toothed, prickly on margin; a rosette the first year, opposite the second year. **Flowers** lilac or white, with 4 petals, in dense ovoid heads with numerous slender bracts that become stiff-hooked prickles at maturity. **Seeds** about 3/16 inch (4.5 mm) long, 4-angled, ridged, hairy, grayish-brown. **Found** in roadsides, pastures, and old fields.

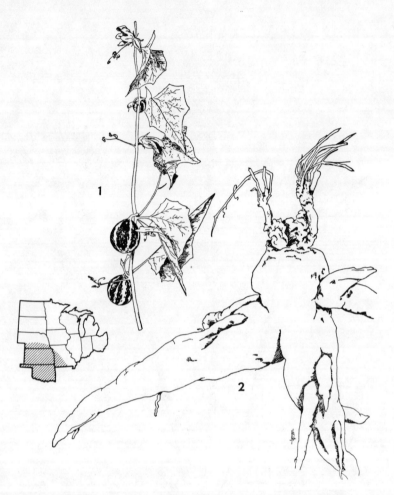

BUFFALO GOURD, *Cucurbita foetidissima* H.B.K. **1,** upper part of plant show-ing fruit; **2,** root system. **Perennial,** reproducing by seed and roots. **Tap-root** yellow inside, carrotlike, very thick and fleshy, often more than 6 inches (15 cm) across, sometimes over 5 feet (1.5 m) long. **Stems** trailing and rooting at joints, 15 to 30 feet (4.5 to 9 m) long, stout, angled, ridged, rough-hairy, many-branched. **Leaves** thick, simple, sharply toothed, 4 inches to 1 foot (10 to 30 cm) long, ovate, long-pointed, rough above, gray-hairy beneath, with strong, rough-hairy petioles. **Flowers** bright yellow, deeply 5-lobed, 3 to 4 inches (7.5 to 10 cm) long and nearly as broad, in leaf axils. Male and female flowers separate but on the same plant. **Fruit** globular, 3 inches (7.5 cm) long, with yellow and green markings and a hard, smooth rind. **Seeds** numerous, oval, flattened, similar to pumpkin seed but about half as large, light straw-colored. **Found** on dry, sandy soil in fields and waste places, and along fence rows. The entire plant has an offensive odor, especially when bruised.

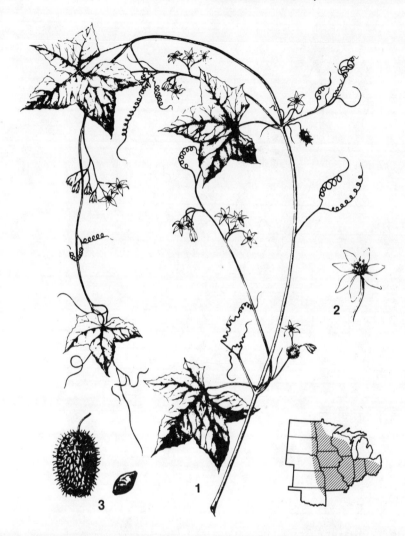

WILD CUCUMBER, *Echinocystis lobata* (Michx.) T. and G. **1**, plant, showing leaves and flower clusters; **2**, flower; **3**, fruit and seed. **Annual**, reproducing by seed. **Stems** vinelike, branched, nearly smooth, except that they are grooved and are sometimes hairy at nodes or joints. Vine may extend 15 to 25 feet (4.5 to 7.5 m). **Leaves** alternate, usually with 5 to 7 sharply pointed lobes, similar in appearance to a cultivated-cucumber leaf. **Flowers** light yellowish-white, in clusters. Male and female flowers separate but often borne together. **Seed pod** a pulpy fruit covered with sharp spines, containing 4 seeds. **Seeds** brown or black, spindle-shaped, flattened, about ¾ inch (1.9 cm) long. **Found** mainly in some river-bottom areas, covering corn and soybeans and making harvest difficult. Occasionally found in fence rows and thickets, especially in low areas.

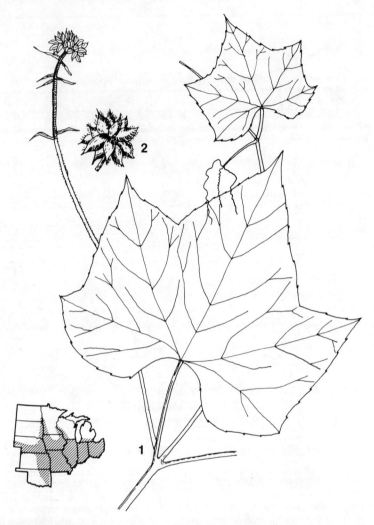

BUR CUCUMBER, *Sicyos angulatus* L. **1**, portion of plant showing stem, leaves, tendrils, and flowers; **2**, cluster of pods containing seeds. **Annual,** reproducing by seeds. **Stem** forms a creeping vine several yards or meters long, with numerous branched, climbing tendrils. **Leaves** alternate, more or less circular in outline but with 3 to 5 shallow lobes, margins finely toothed. Well-developed leaves 4 to 8 inches (10 to 20 cm) wide. **Flowers** unisexual; some are male, producing only pollen; others are female and produce seeds; both are whitish, with 5 united petals about ½ inch (1.3 cm) across. **Seeds** borne singly in a flat, egg-shaped pod, ½ to ¾ inch (1.3 to 1.9 cm) long and ¼ inch (0.6 cm) thick, covered with barbed, prickly bristles. **Found** in wooded areas along stream banks and roadsides and in other shady, damp places. Fast-growing in early summer and very conspicuous, but not usually an aggressive weed in cultivated fields.

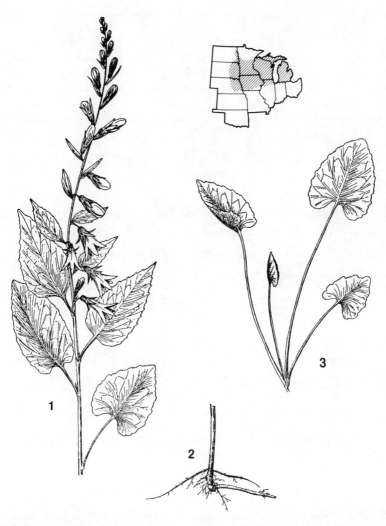

CREEPING BELLFLOWER, *Campanula rapunculoides* L. **1,** upper part of plant; **2,** lower part of plant; **3,** seedling showing basal leaves. **Perennial,** spreading by short stolons, root fragments, and seed. **Roots** tuberlike, both fibrous and fleshy. **Stems** erect, 1 to 3 feet (30 to 90 cm) tall, smooth, leafy, with milky juice. **Basal leaves** long-petioled, heart-shaped; **upper leaves** short-petioled or sessile. **Flowers** numerous, nodding, bell-shaped, about ¾ inch (1.9 cm) long with 5 teeth, purple, scattered along upper portion of the stem. **Seeds** shiny, oval, straw-colored, rounded on one side, ridged on the other, 1 millimeter long. **Found** in dense patches on roadsides, in fence rows, lawns, gardens, and waste places. Often spreads from areas where grown as an ornamental.

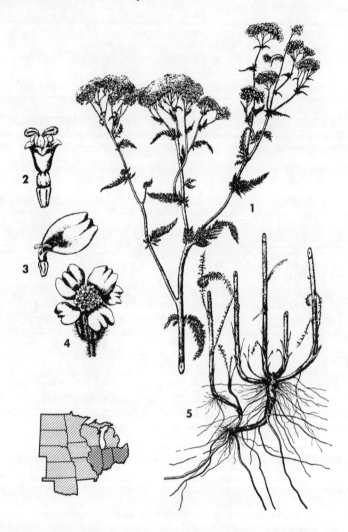

COMMON YARROW, *Achillea millefolium* L. **1**, plant in flower; **2**, disk flower; **3**, ray flower; **4**, flower head; **5**, root system. **Perennial**, reproducing by seed and underground rhizomes. **Stems** 1 to 2 feet (30 to 60 cm) tall, branching at top, covered with grayish-green hairs. Each crown may produce several stems. **Leaves** soft, covered with hairs, finely divided, fernlike. Basal leaves longer than those attached to stems. **Flower heads** small with 5 to 10 white ray flowers and yellow disk flowers, in flat-topped clusters at top of branches. Pink-flowered forms occur rarely. **Seed** tiny, flat, oblong, white or gray. **Found** in meadows, pastures, and waste places; not common in cultivated fields. Persists mostly on thin soil where conditions are unfavorable for the growth of more desirable plants. The plant has an offensive odor and bitter taste.

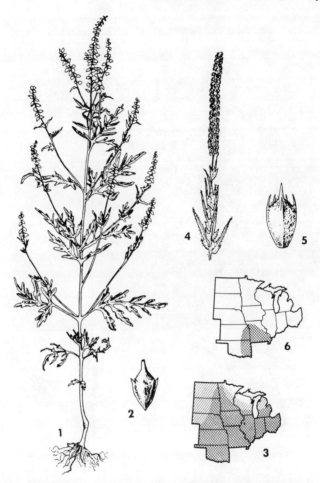

COMMON RAGWEED, *Ambrosia artemisiifolia* L. **1**, plant; **2**, seed; **3**, distribution. **Annual**, shallow-rooted. **Stems** rough, hairy, erect, branched, 1 to 4 feet (0.3 to 1.2 m) tall. **Leaves** nearly smooth, deeply cut into a number of lobes, mostly alternate. **Flowers** of two kinds; male pollen-producing flowers in small inverted clusters at tips of branches; seed-producing flowers fewer, borne at the bases of leaves and in forks of upper branches. **Seed** about ⅛ inch (3 mm) long, enclosed in woody hull, light brown, top-shaped, pointed, bearing several longitudinal ridges ending in short, spiny projections. **Found** in old pastures, wasteland, roadsides, stubblefields, and cultivated land. Produces pollen abundantly and is a hazard to hay fever sufferers.

LANCELEAF RAGWEED, *Ambrosia bidentata* Michx. **4**, portion of stem showing toothed leaves and flowers; **5**, seed; **6**, distribution. Similar to the above. **Leaves** abundant, lanceolate, partly clasping the stem, hairy, bearing 1, 2, or more large sharp teeth on each side of a broad base. **Seeds** 4-angled with 4 sharp spines.

181

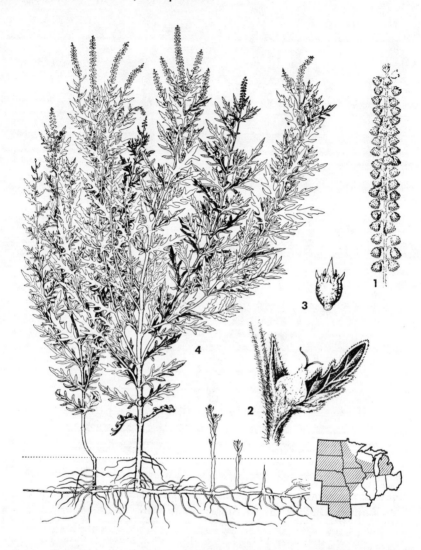

WESTERN RAGWEED, *Ambrosia psilostachya* DC. **1,** male flowers on spike; **2,** female flowers; **3,** seed; **4,** entire plant. **Perennial,** reproducing by rootstocks and seeds. **Stem** erect, normally less than 20 inches (50 cm) tall, hairy, bushy, branched above, often growing in dense patches. **Leaves** with short petioles, alternate or opposite, ovate-lanceolate, with very deep lobes, sometimes compound, rough. **Flowers** of two kinds. Male flowers in clusters on ends of stems and branches; female flowers few, without petals, in axils of upper leaves. **Seed** about ⅛ inch (3 mm) long, with a woody hull that has a pointed tip surrounded by short spines. **Found** in prairies, plains, and uncultivated areas. The pollen is a hazard to hay fever sufferers. Also known as perennial ragweed.

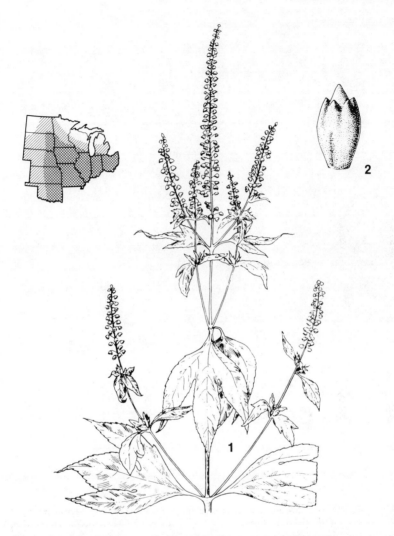

GIANT RAGWEED, *Ambrosia trifida* L. **1,** portion of stem showing leaves and flowers; **2,** seed. **Annual**, reproducing by seed. **Stems** coarse, rough, reaching a height of 12 to 18 feet (3.6 to 5.4 m) on fertile, moist soils; 4 to 8 feet (1.2 to 2.4 m) in less fertile, drier areas. **Leaves** distributed in pairs at nodes; large, slightly hairy, entire, with 3 or, occasionally, 5 lobes. **Flowers** separated, with male flowers abundant in clusters on tips of branches and stems. Female flowers sparse, without petals, in axils of upper leaves. **Seeds** ¼ to ½ inch (0.6 to 1.3 cm) long, with a woody hull bearing blunt ridges that end in several short, thick spines at the tip. **Found** mostly on fertile, moist soils, especially bottomlands. May be serious in corn, soybeans, and other cultivated crops. The abundant pollen is a hazard to hay fever sufferers. Also known as horseweed.

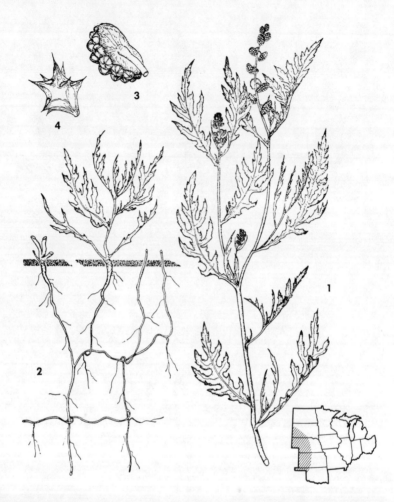

SKELETONLEAF BURSAGE, *Ambrosia tomentosa* Nutt. **1,** top of plant; **2,** root system and young plant; **3,** male flowers; **4,** seed. **Perennial,** reproducing by seeds and deep creeping rhizomes. **Stems** bushy, branched, usually 1 to 2 feet (30 to 60 cm) tall. **Leaves** alternate, divided into narrow lobes, hairy on underside, 2 to 5 inches (5 to 12.5 cm) long. **Flowers** small, male and female borne separately but on the same plant. Male flowers in small drooping heads along tips of branches; female in axils of upper leaves. **Burs** surrounding female flowers bear 1 to 3 seeds, have sharp spines when mature. **Found** in moist cultivated fields, waste places, pastures, and irrigated areas, especially if poorly drained.

WOOLLYLEAF BURSAGE, *Ambrosia grayi* (A. Nels.) Shinners. A species closely related to the above. **Leaves** covered with short woolly hairs on both surfaces, terminal lobe quite large. **Bur** has curved rather than straight spines.

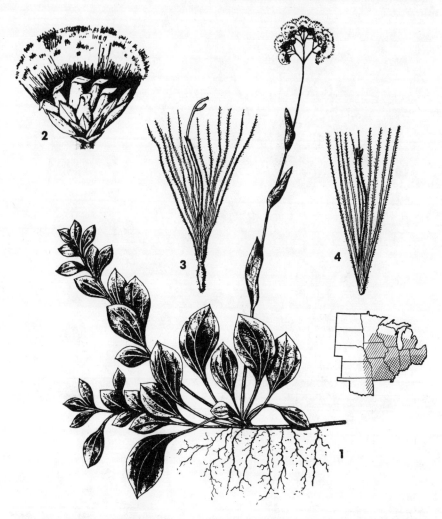

PLANTAINLEAF PUSSYTOES, *Antennaria plantaginifolia* (L.) Hook. **1,** part of plant, showing rooting of creeping stem, and a vertical flowering shoot; **2,** detail of staminate head; **3,** female flower; **4,** male flower. **Perennial,** reproducing by seeds and creeping stems; forms patches. **Stems** decumbent or creeping until flowering, when erect flowering stems 4 to 20 inches (10 to 50 cm) high are formed. **Leaves** at base alternate, petioled, simple, entire, strongly rounded at summit, tapering at base, with hoary upper surface and white-woolly under surface; stem leaves fastened directly to stem with no petiole, small, narrow, white-woolly. **Flowers** borne in small clustered heads, 3 to 30 heads on a stem. Male and female flowers on separate plants; plants bearing male flowers smaller. **Seeds** about 1/32 inch (0.8 mm) long, with circle of long hairs attached at top. **Found** in run-down pastures, meadows, and waste places; one of the typical "poverty weeds."

185

MAYWEED, *Anthemis cotula* L. **1**, portion of plant in flower; **2**, seedling; **3**, seed. **Annual** or **winter annual** with short, thick taproot, reproducing only by seed. **Stems** erect, slender, much branched, nearly smooth, 12 to 18 inches (30 to 45 cm) tall. **Leaves** finely divided, with a strong disagreeable odor. **Flower heads** resembling those of a daisy, ½ to 1 inch (1.3 to 2.5 cm) across, borne singly at ends of branches. Ray flowers white, surrounding a mass of numerous small yellow disk flowers. **Seeds** brown, oblong, 10-ribbed, with a rough seed coat. **Found** most commonly in abandoned fields, barnyards, and waste places. Also known as dog fennel.

COMMON BURDOCK, *Arctium minus* (Hill) Bernh. **1**, root; **2**, crown and first-year leaf; **3**, upper part of second-year growth; **4**, seed. **Biennial**, reproducing by seed only. **Taproot** large, fleshy, living over one winter. **Stem** a crown close to the soil surface the first year; the second year much branched, 3 to 5 feet (0.9 to 1.5 m) tall, hairy, and somewhat grooved or angular. **Leaves** large, with heart-shaped base, covered with hairs; the first year forming a dense rosette, the second year distributed alternately on stem with the larger leaves near the base. **Flower heads** made up of numerous small red-violet disk flowers surrounded by numerous hooked bracts which later form a bur about ½ inch (1.3 cm) in diameter. **Seeds** rather rough, mottled dark gray, about ¼ inch (6 mm) long. **Found** in waste places where soil is productive and not disturbed. Not commonly found in cultivated areas.

GREAT BURDOCK, *Arctium lappa* L. Similar in appearance to above but larger in all respects. Much less common in our region.

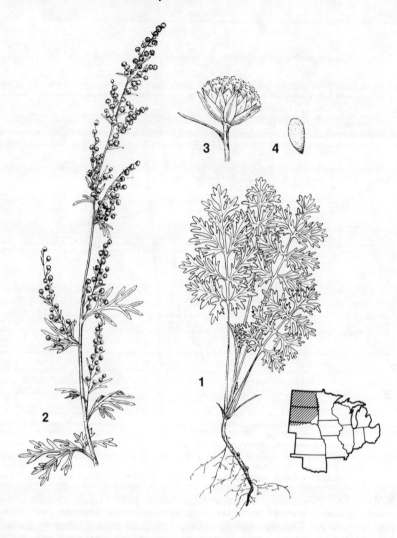

ABSINTH WORMWOOD, *Artemisia absinthium* L. **1**, lower part of leafy stem; **2**, upper part of stem with flowers; **3**, flower head; **4**, seed. **Perennial**, fragrant herb or shrub, reproducing by seed and by branching rootstocks. **Stems** up to about 3 feet (90 cm) tall, clumped, often woody at base and hoary with soft, short gray hairs. **Leaves** alternate, lower leaves with long petioles, upper with short or no petioles. The blade, 2 to 5 inches (5 to 12.5 cm) long, is divided 2 or 3 times into leaflets which are covered with silky hairs. **Flower heads** yellowish, about ⅛ inch (3 mm) in diameter, hanging from leafy panicles. **Fruits** 1-seeded (achenes), smooth, about 1/16 inch (1.5 mm) long, flattened, narrow at base and rounded at tip, light gray-brown. **Found** in pastures, in waste places, and on roadsides, often on dry soils. If grazed by cattle, it is likely to flavor the milk.

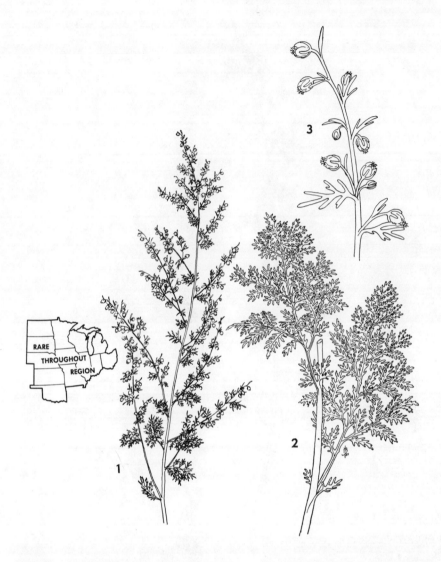

ANNUAL WORMWOOD, *Artemisia annua* L. **1,** upper leaves and flowers; **2,** lower leaves; **3,** flowers. **Annual,** with taproot, reproducing by seed only. **Stem** smooth, erect, without hairs, slender, branched in upper portion, 1 to 4 feet (0.3 to 1.2 m) tall. **Leaves** on lower part of stem alternate, sweet-scented, divided into 3 sharply toothed lobes. Upper leaves much smaller. **Flower heads** drooping, greenish, about 3/16 inch (4.5 mm) in diameter, composed of disk flowers without conspicuous petals, in loose panicles. **Seeds** about 1/16 inch (1.5 mm) long, angled, oval, light yellow. **Found** in sandy soils, especially roadsides, wasteland, and fallow fields. Not a troublesome weed. A number of similar species are found in the area.

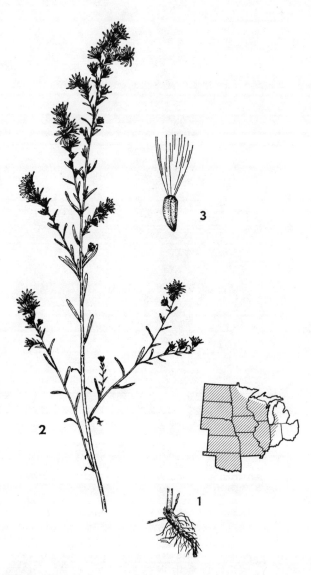

HEATH ASTER, *Aster ericoides* L. **1**, root; **2**, upper part of stem with flower; **3**, seed. **Perennial**, growing from a slender rhizome. **Stems** erect, much branched, 1 to 3 feet (30 to 90 cm) tall, densely covered with hairs. **Leaves** small, ¼ to ½ inch (0.6 to 1.3 cm) long, rigid, linear, entire, numerous. **Flowers** ¼ to ½ inch (0.6 to 1.3 cm) across when open, very numerous; 8 to 20 white ray flowers, yellow disk flowers. **Seeds** silky-hairy, 1/16 inch (1.5 mm) long, light brown. **Found** in pastures, meadows, and waste places, and on roadsides.

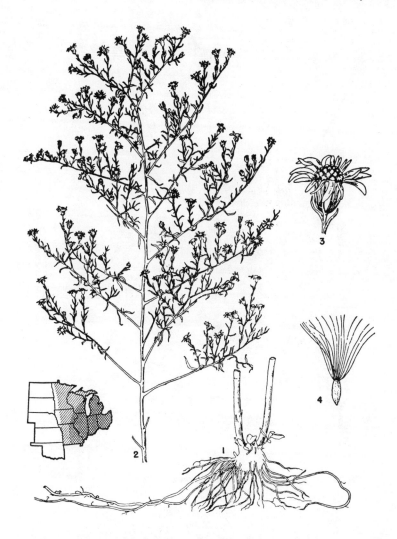

WHITE HEATH ASTER, *Aster pilosus* Willd. **1,** basal part of plant; **2,** flowering part of plant; **3,** flower head; **4,** seed with down attached. **Perennial,** with fibrous roots developing from the hard enlarged crown. **Stems** erect, 1 to 4 feet (0.3 to 1.2 m) tall, hard and tough, smooth or usually hairy or stiff-hairy, upper two-thirds much branched. **Leaves** at base narrowly lance-shaped, those on upper stem becoming very small and narrow, sharp-pointed, numerous. **Flower heads** ½ to ¾ inch (1.3 to 1.9 cm) in diameter, very numerous, mostly on upper sides of branches; white ray flowers surrounding the yellow disk flowers. **Seeds** small, oblong, light brown, with a tuft of silky hairs attached to the top. **Found** in pastures, meadows, roadsides, and waste places. Difficult to control in areas that cannot be cultivated. A number of species resembling the one described are found in the region.

191

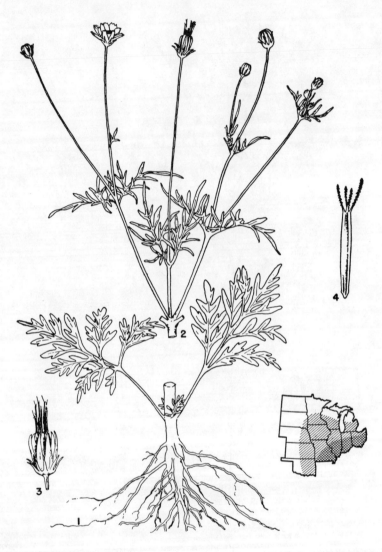

SPANISHNEEDLES, *Bidens bipinnata* L. **1,** lower portion of plant; **2,** upper portion of stem and flower heads; **3,** mature flower; **4,** seed. **Annual,** taprooted with numerous side branches. **Stems** erect, smooth, branching in upper portions. **Leaves** with petioles, divided several times into fine segments; borne opposite at nodes of both stems and branches. **Flower heads** found singly at the ends of long, slender, nearly leafless branches, pale yellow ray flowers surrounding yellow disk flowers. **Seeds** about ½ inch (1.3 cm) long, narrow, sharp-pointed, brown to black, bearing 3 to 4 stiff spines covered with short, down-pointed bristles. **Found** in waste places and grain stubble fields.

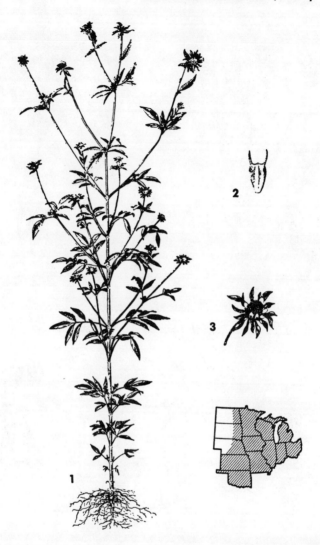

DEVIL'S BEGGARTICKS, *Bidens frondosa* L. **1**, entire plant; **2**, seed; **3**, flower head. **Annual**, reproducing by seed. **Taproot** much branched and shallow. **Stems** 3 to 5 feet (0.9 to 1.5 m) tall, slightly hairy and somewhat 4-sided. Most branching occurs near the top. **Leaves** opposite, 4-ranked, deeply pinnately divided, and covered with minute hairs. **Flower heads** about 1 inch (2.5 cm) in diameter, surrounded by leafy bracts. Ray flowers around the outer edge yellow, disk flowers in the center brownish-yellow. **Seed** flat, brown, about 1/2 inch (1.3 cm) long with 2 barbed spines attached at upper end. **Found** frequently on rich, moist soil in low areas and waste places. Not found in cultivated fields. Several other species similar to this one are found in the region.

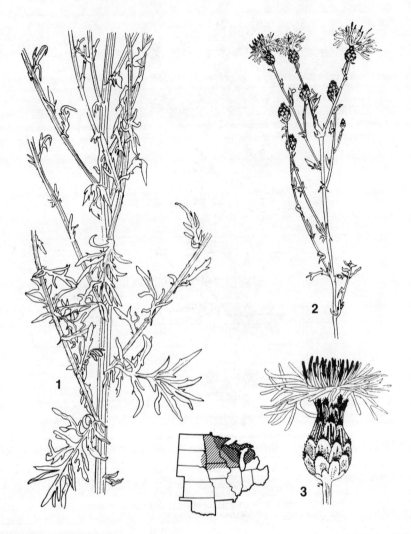

SPOTTED KNAPWEED, *Centaurea maculosa* Lam. **1**, portion of stem with leaves; **2**, upper portion of stem with flower heads; **3**, single flower head. **Biennial**, reproducing by seed. **Stems** erect or ascending, slender, 1 to 3 feet (30 to 90 cm) tall, hairy, branching. **Leaves** alternate, deeply divided into narrow segments, covered with short hairs, much reduced in size near top of the plant. **Flower heads** about ¾ inch (1.9 cm) across, numerous, consisting only of pink to purple disk flowers; heads both terminal and in axils of upper leaves; each head surrounded by leaflike bracts with dark tips bearing a fringe of bristly hairs. **Seed** brownish, ⅛ inch (3 mm) long, notched on one side of base, with a short tuft of bristles on tip end. **Found** in pastures, fields, and roadsides, especially those with dry, gravelly, or sandy soils.

194

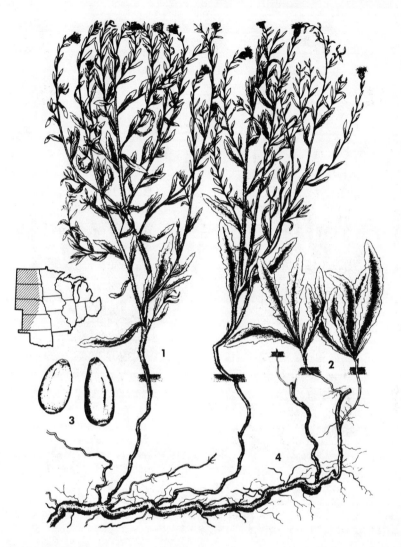

RUSSIAN KNAPWEED, *Centaurea repens* L. **1**, stem and leaves; **2**, new shoots; **3**, seeds; **4**, root. **Perennial**, reproducing by seeds and rhizomes. **Roots** deep and extensive with new shoots coming from various depths. **Stems** 2 to 3 feet (60 to 90 cm) tall, very hairy, ridged, tough, and woody, branches numerous, tipped with flower heads. **Leaves** hairy; lower ones deeply indented, resembling those of dandelions; upper leaves short, narrow, and smooth-edged. **Flower heads** about 1 inch (2.5 cm) in diameter, composed of disk flowers only, which vary from white to light rose or light blue; each head surrounded by small, leafy bracts with smooth tips. **Seed** grayish or yellowish, smooth, about ⅛ inch (3 mm) long. **Found** in waste places or dry-land areas. Persists in cultivated fields when established.

195

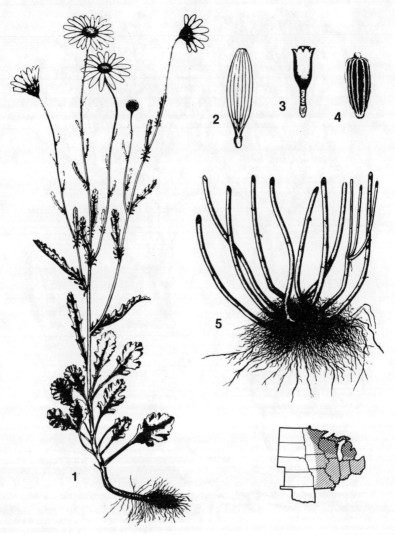

OXEYE DAISY, *Chrysanthemum leucanthemum* L. **1,** entire plant showing flower heads; **2,** ray flower or petal; **3,** disk flower; **4,** seed; **5,** base of plant with numerous stems. **Perennial,** reproducing by rhizomes and seeds. **Root** system fibrous. **Stems** smooth, seldom branched, 1 to 3 feet (30 to 90 cm) high. **Leaves** alternate, simple, usually conspicuously lobed, especially near base of plant. **Flower heads** occurring singly at the ends of the stems, 1 to 2 inches (2.5 to 5 cm) in diameter. Ray flowers with white petals, disk flowers yellow. **Seeds** oval, usually curved, with one side straight and other convex, 1/16 inch (1.5 mm) long, with a prominent knoblike scar on top. **Seeds** black with 8 to 10 white or gray ridges or ribs. **Found** in old pastures, especially those low in fertility. Not a problem in cultivated fields.

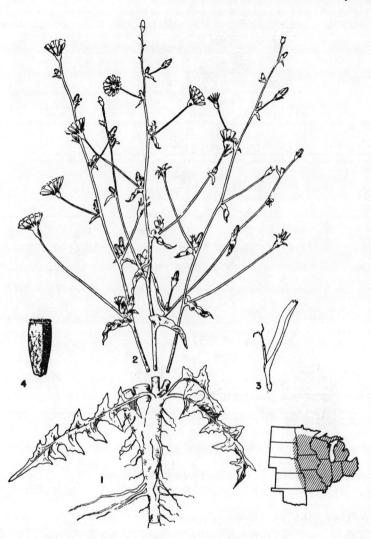

CHICORY, *Cichorium intybus* L. **1**, root and crown; **2**, upper portion of stems with flowers; **3**, individual flower; **4**, seed. **Perennial**, reproducing by seed. **Taproot** large, deep, and fleshy. **Stem** erect, branched, smooth, and with a milky sap. **Leaves** basal and along the stems. Basal leaves forming a rosette, 6 to 8 inches (15 to 20 cm) long, lobed, and resembling those of a dandelion. Leaves on stems smaller and either less lobed or entire. **Flower heads** of ray flowers only, bright blue, about 1 inch (2.5 cm) across, formed at ends of branches and in the axils of leaves of upper part of plant. Flowers are most conspicuous in the morning and close later in the day. **Seeds** dark brown, wedge-shaped, about ⅛ inch (3 mm) long. **Found** along roadsides, in meadows and pastures. Seldom thrives in cultivated fields.

PLUMELESS THISTLE, *Carduus acanthoides* L. **1,** upper portion of plant showing stem, leaves, and flower head; **2,** seed. **Biennial** as a rule, but sometimes winter annual or annual. **Stem** erect, with spiny wings, 3 to 6 feet (0.9 to 1.8 m) tall, branched. **Leaves** deeply divided with alternate lobes. Rosette and lower stem leaves large, decreasing in size up the stem; hairs scattered on upper leaf surface, denser on lower surface, especially along midrib. Lobes on leaves and stem ending with white to yellowish spine. **Flower heads** globe-shaped, erect, single or loosely clustered, with spiny wings to base. Blooms reddish-purple, ½ to 1 inch (1.3 to 2.5 cm) in diameter, occurring from late May through early July. **Seed** maturing 5 to 12 days after full bloom; oblong; usually straight but sometimes slightly curved; straw-colored with brown striations to collar where pappus is attached. Pappus light-colored, not plumed. **Found** in pastures, meadows, and waste areas.

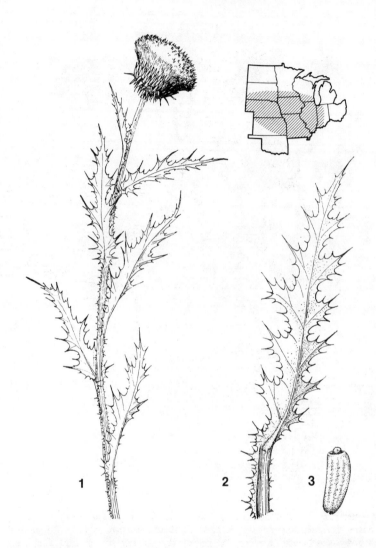

1   2   3

MUSK THISTLE, *Carduus nutans* L. **1**, upper part of stem; **2**, portion of stem showing leaf attachment; **3**, seed. **Biennial**, large, coarse plant. **Stem** erect, spiny, with spiny wings, 3 to 6 feet (0.9 to 1.8 m) tall, lower portion branched. Stems and branches densely covered with short hairs. **Leaves** alternate, coarsely toothed, extending down the stem, very spiny. **Flower heads** as much as 2 inches (5 cm) across, on the ends of long, nearly naked stems, frequently drooping or nodding; flowers purple or lavender; spiny-tipped bracts surrounding the head. **Seeds** about 3/16 inch (4.5 mm) long, glossy yellowish-brown; pappus hairlike. **Found** in pastures, meadows, and waste areas. Considerable variation may be found because this species is a polymorphic complex, with numerous semidistinct phases.

199

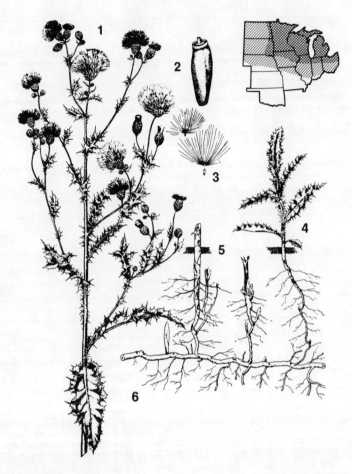

CANADA THISTLE, *Cirsium arvense* (L.) Scop. **1,** upper part of plant; **2,** seed; **3,** down with seed; **4,** new shoot; **5,** base of stem; **6,** root system. **Perennial,** reproducing by seeds and horizontal roots. **Roots** extend several feet deep and some distance horizontally. **Stems** 2 to 5 feet (0.6 to 1.5 m) tall, grooved, branching only at top, slightly hairy when young, increasingly hairy as they mature. **Leaves** usually with crinkled edges and spiny margins, somewhat lobed, and smooth. **Flower heads** numerous, compact, about ¾ inch (1.9 cm) or less in diameter, of lavender disk flowers only. Surrounded by bracts without spiny tips. Male and female flowers usually in separate heads and borne on different plants. **Seed** brown, smooth-coated, slightly tapered, about 3/16 inch (4.5 mm) long and with a ridge around the blossom end. Seed attached to tannish down that is easily broken off. **Found** in all crops; a persistent and troublesome weed. While this description fits most Canada thistles, there are a number of varieties differing slightly in appearance.

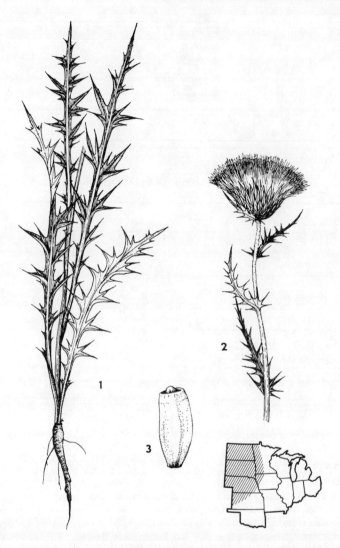

FLODMAN THISTLE, *Cirsium flodmani* (Rydb.) Arthur. **1**, lower part of leafy stem; **2**, upper portion of stem; **3**, seed. **Perennial**, deep-rooted, reproducing from creeping rhizomes and seed. **Stem** 2 to 3 feet (60 to 90 cm) tall, covered with white felt, sparingly branched. **Leaves** in a rosette, light green to grayish on upper side, white with matted hair on lower side. First rosette leaves may be entire; later rosette and stem leaves become increasingly divided into needlelike lobes, cut sometimes to the midrib. **Flowers** reddish-purple, borne in heads surrounded by prickly bracts and often subtended by small, prickly leaves at base of head. Dorsal ridge of bracts may be resinous and sticky. **Fruits** 1-seeded (achenes), about ⅛ inch (3 mm) long. **Found** in pastures, fields, and meadows; often a problem in rural cemeteries.

201

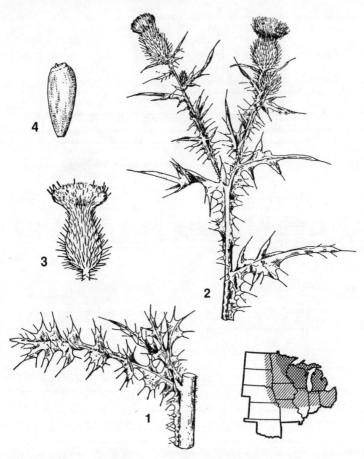

BULL THISTLE, *Cirsium vulgare* (Savi) Tenore. **1**, portion of stem showing leaf attachments; **2**, upper portion of stem; **3**, flower head; **4**, seed. **Biennial**, reproducing by seed. In first year forms rosette with large fleshy taproot. **Stem** second year, 2 to 4 feet (0.6 to 1.2 m) tall, heavy, often branched, more or less hairy. **Leaves** deeply cut, spiny, green on both upper and lower surfaces despite presence of hair. Leaf bases running down stem to give stem winged appearance. Spines on lobes of leaves and stems. **Flower heads** compact, 1 to 2 inches (2.5 to 5 cm) in diameter, rose to reddish-purple; each head surrounded by spiny-tipped bracts. **Seeds** straw-colored, striped with brown, ridged around one end, tipped with an easily detached plumose pappus. **Found** in pastures, meadows, and other unculti-vated land. Does not survive cultivation.

TALL THISTLE, *Cirsium altissimum* (L.) Spreng. Similar to above. **Biennial**, re-producing by seed. **Stems** 3 to 10 feet (0.9 to 3 m) tall. **Leaves** may vary from entire to lobed, and are dark green on upper surface and white woolly on lower surface. **Flower heads** about 1 inch (2.5 cm) in diameter, rose-purple.

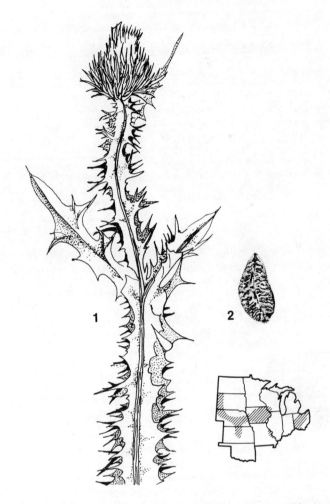

SCOTCH THISTLE, *Onopordum acanthium* L. **1,** upper portion of plant show-ing stem, leaves, and flower heads; **2,** seed. **Biennial,** rarely winter annual, reproducing by seed. **Leaves** at base of plant in rosette first year, coarse, nearly fleshy, grayish with dense hairs, appearing almost cottony at center of rosette. **Stem** erect, 2 to 6 feet (0.6 to 1.8 m) tall, strongly branched with upper branches taller than terminal flower. Stem strongly winged, with wings continuous and lobes spined. Stem leaves lobed, not deeply cut, lobes with sharp spines. **Flower heads** 1 to 2 inches (2.5 to 5 cm) wide, flattened, reddish-purple, short spines on bracts becoming harsh and sharp at maturity. Blooms from mid-June through July with seed maturing through July and August. **Seeds** about 3/16 inch (4 to 5 mm) long, plump, dark brown to black, and rugose or wrinkled. When mature, seeds are forced out of head by crowding. Pappus short, straw-colored, with stiff hairs but not plumed. **Found** in pastures, meadows, and noncropland.

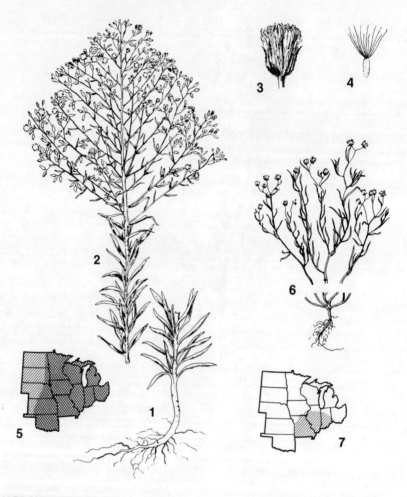

HORSEWEED, *Conyza canadensis* (L.) Cronq. **1**, lower part of leafy stem; **2**, upper part of stem with flowers; **3**, mature flower head; **4**, seed; **5**, distribution. **Annual,** reproducing by seed. **Stem** stout, erect, unbranched at base, 1 to 6 feet (0.3 to 1.8 m) tall, with bristly hairs. **Leaves** numerous, without petioles, linear, dark green, with scattered coarse white bristles, margins toothed or entire. **Flower heads** numerous, small, in axillary panicles, a narrow-pointed bract at the base of each head. Ray flowers greenish-white, scarcely noticeable, surrounding yellow disk flowers. **Seeds** about 1/16 inch (1.5 mm) long with numerous slender white bristles on one end. **Found** in pastures, roadsides, and wasteland. Also known as marestail.

DWARF FLEABANE, *Conyza ramosissima* Cronq. **6**, plant; **7**, distribution. Similar to the above but smaller and bushy. **Stem** 6 to 18 inches (15 to 45 cm) tall, much branched. **Leaves** narrow. **Flower heads** few, scattered. **Found** in dry fields and old pastures.

PLAINS COREOPSIS, *Coreopsis tinctoria* Nutt. **1,** plant showing growth habit; **2,** seed. **Annual,** reproducing by seeds. **Root** system fibrous. **Stems** smooth with many slightly angled branches, up to 4 feet (1.2 m) tall. **Leaves** smooth, opposite or alternate, petioled; lower leaves divided into narrow, linear, or lance-shaped segments, upper leaves narrow and undivided. **Flower heads** numerous, slender-stalked, about 1 inch (2.5 cm) in diameter; ray flowers yellow or orange, with or without purplish-brown base, disk flowers dark purple or brown. **Seed** small, linear-oblong, incurved, wingless, black with a white scar. **Found** in fields and waste places, most abundant on low, moist, poorly drained soils.

205

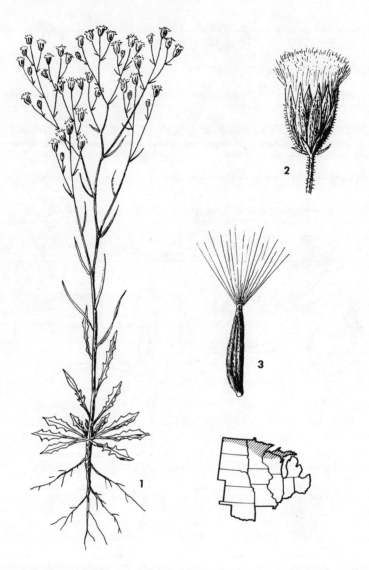

SMOOTH HAWKSBEARD, *Crepis capillaris* (L.) Wallr. **1,** entire plant; **2,** flower head; **3,** seed. **Annual** or **biennial,** reproducing by seeds only. **Stems** slender, erect, leafy, with milky juice, often branching at base, 1 to 2 feet (30 to 60 cm) tall. **Leaves** alternate, nearly free of hairs, spatulate with spreading lobes at base, margins cut or toothed. **Flower heads** about ½ inch (13 mm) in diameter, composed of yellow ray flowers, on long stalks at tips of branches. **Seeds** tapered on both ends, about 1/16 inch (1.5 mm) long, brownish, with numerous soft white bristles at upper end. **Found** in hayfields, pastures, and wasteland.

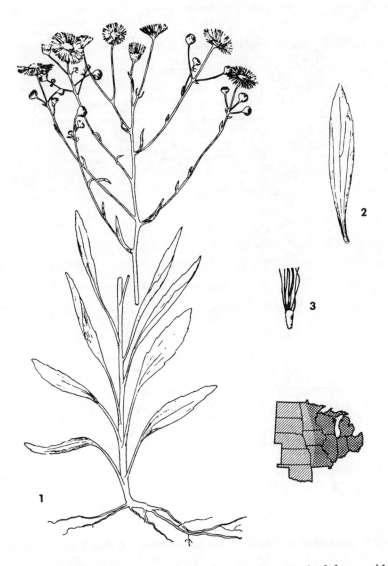

ROUGH FLEABANE, *Erigeron strigosus* Muhl. **1,** plant; **2,** leaf from middle of stem; **3,** seed. **Annual, winter annual,** or **biennial,** reproducing by seeds. **Stems** clustered, 1 to 3 feet (30 to 90 cm) tall, hairy, with numerous branches from the upper part. **Leaves** variable, lower ones ovate, upper lanceolate, blade often tapering toward base to form more or less winged petiole. **Flower heads** ½ to 1 inch (1.3 to 2.5 cm) in diameter, white to lavender ray flowers surrounding the yellow disk flowers. **Seeds** 1/16 inch (1.5 mm) long, wedge-shaped, with a tuft of short white bristles at top. Found most commonly in old hayfields and thin pastures. Several similar species differing slightly from the above occur in the region. Also known as daisy fleabane.

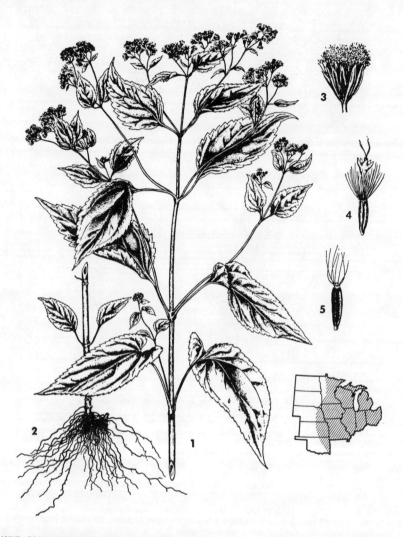

WHITE SNAKEROOT, *Eupatorium rugosum* Houtt. **1,** upper part of plant; **2,** root; **3,** flower head; **4,** single flower; **5,** seed. **Perennial,** spreading by seeds and short rhizomes. **Roots** much branched and fibrous. **Stem** 1 to 3 feet (30 to 90 cm) tall, smooth, and branched near top. **Leaves** opposite, elliptical, thin, smooth, with toothed edges and slender petioles. **Flower heads** small, of white disk flowers only. **Seed** black, angular, about ⅛ inch (3 mm) long, with a tuft of white hairs. **Found** in hardwood timber areas, woodland, pastures, and waste places. It grows only in shaded areas. Contains a cumulative poison that causes the disease known as "trembles" in cattle and horses. Dairy products from animals that have eaten the plant are poisonous to man, causing "milk sickness," one of the serious scourges of pioneers in the region.

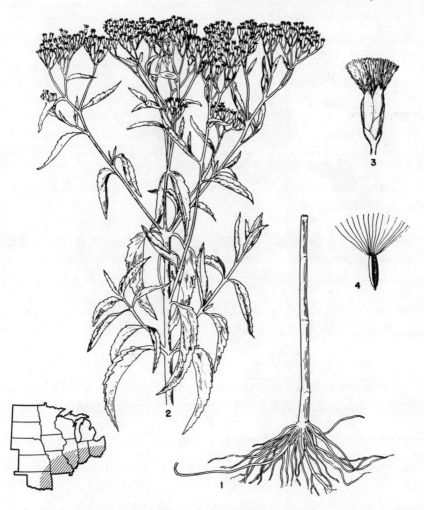

LATE EUPATORIUM, *Eupatorium serotinum* Michx. **1,** lower portion of plant with roots; **2,** upper portion of plant in blossom; **3,** flower head; **4,** seed. **Perennial,** reproducing by seed. **Roots** shallow, fibrous. **Stems** hairy, erect, 3 to 6 feet (0.9 to 1.8 m) tall, upper portion much branched. **Leaves** narrow, tapering to a point, petioled, edges toothed; upper leaves alternate, lower ones opposite. **Flower heads** small, cylindrical, of whitish disk flowers only, borne in a compact, flat-topped cluster at top of plant. **Seed** narrow, oblong to oval with several longitudinal ribs and with a tuft of whitish bristles at top. **Found** on moist soils in feedlots, old pastures, and wasteland. A number of other somewhat similar species of *Eupatorium* (e.g., *E. perfoliatum, E. purpureum, E. altissimum, E. maculatum*) are found in the region, under the common names of thoroughwort, boneset, or joe-pye weed. They are all more or less similar to this illustration. In several states, one or more of these are much more common than *E. serotinum*.

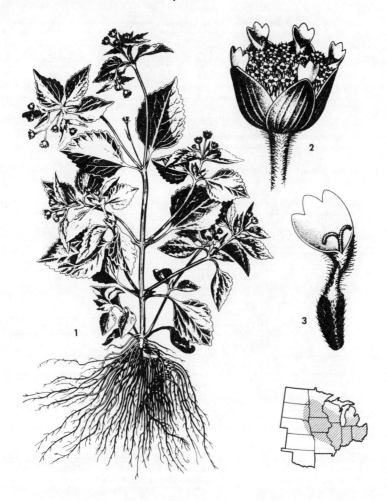

SMALLFLOWER GALINSOGA, *Galinsoga parviflora* Cav. **1,** entire plant; **2,** flower head; **3,** ray flower. **Annual,** reproducing by seeds. **Stem** 1 to 2 feet (30 to 60 cm) tall, erect or spreading, much branched, slender, hairy. **Leaves** opposite, oval to lance-shaped, pointed at tip, thin, with toothed margin. **Flower heads** small, numerous, scattered at ends of branches. Ray flowers very small, white, 4 to 5 in number, surrounding the small yellow disk flowers. **Seed** about 1/16 inch (1.5 mm) long, wedge-shaped, 4-sided, dark brown to black, with a fringe of tiny scales at one end. **Found** in gardens, dooryards, waste places, and lowland fields, especially in damp areas with rich soil. Hairy galinsoga, *Galinsoga ciliata* (Raf.) Blake, is similar to the above and is found in similar places, often more commonly. It has a more pubescent stem than smallflower galinsoga, and has well developed pappus scales on the ray flowers. Ray flowers of smallflower galinsoga have either very small or no pappus scales.

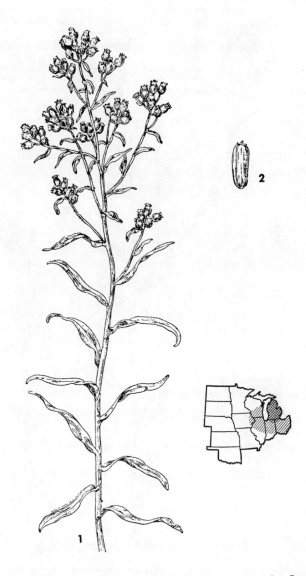

FRAGRANT CUDWEED, *Gnaphalium obtusifolium* L. **1,** plant in flower; **2,** seed. **Biennial,** reproducing by seed. **Stem** slender, 1 to 3 feet (30 to 90 cm) tall, branching mostly in the upper portion; covered with white, feltlike hair. **Leaves** covered with same type of hair; lower leaves a rosette, usually spatulate; stem leaves narrow, without petioles. **Flower head** small, of white disk flowers only, clustered at ends of upper branches. **Seed** about 1/32 inch (0.8 mm) long, wedge-shaped, with a tuft of hairs on one end. **Found** in old fields, pastures, and dry unproductive areas. Does not persist in cultivated fields.

211

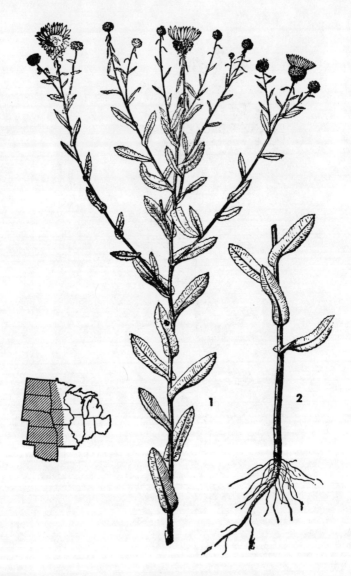

GUMWEED, *Grindelia squarrosa* (Pursh) Dunal. **1**, top of plant; **2**, root and lower stem. **Biennial**, reproducing by seeds. **Stems** erect, 1 to 3 feet (30 to 90 cm) tall, branching near top, rough, somewhat sticky. **Leaves** coarse, oblong, slightly cupped with heavy midrib and toothed edges, alternate, partially clasping stem. **Flower heads** about 1 inch (2.5 cm) in diameter, yellow ray flowers surrounding the yellow disk flowers. Bracts surrounding the head are covered with a sticky resinous substance. **Seeds** light gray, flattened, curved, somewhat 4-angled, with longitudinal lines. **Found** in dry meadows, pastures, and waste places.

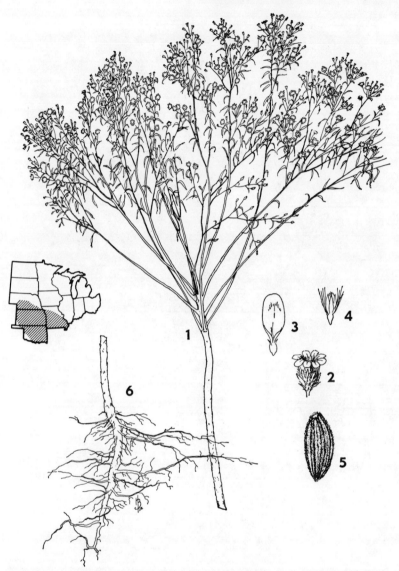

COMMON BROOMWEED, *Gutierrezia dracunculoides* (DC.) Blake. **1,** plant in flower; **2,** flower head; **3,** ray flower; **4,** disk flower; **5,** seed; **6,** root system. **Annual,** reproducing by seed. **Taproot** with many fibrous branches. **Stem** erect, tough or almost woody, bushy-topped, 15 to 30 inches (37.5 to 75 cm) tall. **Leaves** linear, about 1 inch (2.5 cm) long and ⅛ inch (3 mm) wide. **Flower heads** small, at tips of the many fine branches. Ray flowers 5 to 10 in number, bright yellow, surrounding the pale yellow disk flowers. **Found** mostly in pastures. Sometimes the dominant weed in many pastures, although its abundance varies greatly from year to year.

213

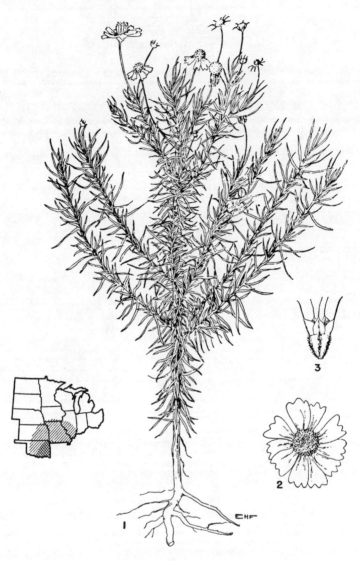

BITTER SNEEZEWEED, *Helenium amarum* (Rafin.) H. Rock. **1,** plant; **2,** flower head; **3,** seed. **Annual,** with short branching taproot. **Stems** smooth, erect, 6 to 30 inches (15 to 75 cm) tall, branching in upper portion. **Leaves** numerous, smooth, threadlike, without petioles, alternate, and crowded along main stem and branches. **Flower heads** about ¾ inch (1.9 cm) in diameter, ray flowers yellow with toothed tip, surrounding dome-shaped mass of yellow disk flowers. **Seed** reddish-brown, hairy along edges, wedge-shaped, bearing bristle-tipped scales at top. **Found** in old feedlots, pastures, idle land, and wasteland. Does not persist under cultivation.

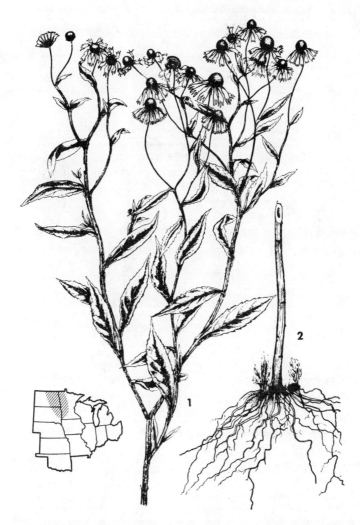

COMMON SNEEZEWEED, *Helenium autumnale* L. **1**, upper part of plant; **2**, lower stem and roots. **Perennial,** reproducing by seeds and a spreading crown. **Roots** much branched, somewhat fleshy. **Stems** slender, erect, 2 to 5 feet (0.6 to 1.5 m) tall, smooth to rough, narrowly branched, with winged appendages along the stem, especially on upper part. **Leaves** alternate, slender, oblong to lanceolate, 2 to 4 inches (5 to 10 cm) long, gray and hairy when young, becoming greenish and smooth later. **Flower heads** sunflower-like, about 1 inch (2.5 cm) across. Ray flowers yellow, drooping, surrounding the greenish-yellow disk flowers. **Seed** about 1/16 inch (1.5 mm) long, hairy. **Found** around water holes and ditches where water is readily available. Whether dry or fresh, poisonous to livestock, especially sheep. Most serious in the western areas.

215

COMPOSITE FAMILY, *Compositae*

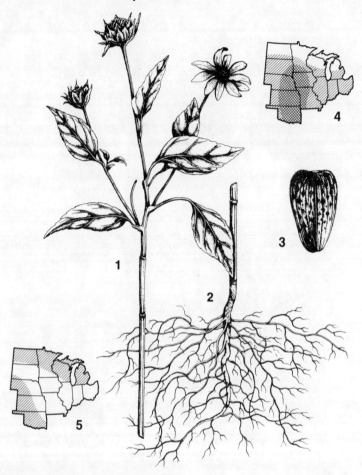

COMMON SUNFLOWER, *Helianthus annuus* L. **1**, upper stem with flowers; **2**, lower stem and root system; **3**, seed; **4**, distribution. **Annual**, reproducing only by seed. **Root** system fibrous. **Stem** erect, stout, rough, 2 to 10 feet (0.6 to 3 m) tall, freely branching. **Leaves** alternate, simple, rough, hairy, mostly with saw-toothed margins; lower ones long-petioled. **Flower heads** 1 to 5 inches (2.5 to 12.5 cm) in diameter. Ray flowers yellow, surrounding brown or reddish-brown disk flowers. **Seed** ⅛ to nearly ½ inch (0.3 to 1.3 cm) long, ovate to wedge-shaped, slightly 4-angled and flattened, white, or gray or dark brown with lighter stripes or spots, without hairs except at the tip. **Found** in cultivated land, pastures, and waste places.

PRAIRIE SUNFLOWER, *Helianthus petiolaris* Nutt. **5**, distribution. Similar to the above but smaller and more slender. **Annual. Stems** 6 inches to 6 feet (15 cm to 1.8 m) tall, rough. **Leaves** usually pale green, simple, slender, petioled, rough on both sides, all but lowest alternate. **Flower heads** 1 to 2 inches (2.5 to 5 cm) in diameter. **Found** in dry prairies and uncultivated land.

MAXIMILIAN SUNFLOWER, *Helianthus maximiliani* Schrad. **1,** plant in flower; **2,** disk flower; **3,** ray flower. **Perennial,** reproducing by seed and fleshy roots and thickened rhizomes. **Stem** stout and rough, 1 to 5 feet (0.3 to 1.5 m) tall. **Leaves** numerous, alternate or lower ones opposite, lanceolate, 3 to 7 inches (7.5 to 17.5 cm) long, with short petioles or none at all, rough on both sides, folding in drying. **Flower heads** 3 to 4 inches (7.5 to 10 cm) in diameter, few to many, ray and disk flowers both yellow. **Seed** gray, mottled with black, wedge-shaped, flattened, about ¼ inch (6 mm) long. **Found** on dry prairies and in pastures.

217

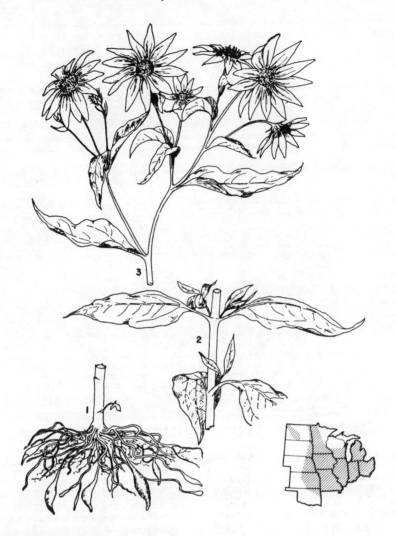

JERUSALEM ARTICHOKE, *Helianthus tuberosus* L. **1,** lower part of stem with roots, rhizomes, and immature tubers; **2,** section from middle of stem; **3,** upper portion of stem with flower heads. **Perennial,** reproducing by rhizomes, tubers, and seeds. **Roots** fibrous, from short rhizomes which bear edible white tubers at tips. **Stems** erect, usually branching above, rough-hairy, up to 9 feet (2.7 m) high. **Leaves** simple, large, opposite on lower part and alternate on upper part of stem, upper surface very rough, lower surface hairy, varying from egg-shaped to lance-shaped, edges saw-toothed. **Flower heads** about 2 inches (5 cm) in diameter, with large yellow ray flowers surrounding yellow disk flowers. **Seed** flattened, wedge-shaped, smooth, often mottled with black. **Found** in moist fields, fence rows, roadsides, and woods. Troublesome when established in cultivated fields.

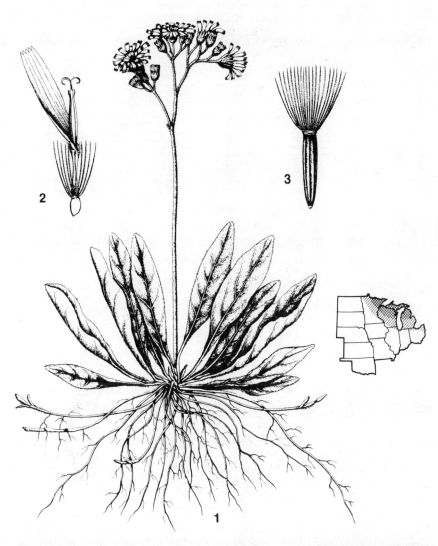

ORANGE HAWKWEED, *Hieracium aurantiacum* L. **1**, entire plant, showing roots, stolons, leaves, and flower stalk; **2**, single flower; **3**, seed. **Perennial**, reproducing by seeds and stolons. **Roots** fibrous. Stolons run along ground, rooting at the nodes. **Stems** erect, 6 to 18 inches (15 to 45 cm) tall, covered with stiff hairs, containing a milky juice. **Leaves** basal, without petioles, simple, covered with stiff hairs. **Flower heads** about ¾ inch (1.9 cm) in diameter, clustered at the top of the leafless stems, composed of conspicuous orange-red ray flowers only. **Seeds** about 1/16 inch (1.5 mm) long, dark brown or black, cylindrical, elongated, and covered with longitudinal ridges. **Found** in poor pastures and other poor noncultivated soils. Does not persist in cultivated crops.

219

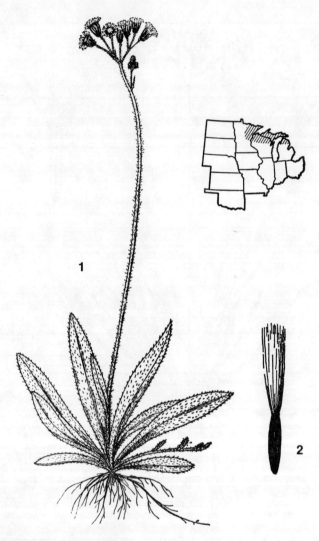

YELLOW HAWKWEED, *Hieracium pratense* Tausch. **1**, entire plant; **2**, seed.
Perennial, reproducing by seeds, by slender rhizomes, and by occasional
stolons that develop late in summer. **Stems** 6 inches to 3 feet (15 to 90 cm)
tall, coarse, hairy, containing milky juice; upper parts with blackish, gland-
tipped hairs. **Leaves** simple, without petioles, about 10 inches (25 cm) long,
spatula-shaped, with bristles on both surfaces. Usually they grow from the
base of the stem, although 1 to 3 well-developed leaves are borne higher on
the stem. **Flower heads** each have 12 or more yellow flowers. **Fruits** 1-seeded
(achenes), about 1/16 inch (1.5 mm) long, dark brown or black, and cylindrical with vertical ridges. **Found** in clearings, meadows, pastures, grass-
lands, and old fields on dry, gravelly, and somewhat acid soil.

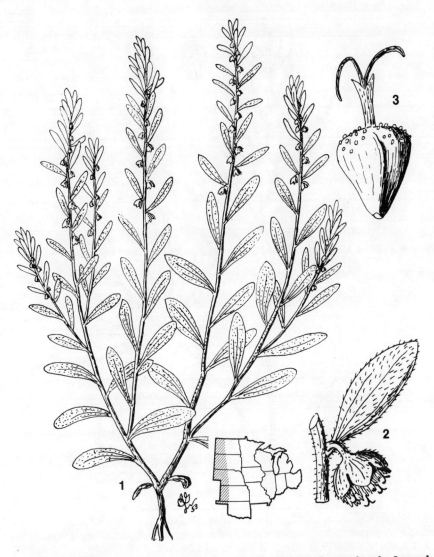

POVERTYWEED, *Iva axillaris* Pursh. **1**, entire plant; **2**, flower head; **3**, seed. **Perennial**, reproducing by seeds and creeping rootstocks. **Stems** 6 inches to 2 feet (15 to 60 cm) tall, erect, branched, very leafy. **Leaves** without petioles, opposite or the upper ones alternate, narrowly oblong, somewhat thick or fleshy, stiff, and rough to the touch. **Flower heads** small, drooping, surrounded by bracts in the form of a 5-lobed cup, borne in axils of the upper leaves. Several greenish-yellow disk flowers included in each head. **Seeds** egg-shaped, flattened, sometimes curved, grayish-brown in color. **Found** in grain fields, meadows, cultivated crops, and waste places. Common in dry areas on alkaline or saline soils.

221

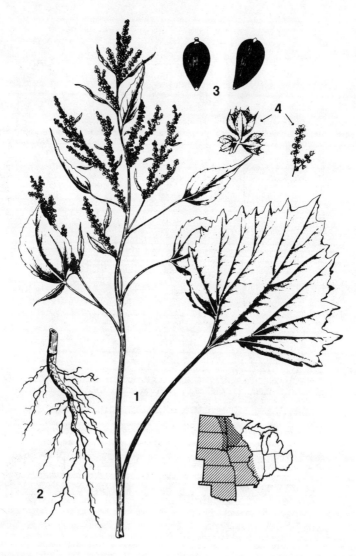

MARSHELDER, *Iva xanthifolia* Nutt. **1**, plant in bloom; **2**, root; **3**, seeds; **4**, flowers. **Annual** with taproot, reproducing by seeds. **Stem** 3 to 8 feet (0.9 to 2.4 m) tall, moderately branched, grayish-green, smooth. **Leaves** broad, mostly opposite, light grayish-green, covered with small short hairs, with toothed margins. **Flower heads** small, drooping, borne in panicles at top of stem and in axils of upper leaves. **Flowers** either male or female but borne in the same head, without petals, greenish-yellow in color. **Seeds** gray to black, triangular, somewhat flattened with a ridged surface, about ⅛ inch (3 mm) long, produced in abundance. **Found** along roadsides, in farmyards, ditches, and pastures. Infrequent in cultivated fields.

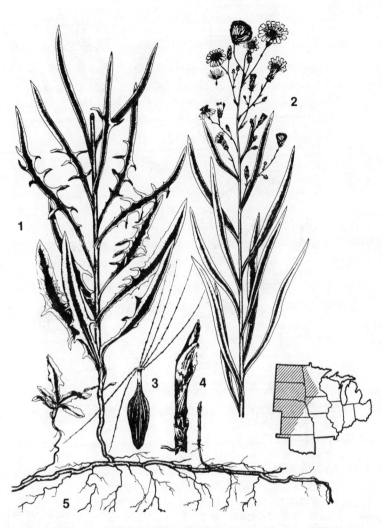

BLUE LETTUCE, *Lactuca pulchella* (Pursh) DC. **1,** lower portion of stem showing long leaves with notched margins; **2,** upper stem showing smooth leaf
margins and flowering habit; **3,** seed with bristles; **4,** new shoots as they
emerge from soil; **5,** root system. **Perennial,** reproducing by seeds and
creeping roots. **Stems** 1 to 4 feet (0.3 to 1.2 m) tall, branching at top, smooth
and leafy. **Leaves** bluish-green, with smooth surface. Those on lower stem
2 to 8 inches (5 to 20 cm) long with notched margins; those on upper stem
shorter with smooth margins. **Flower heads** about 1 inch (2.5 cm) in diameter, composed of pale blue or violet ray flowers. **Seed** oblong, flat, gray or
reddish-brown, with 3 ridges on face, and tapering to a beak with soft white
bristles. Entire plant contains a bitter, milky white juice. **Found** in pastures,
grain fields, and waste areas. Difficult to eradicate from cultivated areas.

223

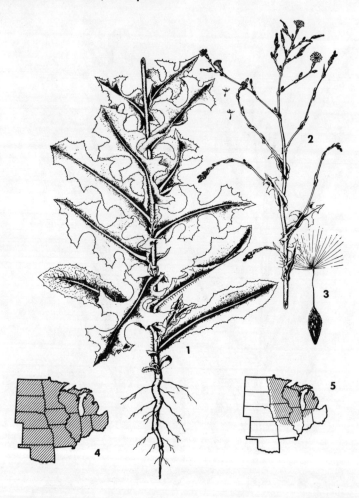

PRICKLY LETTUCE, *Lactuca serriola* L. **1**, lower portion of plant; **2**, upper part of plant with flowers; **3**, seed; **4**, distribution. **Annual** or **winter annual**, reproducing by seed. **Taproot** large. **Stem** erect, 2 to 6 feet (0.6 to 1.8 m) tall, stiff, leafy, hollow, prickly on the lower part and containing milky juice. **Leaves** large, coarse; lower leaves more or less lobed, upper ones small, linear; all with prickles along margin and along center of lower surface of midrib. **Flower heads** about 3/16 inch (4.5 mm) across, in open terminal clusters, composed of yellow ray flowers only. **Seed** black, rough, slender-tipped with a tuft of white bristles at upper end. **Found** in roadsides, fence rows, and wasteland.

TALL LETTUCE, *Lactuca canadensis* L. **5**, distribution. Similar to the above. **Biennial,** reproducing by seed. **Leaves** basal the first year, covered with powdery bloom, usually lanceolate, entire or with wavy margins, edges smooth, midrib without prickles but may have a few hairs.

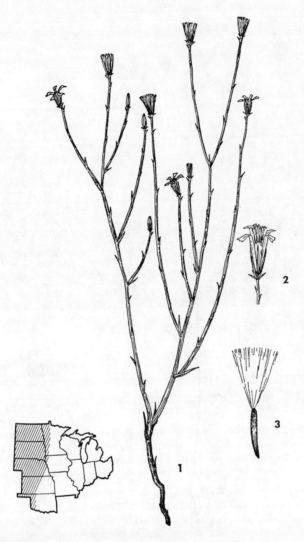

SKELETONWEED, *Lygodesmia juncea* (Pursh) D. Don. **1,** upper part of stem with flowers; **2,** flower head; **3,** seed. **Perennial,** reproducing from long taproot and by seeds. **Stem** 10 to 20 inches (25 to 50 cm) tall, rigid, much branched, usually tufted, finely grooved, containing milky juice, rushlike. **Leaves** alternate, narrow, lower ones about 1 to 2 inches (2.5 to 5 cm) long, upper ones reduced to scales or sharp-pointed bracts making the stem appear leafless. **Flowers** pink or white, mostly 5 per head at end of stems. **Fruits** are 1-seeded (achenes), 3/16 to ¼ inch (4.5 to 6 mm) long, narrow with 8 to 10 ribs on each side of achene. **Found** in meadows, plains, and waste places, mostly on light dry soils. The bitter milky juice of stems and leaves is suspected of being poisonous to livestock.

225

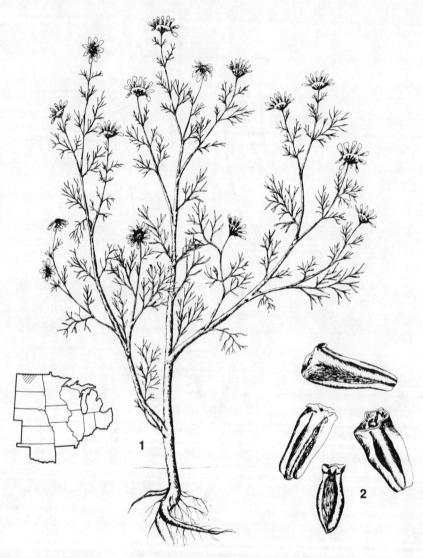

FALSE CHAMOMILE, *Matricaria maritima* L. var. *agrestis* (Knaf) Wilmott.
1, stems, leaves, flowers; **2,** seeds. **Winter annual** or **annual**, reproducing
by seed. **Taproot** system with extensive secondary roots. **Stems** 1 to 3 feet
(30 to 90 cm) tall, frequently branched, especially from the crown area.
Leaves dark green, 1 to 3 inches (2.5 to 7.5 cm) long, finely divided. **Flowers**
occurring singly at end of branches, ½ inch (1.3 cm) in diameter, with
center of yellow disk flowers and with ray flowers having white petals.
Seeds gray to black, 1/16 inch (1.5 mm) long, 3-angled. **Found** along roadsides, fences, tree belts, and ponds. It may be a problem in cultivated fields
when fall rosettes are not destroyed with spring tillage before planting.

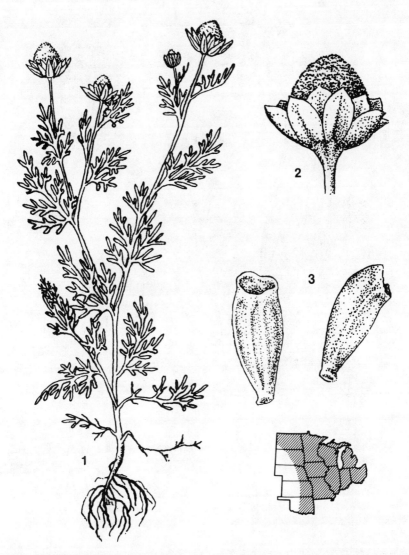

PINEAPPLEWEED, *Matricaria matricarioides* (Less.) Porter. **1,** entire plant; **2,** flower head; **3,** seed. **Annual. Stems** smooth, without hairs, much-branched, 6 to 18 inches (15 to 45 cm) tall. **Leaves** alternate, finely divided, smelling like pineapple when bruised. **Flower heads** numerous, on the ends of branches, without ray flowers, consisting of a mass of greenish-yellow disk flowers grouped into a cone-shaped head about ¼ inch (6 mm) in diameter. **Seeds** about 1/16 inch (1.5 mm) long, 3- to 5-ribbed. **Found** on roadsides and in barnyards, waste places, gardens, and sometimes cultivated fields.

227

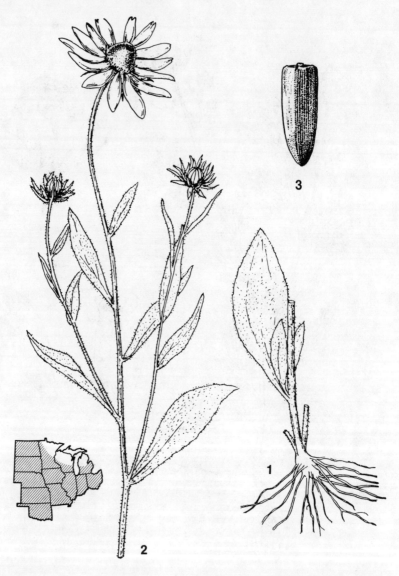

BLACKEYED SUSAN, *Rudbeckia hirta* L. **1**, lower part of plant; **2**, upper part of plant with flowers; **3**, seed. **Perennial**, reproducing by seeds. **Stems** bristly-hairy, erect, 1 to 3 feet (30 to 90 cm) tall, with a few branches. **Leaves** at base of stem ovate; upper leaves somewhat linear, coarsely toothed or entire, without petioles. **Flower heads** 2 to 3 inches (5 to 7.5 cm) in diameter, on long terminal stalks. Ray flowers orange-yellow, surrounding a conelike mass of purplish-brown disk flowers. **Seed** 4-angled, about ⅛ inch (3 mm) long. **Found** in old hay fields and upland pastures with dry soil.

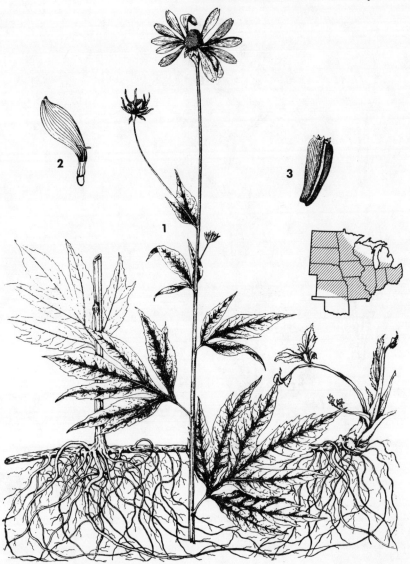

CUTLEAF CONEFLOWER, *Rudbeckia laciniata* L. **1**, plant in flower; **2**, ray flower; **3**, seed. **Perennial**, reproducing by rhizomes and seed. **Root** system fibrous. **Stems** 3 to 7 feet (0.9 to 2 m) tall, often whitish. **Leaves** alternate, deeply pinnately lobed or compound, long-petioled. **Flower heads** 2 to 4 inches (5 to 10 cm) in diameter on long bare stalks. Ray flowers long, yellow, soon drooping, surrounding a conelike mass of yellowish disk flowers. **Seed** gray, about ⅜ inch (9 mm) long, straight or curved, 4 angled, with 4 short teeth on one end. **Found** in rich low ground, pastures, and woodland, especially along streams. Also called goldenglow.

229

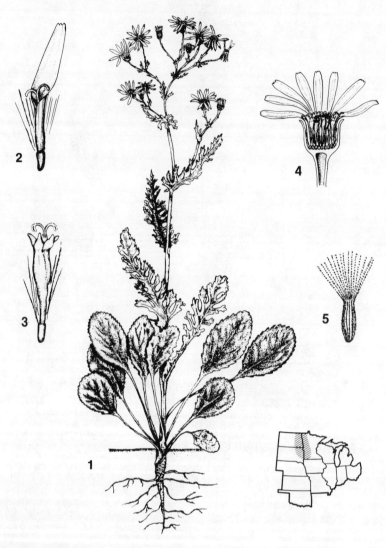

GOLDEN RAGWORT, *Senecio aureus* L. **1**, plant in flower; **2**, ray flower; **3**, disk flower; **4**, section of flower head; **5**, seed. **Perennial**, reproducing by seed and short rhizomes. **Stems** erect, usually 1 to 2 feet (30 to 60 cm) tall, smooth, branched near top. **Leaves** on lower part of stem with long petioles and ovate blades rounded at the tip and with round-toothed margins. Leaves on upper part of stem with deeply cleft margins, the segments often toothed, alternate, without petioles. **Flower heads** on slender branches, ½ to 1 inch (1.3 to 2.5 cm) in diameter. Ray flowers numerous, deep yellow, surrounding a mass of yellow disk flowers. **Seeds** elongated, smooth, with a tuft of barbed white hairs at the tip. **Found** in swamps and wet meadows.

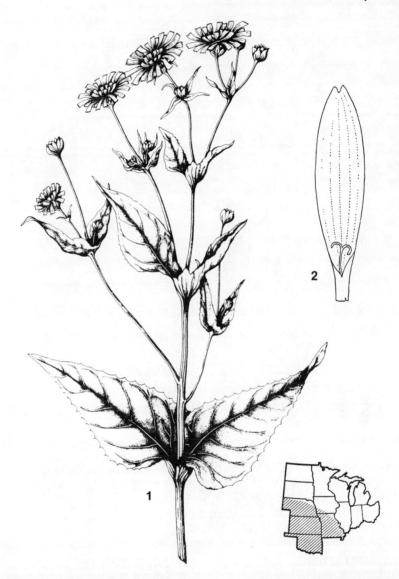

CUPPLANT, *Silphium perfoliatum* L. **1,** upper portion of plant; **2,** ray flower. **Perennial,** reproducing by seed. **Stem** stout, square, erect, 4 to 8 feet (1.2 to 2.4 m) tall, branching slightly at the top. **Leaves** opposite, bases extending around stem to form a cup, rough on both sides, with saw-toothed edges. Larger leaves 6 to 12 inches (15 to 30 cm) long, 4 to 8 inches (10 to 20 cm) wide. **Flower heads** 2 to 3 inches (5 to 7.5 cm) across, composed of bright yellow ray flowers surrounding yellow disk flowers. **Seeds** gray to black, oblong, flat, notched at end. **Found** in fence rows, roadsides, waste places. Does not persist in cultivated land. Also known as cup rosinweed.

GRAY GOLDENROD, *Solidago nemoralis* Ait. **1,** basal part of stem and rootstock; **2,** upper stem and flower clusters; **3,** flower head; **4,** seed. **Perennial,** reproducing by seeds and by persistence of the stout, branched base of the stem. **Stems** 6 to 30 inches (15 to 75 cm) tall, hairy, grayish. **Leaves** on lower part of plant petioled and tongue-shaped; upper leaves smaller, oblong, grayish-hairy. **Flower heads** small, cylindrical in a slender, curving, 1-sided cluster, 2 to 8 inches (5 to 20 cm) long. Ray flowers few, small, yellow; disk flowers few, small, yellowish. **Seeds** oblong, about 1/16 inch (1.5 mm) long, bearing a tuft of white bristles on the top. **Found** in recently abandoned fields, fence rows, and open woods especially on dry sites. A number of species resembling the one described are found in the region.

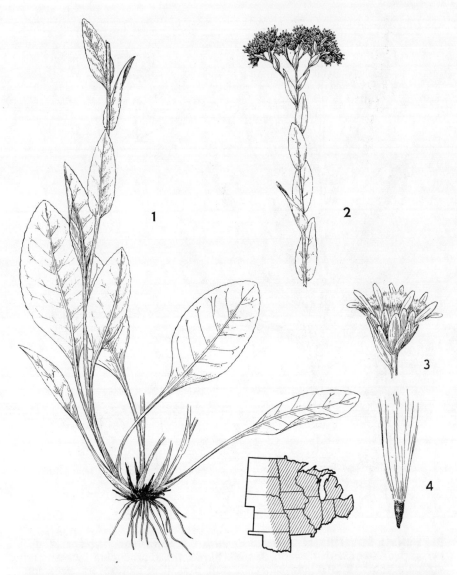

RIGID GOLDENROD, *Solidago rigida* L. **1,** lower part of plant; **2,** upper part of plant; **3,** flower head; **4,** seed. **Perennial,** reproducing by seeds and by persistence of a stout, branched base of the stem. **Stem** coarse, slightly hairy, up to 5 feet (1.5 m) tall. **Leaves** alternate, stiff and thick, grayish-hairy, margins smooth or with shallowly rounded teeth; lower leaves longer petioled than upper, upper may be without petioles. **Flowers** terminal in dense heads, large with 30 to 40 yellow flowers per head. **Fruits** 1-seeded (achenes), smooth or hairy at tips, with 10 to 15 ridges on the surface. **Found** in dry, gravelly open places of woods or on prairies.

233

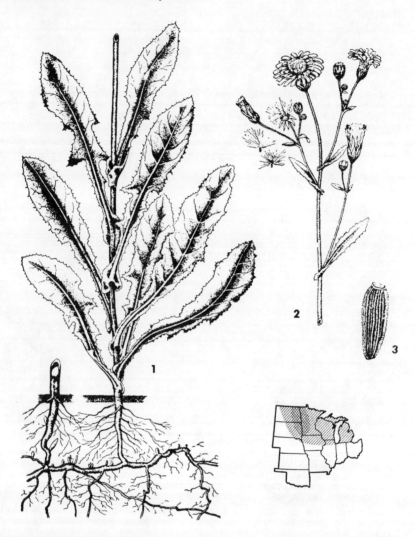

PERENNIAL SOWTHISTLE, *Sonchus arvensis* L. **1**, lower part of plant; **2**, upper part of stem with flowers; **3**, seed. **Perennial**, reproducing by seed and creeping roots. **Roots** may penetrate soil to a depth of several feet and spread horizontally, producing shoots from buds on the roots. **Stems** smooth, 3 to 7 feet (0.9 to 2 m) tall, erect, with a milky juice and a whitish bloom on the surface. **Leaves** 4 to 8 inches (10 to 20 cm) long, alternate, irregularly toothed, lobed, edges spiny. **Flower heads** about 1½ inches (3.8 cm) across, composed of deep yellow ray flowers. **Seed** dark reddish-brown, about ⅛ inch (3 mm) long, slightly flattened, 5- to 7-ribbed with smaller cross wrinkles and with a tuft of hair on one end that is easily broken off. **Found** in cultivated fields, pastures, and wasteland. It is not easily destroyed and becomes a serious problem in grain and row crops.

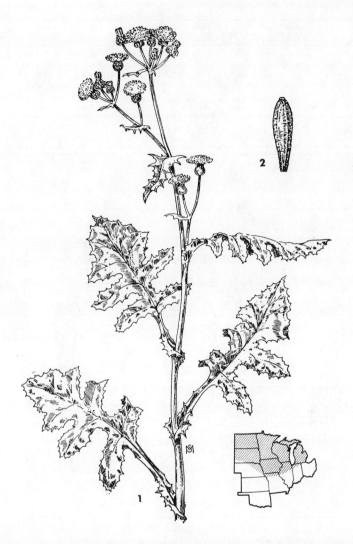

ANNUAL SOWTHISTLE, *Sonchus oleraceus* L. **1**, top of plant in bloom; **2**, seed. **Annual**, reproducing by seed. **Stem** smooth, erect, 1 to 6 feet (0.3 to 1.8 m) tall, with a milky juice. **Leaves** at base of stem more or less petioled; upper leaves clasping the stem with pointed projections; deeply cut, usually with a large end segment, margins with soft prickles. **Flower heads** about ¾ inch (1.9 cm) across, of light yellow ray flowers; borne on numerous branches at top of plant. **Found** in gardens, pastures, wasteland, and road-sides.

SPINY SOWTHISTLE, *Sonchus asper* (L.) Hill. Similar to the above. **Annual.** **Leaves** nearly entire, prickly-edged, stem leaves clasping the stem with large, rounded, earlike lobes.

235

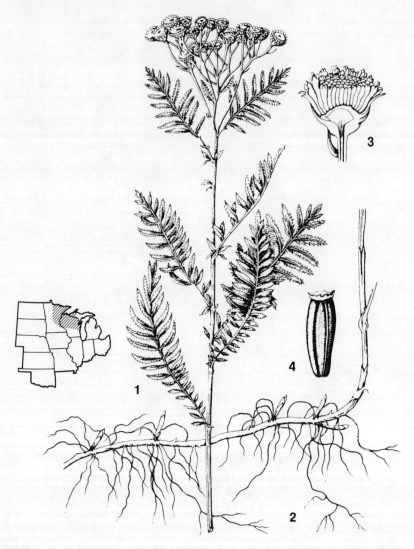

TANSY, *Tanacetum vulgare* L. **1,** plant in flower; **2,** root system showing rhizome; **3,** section of a flower head; **4,** seed. **Perennial,** reproducing by seed and short rhizomes. **Root** system strong, fibrous. **Stems** stout, erect, smooth or slightly hairy, 1 to 4 feet (0.3 to 1.2 m) tall, unbranched, except for the flowering portion. **Leaves** alternate, compound with oblong segments having toothed edges, smooth or nearly so, lower leaves sometimes 12 inches (30 cm) long. **Flower heads** numerous, button-shaped, about ½ inch (1.3 cm) in diameter, composed of many small yellow ray flowers, in a flat-topped cluster at the top of the stem. **Seed** flat, about 1/16 inch (1.5 mm) long, 5-angled, yellowish-brown, tipped with small scales. **Found** along roadsides, in gardens and waste places. The plant has an unpleasant odor.

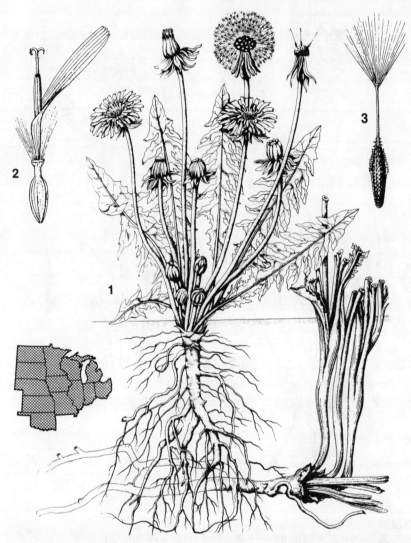

COMMON DANDELION, *Taraxacum officinale* Weber. **1**, plant in flower; **2**, single ray flower; **3**, seed. **Perennial**, reproducing by seed. **Root** thick, fleshy, often with branches. New sprouts can come from roots or root segments. **Stem** never elongates but produces a rosette of leaves. **Leaves** simple, variously lobed, 3 to 10 inches (7.5 to 25 cm) long, containing a milky juice, arising from a crown at or slightly below the surface of the ground. **Flower heads** 1 to 2 inches (2.5 to 5 cm) in diameter, of yellow ray flowers, borne on a long, bare, hollow stalk. **Seed** tannish, about 3/16 inch (4.5 mm) long, elongated, with a slender tip bearing a tuft of hairs that are easily broken off. One variety has reddish-brown seeds. **Found** in lawns, meadows, gardens, and waste places.

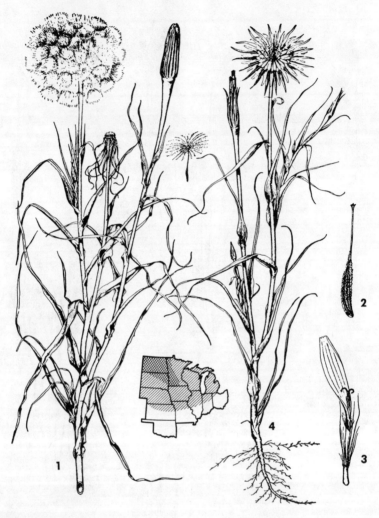

WESTERN SALSIFY, *Tragopogon dubius* Scop. **1,** plant with head of mature seed; **2,** seed; **3,** single flower; **4,** plant in flower. **Biennial,** reproducing by seeds. **Taproot** fleshy. **Stem** erect, branched, smooth, 1 to 3 feet (30 to 90 cm) tall, containing milky juice. **Leaves** grasslike, with a clasping base that encloses the stem, alternate, long, narrow, light green, smooth with smooth margins. **Flower heads** 1 to 2 inches (2.5 to 5 cm) in diameter, solitary at top of stem, composed of bright yellow ray flowers. **Seeds** about ½ inch (1.3 cm) long, narrow, rough, ridged with slender tip on one end, to which is attached a parachutelike appendage. **Found** in meadows, pastures, waste places, roadsides, and fence rows. The white, sticky juice of this plant is bitter, making the plant unpalatable to livestock. A similar species having purple flowers is found in some areas. Also commonly known as yellow goatsbeard.

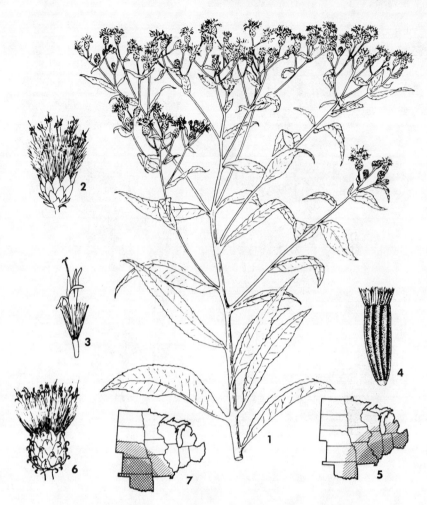

TALL IRONWEED, *Vernonia altissima* Nutt. **1,** upper portion of stem; **2,** flower head; **3,** single flower; **4,** seed; **5,** distribution. **Perennial,** reproducing by rhizomes and seed. **Roots** strong, fibrous. **Stems** erect, 3 to 6 feet (0.9 to 1.8 m) tall, widely branched in the upper portion. **Leaves** long, lanceolate to narrowly ovate, sharply toothed, with short hairs on the lower surface. **Flower heads** about ⅜ inch (9 mm) across, numerous, surrounded by smooth-tipped leafy bracts, borne in a flat-topped cluster at the ends of the branches. Disk flowers reddish-purple. **Seed** mostly oblong, prominently ribbed, with short bristles at the tip. **Found** in meadows, pastures, and wastelands.

WESTERN IRONWEED, *Vernonia baldwini* Torr. **6,** flower head; **7,** distribution. Similar to the above species. **Leaves** densely hairy on lower surface. **Flower heads** surrounded by bracts with hooked tips. **Found** in prairie pastures.

239

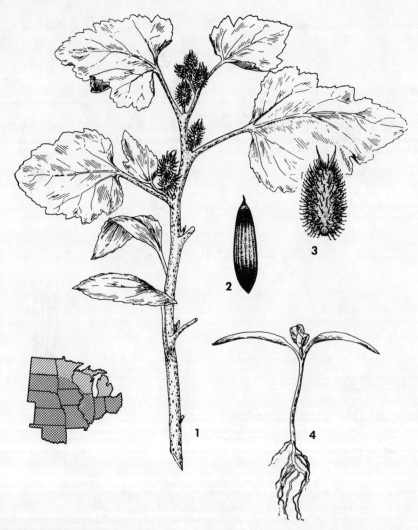

COMMON COCKLEBUR, *Xanthium strumarium* L. **1,** upper part of plant; **2,** seed; **3,** bur; **4,** seedling plant. **Annual,** reproducing by seed. **Taproot** rather woody, stout. **Stem** erect, normally bushy, 2 to 4 feet (0.6 to 1.2 m) tall, ridged, rough-hairy, often spotted. **Leaves** alternate, simple, triangular in outline, toothed or lobed, rough, with long petioles. **Flowers** small, male and female flowers separate but borne together in clusters in axils of the upper leaves. Two female flowers are enclosed in each oval bur. At maturity the bur is hard, woody, and covered with hooked prickles, and ends in 2 curved spines. Male flowers numerous, in clusters on short stalks, dropping soon after pollen is shed. **Seeds** about ½ inch (1.3 cm) long, dark brown, rather slender with pointed tips. **Found** in cultivated fields, abandoned land, poor pastures, and roadsides.

Keys
Glossary
Indexes

KEYS FOR IDENTIFYING WEEDS[1]

How a Key Is Used

A key is a device for identifying plants. It is an outline consisting of alternative statements about structure or appearance. From each pair of statements, you choose the one that applies to the plant you are identifying. After you have made your first choice, you then choose from the next pair subordinate to the first, and so on, until you come to the name of the plant.

As an example, a short key to certain well-known legumes is given below. First look at the two headings labeled "1." If the plant to be identified has a rounded head of flowers, it will be found under the second "1," and you will ignore everything under the first "1," since all the plants under that heading will have flowers in slender spikes. Next, you look at the flowers, which are white, so you choose the second "3." Under the second "3" is a pair of "4's." The plant has a prostrate stem that seemingly roots at the nodes. It is white clover.

1. Flowers in slender spikes.
  2. Flowers yellow.   YELLOW SWEETCLOVER
  2. Flowers white.   WHITE SWEETCLOVER
1. Flowers in rounded heads.
  3. Flowers pink to red.   RED CLOVER
  3. Flowers white or pinkish.
    4. Plants trailing, rooting at nodes; flowers white.
                WHITE CLOVER
    4. Plants ascending, not rooting at nodes; flowers white, becoming pink.
                ALSIKE CLOVER

Note that you always choose between two alternatives, and that the two alternatives bear the same number. Note also that a given number is used for only one pair of headings and is not repeated.

When you use the longer keys beginning on page 247, you will find that often one of a pair of statements will be widely separated from the other. For example, under the first "1" in Key 1, there are pairs of "2's," "3's," "4's," "5's," and "6's" before you come to the second "1." Sometimes the separation is so wide that you have to turn a couple of pages before you come to the second of a pair of statements. In all cases, choose between two statements bearing the same number and keep on choosing until the plant is identified.

[1] Prepared by DUANE ISELY, Iowa State University. Journal paper No. J-9255 of the Iowa Agriculture and Home Economics Experiment Station, Ames, Iowa. Project 1983.

Use of Technical Plant Characters in a Key

Individuals who easily recognize plants sometimes wonder why it is necessary to use technical details in a key, details that need not be observed in recognizing a plant. However, recognizing a known plant and identifying an unknown one are two different processes.

An analogy: Most people interested in cars can usually differentiate, even at a distance, between popular makes, regardless of model, year, or body type. This recognition is based on a knowledge both of general form and of the detailed variations from model to model and from year to year, and involves a rapid, subconscious sorting of these details. But if one is to write down features that will allow a person who doesn't know cars to distinguish between makes, one must turn to characteristics that are consistent regardless of year or model. For example, the insignias on the front of the hood may be constant enough to furnish a means of identification. And possibly characters of the grille, the curvature of the fenders, or the nature of the hubcaps would also be valuable.

A plant is usually recognized by a combination of superficial and often variable characters that, if put into words, would require an involved description. Plants must be identified by consistent characters, sometimes small or technical, that serve as "signposts."

Technical Terms

Arising from the need for technical characters is the necessity for technical terms. Most botanical keys contain many. Such words make it hard for the person who has little familiarity with plants to use the key. But — returning to automobiles — one could scarcely discuss the ailments of his car intelligently with a mechanic if he did not know a few words such as carburetor, water pump, and rings. In the same way, if plants are to be described with any precision, it is necessary to have words for their parts.

I've tried to use as few technical terms as possible in the following keys. Usually descriptive phrases are substituted. Sometimes the more exact technical term is placed in parentheses after the descriptive phrase or vice versa. The following paragraphs define words that are used most frequently without definition in the keys. A glossary beginning on page 291 defines other words sometimes used in the keys and also in the weed descriptions.

Duration of weed. *Annual* — lives one year. *Biennial* — lives two years, usually forming a rosette the first year and sending up an inflorescence the second. *Perennial* — lives several years. Annuals and biennials usually have only a taproot with small branches or, if grasses, a fibrous root system. Perennials possess overwintering parts — for example, thickened crowns from which new shoots arise, bulbs or tubers, or creeping underground rootstocks, which may be either stems (rhizomes) or roots.

Arrangement of leaves. *Alternate* — one leaf at each level on the stem. *Opposite* — two leaves opposite one another and paired. *Whorled* — three or more leaves at each level on the stem.

Nature of leaf. *Simple* — the leaf blade consists of a single piece and is not divided into separate leaflets. However, simple leaves are frequently toothed or lobed. Maple and elm leaves are simple leaves. *Compound* — the leaf blade is divided into several leaflike parts called leaflets. A hickory, locust, or marijuana leaf is compound.

Leaf shape. *Ovate* — egg-shaped, nearly elliptic but broadest at base. *Lanceolate* — lance-shaped, longer than ovate and usually pointed at tip. *Linear* — long and narrow with nearly parallel sides. Grass leaves are linear.

Arrangement of flowers. If the flowers are in a definite cluster, usually at the top of the plant, they are said to be in an *inflorescence*. On some plants the flowers may be borne along the stem, in the angles (leaf axils) between the stems and the leaves. Such flowers are said to be *axillary*, and if in groups, comprise axillary clusters.

Flower parts. The details of flower and fruit structure provide the best characters for identifying plants. But because of the technical nature of these parts, they are little used in these keys. The expanded and usually colored parts of the flower are the *petals*. The *sepals* form the greenish hull around the flower when it is in bud; when the flower is open, they lie outside and below the petals. Many flowers have no petals and are usually greenish or inconspicuous.

The "flowers" of members of the composite family (e.g., dandelion, sunflowers, thistle) are in reality whole inflorescences (heads) of tiny flowers.

Nature and Arrangement of the Keys

In the following keys, precision of statement has been sacrificed to minimize the use of technical terms. As a result, some leads are ambiguous. As far as possible, such difficulties have been anticipated and the plants concerned have been entered under both alternatives, that is, they may be keyed out in either "direction."

The keys on pages 247 to 288 include all the weeds described in this manual except dodder, bracken, and field horsetail. Key 1 (page 247) includes plants with yellow, orange, or cream flowers; Key 2 (page 257), plants with white flowers; Key 3 (page 267), plants with red, pink, blue, lavender, or purple flowers; Key 4 (page 274), grassy plants with green flowers; Key 5 (page 280), broadleaf plants with green flowers; Key 6 (page 286), woody plants.

Usually flower color will indicate the key to be used. In doubtful cases, the following analysis in the form of a key will help.

1. Plant a yellowish, twining vine without leaves, growing parasitically on legumes or flax.   DODDER (*Cuscuta* spp.)[2] p. 141
1. Plants not as above.
  2. Plants producing neither flowers nor seeds; leaves (as described below) fernlike, or absent.
    3. Plant a fern; leaves (fronds) large, divided into numerous segments.   BRACKEN (*Pteridium aquilinum*) p. 12
    3. Plant(s) with hollow, jointed stems and no leaves; stems of two kinds; one coming up early in the spring is whitish, unbranched, with a conelike structure at tip; the second is green, with clusters of branches arising at each level.
        FIELD HORSETAIL (*Equisetum arvense*) p. 11
  2. Plants producing flowers and seeds; leaves present, various in nature.
    4. Plants not woody.
      5. Flowers with yellow, orange, cream, or white petals or petallike structures, occasionally greenish white or faintly streaked with pink (the center of the flower, or flower head, is sometimes colored differently).
        6. Flowers yellow to orange, or cream.   KEY 1, page 247
        6. Flowers white or greenish white.   KEY 2, page 257
      5. Flowers other than yellow, orange, cream, or white.
        7. Flowers red, pink, lavender, blue, or purple; petals usually present.   KEY 3, page 267
        7. Flowers greenish to greenish brown; petals usually absent.
          8. Plants grasslike; leaf blades sessile (without a stalk or petiole) and attached to a sheath that encircles the stem; blades narrowly strap-shaped or linear, entire (without teeth or lobes), with numerous parallel veins.
            KEY 4, page 274.
          8. Plants neither grasses nor grasslike; leaves without a basal sheath, not parallel-veined; with 1 main vein and branches (pinnately veined) or with 3 to 5 main veins from base of blade (palmately veined), the interspaces net-veined; leaf blades various in shape, usually not linear, often toothed or lobed or compound.   KEY 5, page 280
    4. Plants woody vines or shrubs.   KEY 6, page 286

[2] Several kinds of dodder may attack leguminous crops. Dodders also infest a variety of wild plants.

KEY 1. PLANTS WITH YELLOW, ORANGE, OR CREAM FLOWERS

1. Plants (leaves or stems) spiny or prickly; plants commonly possessing a milky juice.
    2. Plants consisting of spiny pads or disks, without leaves; flowers more than 2 inches (5 cm) in diameter.   PRICKLYPEAR (*Opuntia* spp.) p. 128
    2. Plants not as above, with leaves; flowers or flower heads less than 2 inches (5 cm) in diameter.
        3. Leaves and stems densely covered with rigid spines; flowers separate; juice not milky.   BUFFALOBUR (*Solanum rostratum*) p. 163
        3. Leaves prickly along margins and sometimes lower midrib but stems not spiny; flowers tiny, in heads that look like single flowers (e.g., dandelion); juice milky.
            4. Flowers (flower heads) less than ½ inch (1.3 cm) across, straw-yellow, numerous, in a branched flower cluster (panicle); leaves prickly on lower midrib as well as margins.
                        PRICKLY LETTUCE (*Lactuca serriola*) p. 224
            4. Flower heads ½ to 1½ inches (1.3 to 3.8 cm) across, bright yellow, usually 5 to 20 in number; leaves not prickly on lower midrib.
                5. Flower heads more than 1 inch (2.5 cm) in diameter (slightly smaller than those of a dandelion); plants perennial from creeping roots.   PERENNIAL SOWTHISTLE (*Sonchus arvensis*) p. 234
                5. Flower heads ½ to 1 inch (1.3-2.5 cm) in diameter (about half the size of those of a dandelion); plants from an annual taproot.
                    6. Leaf margin sharply prickly; base of the blade usually curled and clasping the stem (auriculate); seeds (achenes) not cross-wrinkled.   SPINY SOWTHISTLE (*Sonchus asper*) p. 235
                    6. Leaf margin soft-prickly; leaf base tapering, not clasping the stem, or some of upper leaves slightly clasping; achenes irregularly ridged and cross-wrinkled.
                        ANNUAL SOWTHISTLE (*Sonchus oleraceus*) p. 235
1. Plants (leaves or stems) not spiny; in a few cases, the fruit is spiny or prickly.
    7. Plants with neither a leafy stem nor prostrate stolons; leaves all in a cluster (rosette) at ground level; flower heads solitary on hollow, leafless stalks.
        8. "Seeds" (achenes) olive-drab to dull brown; leaves extremely variable, deeply dissected or only irregularly toothed; inner bracts around head not appendaged; the usual dandelion.
                    COMMON DANDELION (*Taraxacum officinale*) p. 237
        8. Achenes red-brown to reddish purple; leaves usually dissected nearly to the midrib with narrow, frequently downwardly curved (runcinate) lobes; inner bracts around head with hornlike appendages; uncommon.
        REDSEED DANDELION (*Taraxacum erythrospermum*) not illustrated
    7. Plants with an erect or prostrate leaf-bearing stem; flowers or flower heads various, not arising directly from a basal rosette (stem leaves are few or reduced in hawkweeds, *Hieracium*, which, however, usually have stolons).
        9. Plants prostrate, trailing, or spreading.
            10. Leaves compound.
                11. Leaflets 8 to 16; fruit a spiny bur
                        PUNCTUREVINE (*Tribulus terrestris*) p. 113

11. Leaflets 3; fruit a 1-seeded pod.

BLACK MEDIC (*Medicago lupulina*) p. 109

10. Leaves simple.

12. Plant fleshy with small, entire leaves, flowers less than ½ inch (1.3 cm) across; fruit a small capsule, less than 1 inch (2.5 cm) long. PURSLANE (*Portulaca oleracea*) p. 71

12. Plant not fleshy, with large, irregularly toothed or lobed leaves; flowers large, 1-2 inches (2.5-5 cm) long; fruit large, more than 1 inch (2.5 cm) long.

13. Plant with tendrils; flowers 3-4 inches (7.5-10 cm) long, solitary in leaf axils, fruits gourdlike, not beaked.

BUFFALO GOURD (*Cucurbita foetidissima*) p. 176

13. Plants lacking tendrils; flowers to 2 inches (5 cm) long, in inflorescenses; fruit a capsule with an incurved or hooked beak several inches long.

DEVILSCLAW (*Proboscidea louisianica*) p. 168

9. Plants erect or ascending (some may root at lower nodes or have trailing stolons as well as erect stems).

14. Leaves compound, divided into distinct leaflets; or some or all of leaves dissected into numerous fine segments and usually appearing fernlike.

15. Leaves compound, divided into distinct leaflets that are ordinarily more than ¼ inch (6 mm) wide.

16. Leaves opposite; flowers in heads that look like single flowers; fruits 1-seeded (achenes), with 2 barbed, sharp projections (awns) at top.

DEVIL'S BEGGARTICKS (*Bidens frondosa*) p. 193

16. Leaves alternate; flowers not in heads; fruits various.

17. Leaflets 3, entire except for a notch at apex (obcordate); each flower producing a single, many-seeded fruit (capsule).

COMMON YELLOW WOODSORREL

(*Oxalis stricta*) p. 111

17. Leaflets various in number, toothed or lobed; fruits not capsular, several frequently produced by each flower.

18. Leaves pinnately compound (leaflets arising from an elongated midrib or axis); flowers umbellate (numerous flower stalks arising from same point); each flower producing 1 fruit, which, at maturity, splits into 2 flat, 1-seeded segments (mericarps).

WILD PARSNIP (*Pastinaca sativa*) p. 133

18. Leaves palmately compound (leaflets arising fingerlike from apex of leaf stalk); flowers not umbellate; each flower producing several 1-seeded fruits (achenes).

19. Leaflets lobed or dissected, frequently running together at base, their exact number difficult to determine; stipules (appendages where leaf stalk joins stem) not evident.

TALL BUTTERCUP (*Ranunculus acris*) p. 83

19. Leaflets toothed, clearly distinguishable and easy to count; stipules present.

19a. Under surface of leaves silvery-hairy.
SILVERY CINQUEFOIL
(*Potentilla argentea*) p. 105

19a. Under surface of leaves greenish.

20. Leaflets 5 to 9; petals large, longer than other flower parts.
SULPHUR CINQUEFOIL
(*Potentilla recta*) p. 106

20. Leaflets 3; petals small and inconspicuous, scarcely longer than sepals.
ROUGH CINQUEFOIL
(*Potentilla norvegica*) p. 106

15. Leaves not divided into distinct leaflets; but some or all of leaves dissected into numerous fine segments usually less than ¼ inch (6 mm) wide, the whole leaf presenting a fernlike appearance.

21. Leaves all alternate.

22. Flowers with 4 distinct petals set at right angles to one another; fruit resembling a slender pod (silique) and containing several yellowish seeds; plants not strongly scented.

23. Mature pods more than 2 inches (5 cm) long; main segments of basal (rosette) leaves usually not dissected into secondary segments (1-pinnatifid).
TUMBLE MUSTARD (*Sisymbrium altissimum*) p. 102

23. Mature pods less than 1 inch (2.5 cm) long, main segments of basal leaves usually dissected into secondary segments (2-pinnatifid).
TANSY MUSTARD (*Descurainia pinnata*) p. 94

22. Flowers (flower heads) without petals or marginal petal-like structures, the heads button- or bell-shaped; fruits 1-seeded, not podlike, clustered together in the heads; plants usually strongly scented.

22a. Flower heads yellow or orange, erect, ¼ inch (6 mm) or more wide.

22b. Plants perennial: stems usually a foot (0.3 m) or more high; main leaf segments crowded, pinnatifid; flower heads orange, in a dense, flat-topped cluster.
TANSY (*Tanacetum vulgare*) p. 236

22b. Plants annual; stems less than a foot (0.3 m) high; leaf segments slender, entire, distant; flower heads yellowish, not densely clustered.
PINEAPPLEWEED
(*Matricaria matricarioides*) p. 227

22a. Flower heads yellowish-white, gray, yellow, or greenish, frequently bent over (nodding), distinctly less than ¼ inch (6 mm) wide.

24. Plants greenish, relatively smooth, strong-scented annuals arising from a taproot.
ANNUAL WORMWOOD
(*Artemisia annua*) p. 189

24. Plants white-silky or woolly, scarcely scented; perennials from spreading rhizomes. ABSINTH WORMWOOD

(*Artemisia absinthium*) p. 188

21. Leaves all opposite, or only the lower opposite.

25. Flower heads with a dark center and large, petallike marginal (ray) flowers; lower leaves with threadlike (filiform) segments, the upper mostly undivided. PLAINS COREOPSIS (*Coreopsis tinctoria*) p. 205

25. Flower heads without a dark center; ray flowers, if present, small and inconspicuous; leaves fernlike.

26. Leaves all opposite; flower heads single or in small groups at tips of branches, with small ray flowers; seeds columnar with points at the tip that readily adhere to clothing. SPANISHNEEDLES (*Bidens bipinnata*) p. 192

26. Leaves alternate above, opposite below; upper flower heads in slender spikes, producing pollen only and not setting seed; seeds broad, produced in axils of upper leaves, not adhering to clothing.

27. Plants annual, very common; leaves smooth above, usually much divided, i.e., the main segments dissected into secondary divisions (2-pinnatifid); fruits with a distinct crown of points at tip. COMMON RAGWEED

(*Ambrosia artemisiifolia*) p. 181

27. Plants perennial from creeping roots (first-year plants appear annual), similar in appearance to common ragweed but much less common; leaves rough on upper surface, less divided than those of common ragweed, the main segments frequently lobed but not again divided (1-pinnatifid); fruits with a very short crown of points or nearly smooth at tip. WESTERN RAGWEED

(*Ambrosia psilostachya*) p. 182

14. Leaves neither compound nor dissected into fine segments; if lobed or divided (pinnatifid), the blades not fernlike, or the segments relatively broad or coarse.

28. Petals 4, placed at right angles to one another (flowers crosslike); fruit podlike (a silique), elongate or "ball-shaped," severalseeded (one exception), frequently with a beak at the tip.

29. Pods upwardly appressed against stem.

30. Flowers less than ¼ inch (6 mm) across; beak of pod indistinct, less than 1/16 inch (1.5 mm) long; upper leaves with 3 narrow lobes. HEDGE MUSTARD (*Sisymbrium officinale*) p. 103

30. Flowers more than ¼ inch (6 mm) across; beak of pod evident, about ⅛ inch (3 mm) long; upper leaves irregularly toothed. BLACK MUSTARD (*Brassica nigra*) p. 88

29. Pods spreading, ascending, or nearly erect, but not appressed against stem.

31. Pods spherical (globose) to egg-shaped (ovoid); leaves clasping the stem by basal lobes.

250

32. Plants perennial from creeping roots; pods splitting open at maturity (dehiscent), with numerous tiny seeds. AUSTRIAN FIELDCRESS (*Rorippa austriaca*) p. 101

32. Plants annual; pods not splitting open at maturity (indehiscent), with 1 large seed, or sometimes 2. BALL MUSTARD (*Neslia paniculata*) p. 99

31. Pods oblong to linear; leaves clasping or not.

33. Plants smooth or with a few scattered hairs or very tiny appressed hairs.

34. Leaves with a pair of basal lobes clasping about the stem, otherwise entire (neither toothed nor lobed); seed pods frequently 3 inches (7.5 cm) long, and often nearly vertical in position. HARE'S EAR MUSTARD (*Conringia orientalis*) p. 93

34. Leaves entire, toothed or lobed, not clasping the stem; seed pods various, if vertical, shorter than above.

35. Leaves not lobed, usually nearly entire, narrow (linear-lanceolate); pod stalk (pedicel) slender, often ½ to ¾ inch (13 to 19 mm) long. WORMSEED MUSTARD (*Erysimum cheiranthoides*) p. 95

35. Leaves lobed, usually broad; pod stalk coarser and shorter than above.

36. Basal leaves with a broadly rounded terminal lobe; foliage shiny green; seed pods usually not longer than 1 inch (2.5 cm); seeds somewhat flattened. YELLOW ROCKET (*Barbarea vulgaris*) p. 86

36. Basal leaves with pointed lobes; foliage often somewhat whitish-green; seed pods usually longer than 1 inch (2.5 cm); seeds spheroidal. INDIAN MUSTARD (*Brassica juncea*) p. 88

33. Plants conspicuously bristly-hairy.

37. Fruit jointed at maturity, breaking crosswise into segments containing 1 or 2 seeds; basal leaves usually divided to the midrib into separate segments. WILD RADISH (*Raphanus raphanistrum*) p. 100

37. Fruit splitting longitudinally to release seeds at maturity; basal leaves irregularly toothed or pinnatifid, but not divided to midrib. WILD MUSTARD (*Brassica kaber*) p. 89

28. Petals not 4 in number; fruit various, not a silique.

38. Leaves alternate, occasionally the uppermost or the lower opposite, or (rarely) nearly all in basal clusters (rosettes).

39. Fruit a 3-lobed, 3-seeded capsule that hangs downward at maturity; leaves narrowly strap-shaped, crowded on the mostly unbranched stem; juice milky.

40. Leaves about ⅛ inch (3 mm) wide.
      CYPRESS SPURGE (*Euphorbia cyparissias*) p. 117
40. Leaves ¼ to ¾ inch (6 to 19 mm) wide.
      LEAFY SPURGE (*Euphorbia esula*) p. 118
39. Fruit not a 3-lobed, 3-seeded capsule; plants otherwise not with the above combination of characters.
  41. Flowers without petals or petallike structures; inflorescences appearing as erect or drooping yellow disks, or as a cluster of short, flat spikes.
    42. Leaves grasslike; stems 3-angled; triangular in cross section; inflorescence a cluster of short, flat spikes.
    YELLOW NUTSEDGE (*Cyperus esculentus*) p. 44
    42. Leaves not grasslike; stems rounded; inflorescence of disklike flower heads.
      43. Flowers (flower heads) on stalks in a branched flower cluster; stem leaves strap-shaped, not toothed; seeds with a cluster of hairs (pappus) at tip.
        44. Stem unbranched below inflorescence, often 3 to 6 feet (0.9 to 1.8 m) tall; leaves crowded, strap-shaped.
        HORSEWEED (*Conyza canadensis*) p. 204
        44. Stem branched, low, usually not much exceeding 1 foot (0.3 m); leaves narrowly linear.
        DWARF FLEABANE
                (*Conyza ramosissima*) p. 204
      43. Flower heads not stalked (sessile), arising directly from an unbranched axis; leaves usually with a pair of teeth at base; seeds not possessing a pappus.
      LANCELEAF RAGWEED
            (*Ambrosia bidentata*) p. 181
  41. Flowers with petals or petallike structures.
    45. Flowers closely associated in heads, each head simulating a single flower; flowers in the head either all similar — strap-shaped, with each appearing like a single petal (ray flowers); or of two kinds — small tubular flowers crowded together in a central disk (disk flowers), and marginal (ray) flowers that look like petals; each head setting several to many seeds (achenes), which often bear a cluster of hairs or bristles (pappus) at the apex.
    46. Heads with no central disk; flowers all strap-shaped and petallike (ray-flowers); fresh plants frequently with a milky juice.
      47. Leaves entire, grasslike; heads large, 1½ to 2½ inches (3.8 to 6.3 cm) across.
      WESTERN SALSIFY
             (*Tragopogon dubius*) p. 238
      47. Leaves not grasslike, some or all usually toothed or lobed; heads usually less than 1 inch (2.5 cm) across.

48. Leaves mostly in basal rosettes; erect stems bearing only 1 to 3 reduced blades; prostrate leaf-bearing stolons often evident.

48a. Flower heads orange.
ORANGE HAWKWEED
(Hieracium aurantiacum) p. 219

48a. Flower heads yellow.
YELLOW HAWKWEED
(Hieracium pratense) p. 220

48. Leaves of mature plants not mostly in rosettes, those on stems numerous; stolons not present.

49. Leaves soft-prickly, the teeth or lobes drawn out into bristles, or leaves soft-prickly on lower midvein.

50. Midvein on undersurface of leaves prickly with a row of bristles; most of stem leaves twisted sidewise so that blade is in a vertical position (one edge above the other); heads less than ½ inch (1.3 cm) in diameter.
PRICKLY LETTUCE
(Lactuca serriola) p. 224

50. Midvein not prickly; leaves horizontal; heads more than ½ inch (1.3 cm) in diameter.
ANNUAL SOWTHISTLE
(Sonchus oleraceus) p. 235

49. Leaves not prickly-margined.

51. Branches bearing flower clusters arched or recurving, bearing the crowded flowering heads primarily on one side in a curved wand; leaves mostly stalked, not clasping the stem.
GRAY GOLDENROD
(Solidago nemoralis)[3] p. 232

51. Branches of inflorescence erect or ascending, bearing upright heads at tip; stem leaves mostly without stalks (sessile), with lower portion of the blade clasping.

52. Plants 3 to 8 feet (0.9 to 2.4 m) tall with densely leafy stems; heads numerous, less than ½ inch (1.3 cm) wide; seeds (achenes) black, beaked.
TALL LETTUCE
(Lactuca canadensis) p. 224

[3] And other species of goldenrod, including rigid goldenrod *(Solidago rigida)* p. 233.

52. Plants low, usually about 1 foot (30 cm) tall, often with several branches from base; heads ⅜ to ¾ inch (10 to 19 mm) in diameter; seeds (achenes) brown, not beaked.
SMOOTH HAWKSBEARD
(*Crepis capillaris*) p. 206

46. Heads with a central disk that is margined by petallike ray flowers; plants without a milky juice.

53. Central disk of head (tubular flowers) black or dark brown.

54. Seeds (achenes) black, brick-shaped, ⅛ inch (3 mm) or less long; leaves oblong to strap-shaped, less than 1 inch (2.5 cm) wide.
BLACKEYED SUSAN
(*Rudbeckia hirta*) p. 228

54. Seeds white, gray, or brown, larger than above; leaves usually broadly ovate to lanceolate and 1 inch (2.5 cm) or more wide.

55. Leaves rough (scabrous); seeds (achenes) dull white to gray, hairy at tip, ¼ to ⅜ inch (6 to 10 mm) long; common.
COMMON SUNFLOWER
(*Helianthus annuus*) p. 216

55. Leaves hairy but not markedly rough; seeds pale brown, hairy all over, less than ¼ inch (6 mm) long; not common in agricultural areas.
PRAIRIE SUNFLOWER
(*Helianthus petiolaris*) p. 216

53. Entire head yellow.

56. Seeds bearing at apex a cluster (pappus) of numerous fine bristles. (In immature flowering heads, the pappus is hidden by the flowers and the head must be split to find it; after the head begins to ripen, the pappus is easily visible externally.)

57. Stem leaves pinnatifid (lobed along an elongated midrib); flower heads more than ½ inch (1.3 cm) across.
GOLDEN RAGWORT
(*Senecio aureus*) p. 230

57. Stem leaves toothed or entire; flower heads not exceeding ½ inch (1.3 cm).
GRAY GOLDENROD
(*Solidago nemoralis*)[4] p. 232

---

[4] And other species of goldenrod including rigid goldenrod (*Solidago rigida*) p. 233.

56. Seeds not bearing a pappus of fine bristles; pappus absent, or of scales, or of a few (5 to 10) somewhat flattened, stiff bristles.

58. Stem leaves narrowly linear or threadlike; southern.

59. Heads ½ to ¾ inch (1.3 to 1.9 cm) wide; marginal ray flowers lobed at tip.
BITTER SNEEZEWEED
(*Helenium amarum*) p. 214

59. Heads less than ½ inch (1.3 cm) wide; ray flowers not lobed.
COMMON BROOMWEED
(*Gutierrezia dracunculoides*) p. 213

58. Leaves broader than above, not linear; central and northern.

60. Stems winged by attached basal portions of leaf blades (leaves decurrent); ray flowers 3-toothed or lobed at tip.
COMMON SNEEZEWEED
(*Helenium autumnale*) p. 215

60. Stems not winged; ray flowers not toothed.

61. Plants finely hairy, often somewhat rough; perennial from rhizomes and tubers; heads not sticky or gummy.

62. Central disk of heads (not including petallike rays) usually ⅜ to ¾ inch (1 to 1.9 cm) broad; lowermost leaves opposite; rhizomes bearing enlarged tubers.
JERUSALEM ARTICHOKE
(*Helianthus tuberosus*) p. 218

62. Central disk of heads ¾ to 1½ inches (1.9 to 3.8 cm) broad; leaves all alternate; rhizomes not tuber-bearing.
MAXIMILIAN SUNFLOWER
(*Helianthus maximiliani*) p. 217

61. Plants smooth (glabrous), without rhizomes or tubers; heads gummy.
GUMWEED
(*Grindelia squarrosa*) p. 212

45. Flowers separate, not associated in heads; fruits and seeds various, without a pappus.

63. Leaves velvety-hairy or densely woolly.

64. Fruit a berry enclosed in an angular, papery husk; plant perennial from creeping rootstocks.
CLAMMY GROUNDCHERRY
(*Physalis heterophylla*) p. 158

64. Fruit a dry capsule which splits open at maturity, not enclosed within a husk; plants annual or biennial, without creeping rootstocks.

65. Plants gray-woolly; flowers in a dense spike; leaves not heart-shaped at base.
COMMON MULLEIN
(*Verbascum thapsus*) p. 165

65. Plants velvety; flowers not in a spike; leaves heart-shaped at base.
VELVETLEAF
(*Abutilon theophrasti*) p. 122

63. Leaves smooth (glabrous) or hairy, but neither velvety nor densely woolly.

66. Basal leaves palmately divided into 3 to 7 main segments which are further subdivided.

67. Flowers pale yellow, purplish in center; each flower produces a single, large, several-seeded fruit (capsule) partially surrounded by a bladdery hull; plants annual.
VENICE MALLOW
(*Hibiscus trionum*) p. 123

67. Flowers bright yellow throughout; each flower produces numerous small seed-like fruits; plants perennial.
TALL BUTTERCUP
(*Ranunculus acris*) p. 83

66. Basal leaves not palmately dissected.

68. Basal (rosette) leaves as broad as long, heart-shaped.
SMALLFLOWER BUTTERCUP
(*Ranunculus abortivus*) p. 82

68. Basal leaves longer than broad, not heart-shaped.

69. Leaves entire, strap-shaped, not hairy; flowers not symmetrical, the petals of different sizes (irregular).
YELLOW TOADFLAX
(*Linaria vulgaris*) p. 164

69. Leaves not strap-shaped, usually toothed or shallowly lobed, hairy; flowers with petals of same size (regular) or fused together.

70. Petals fused into a single piece like a petunia (gamopetalous); fruit a berry enclosd in a husk.
SMOOTH GROUNDCHERRY
(*Physalis subglabrata*) p. 159

70. Petals separate; fruit not a berry.
71. Leaves stalked (petioled); flowers scattered; fruit splitting into 5 seeds.
PRICKLY SIDA
(*Sida spinosa*) p. 126
71. Leaves not stalked (sessile); flowers in a terminal spike; fruit with many seeds.
COMMON EVENINGPRIMROSE
(*Oenothera biennis*) p. 129
38. Leaves all opposite.
72. All leaves, or only the lower, lobed or cleft into segments.
73. Flowers (flower heads) in narrow spikes, without petals or petallike structures; leaves mostly with 3 to 5 big lobes (palmately lobed).
GIANT RAGWEED (*Ambrosia trifida*) p. 183
73. Flower heads separate at stem tips, with large petallike ray flowers; lower leaves with 3 to 7 lobes (pinnately lobed), upper blades often unlobed.
CUTLEAF CONEFLOWER
(*Rudbeckia laciniata*) p. 229
72. Leaves toothed or entire.
74. Bases of upper, paired leaves joined together and forming a cup about stem at nodes.
CUPPLANT (*Silphium perfoliatum*) p. 231
74. Bases of leaves not joined together.
ST. JOHNSWORT (*Hypericum perforatum*) p. 127

KEY 2. PLANTS WITH WHITE FLOWERS

1. Leaves opposite or whorled.
2. Leaves whorled (several at each level on stem).
3. Plants forming prostrate mats; flowers in small axillary clusters; seeds very small, reddish.   CARPETWEED (*Mollugo verticillata*) p. 70
3. Plants spreading or erect, not forming prostrate mats; flowers in branched or rounded inflorescences; seeds not as above.
4. Stems spreading or nearly prostrate (decumbent), covered with fine hooked bristles and readily adhering to clothing; fruit separating into two globular, 1-seeded sections.
CATCHWEED BEDSTRAW (*Galium aparine*) p. 174
4. Stems erect or ascending, without hooked bristles; fruits many-seeded.
5. Stems nearly simple (unbranched); flowers in umbels (numerous flower stalks arising from the same place); pods milkweedlike, more than 1 inch (2.5 cm) long; seeds large, tufted with long hairs.
EASTERN WHORLED MILKWEED (*Asclepias verticillata*) p. 138
5. Stems much branched; flowers in branched inflorescences; fruits a fraction of an inch long; seeds small, without hairs.
CORN SPURRY (*Spergula arvensis*) p. 79
2. Leaves opposite (uppermost rarely alternate).

6. Plant a twining or climbing vine; leaves heart-shaped at base; fruits milkweedlike. **HONEYVINE MILKWEED** (*Ampelamus albidus*) p. 135

6. Plants not vines; leaves and fruits various, not as above.

　7. Leaves pinnately lobed (lobes approximately at right angles to midrib of blade); mature fruits (capsules) hanging downward; plants evident in spring. **WATERPOD** (*Ellisia nyctelea*) p. 144

　7. Leaves various, not as above; mature fruits not hanging down; plants flowering at various times of the season.

　　8. Leaves entire (edge without teeth), or (rarely) the lowermost toothed; flowers not borne in heads; fruits often capsules containing several seeds.

　　　9. Long bristles (stipules) present at leaf bases; fruits splitting into 2 or 3 large seedlike fragments, each with 3 or 4 scalelike appendages at tip. **POORJOE** (*Diodia teres*) p. 173

　　　9. Stipules not present; seeds not as above, released from within fruits at maturity.

　　　　10. Flowers borne in the axils of conspicuous alternate bracts (reduced leaves); plants appearing fleshy; fruits somewhat 2-lobed.
PURSLANE SPEEDWELL (*Veronica peregrina*) p. 166

　　　　10. Flowers not borne in the axils of alternate bracts; bracts and leaves all opposite; plants not fleshy; fruits not 2-lobed.

　　　　　11. Plants with a milky juice; fruit long and slender, shaped somewhat like a pencil; seeds with a tuft of long, fine hairs. **HEMP DOGBANE** (*Apocynum cannabinum*) p. 134

　　　　　11. Plants without a milky juice; fruit short; seeds without hairs.

　　　　　　12. Plants low or creeping, rarely more than a few inches high; flowers 1/8 inch (3 mm) or less in diameter.

　　　　　　　13. Lower leaves stalked (petioled); plants hairy only on angles of stems and leaf stalks.
COMMON CHICKWEED (*Stellaria media*) p. 80

　　　　　　　13. Leaves without stalks (sessile); plants densely hairy all over.
MOUSE-EAR CHICKWEED
(*Cerastium vulgatum*) p. 73

　　　　　　12. Plants erect, frequently exceeding 1 foot (0.3 m) in height; flowers usually 1/2 inch (1.3 cm) or more across.

　　　　　　　14. Plants glabrous (not hairy).

　　　　　　　　15. Stem sticky; fruit (capsule) surrounded by a tight-fitting hull (calyx); plant annual.
SLEEPY CATCHFLY (*Silene antirrhina*) p. 76

　　　　　　　　15. Stem not sticky; capsule surrounded by swollen, bladdery calyx hull; plant perennial.
BLADDER CAMPION (*Silene cucubalus*) p. 77

　　　　　　　14. Plants hairy (pubescent).

　　　　　　　　16. Stems sticky, or viscid-hairy; 3 styles (branches of the stalk from the pistil); plant annual, with single stout stem.
NIGHT-FLOWERING CATCHFLY
(*Silene noctiflora*) p. 78

16. Stems soft-hairy, not sticky or viscid; 5 styles; plant biennial or perennial, with several stems from its base.
WHITE COCKLE (*Lychnis alba*) p. 74

8. Leaves toothed or lobed; flowers in dense clusters (often in heads that superficially appear like single flowers), or spikes; fruits not capsules.

17. Leaves lobed, the lower somewhat maplelike; flower clusters becoming spiny in fruit.
MOTHERWORT (*Leonurus cardiaca*) p. 152

17. Leaves toothed; flower spikes or clusters not becoming spiny in fruit.

18. Flowers in spikes or in dense clusters in leaf axils; fruits splitting into four 1-seeded segments; stems conspicuously square.

19. Flowers in spikes terminating stems.

20. Flowers closely overlapping in dense spikes; plants aromatic (leaves with a strong odor when crushed); seeds (nutlets) with a pair of white spots at base.
CATNIP (*Nepeta cataria*) p. 154

20. Flowers not closely crowded, but in loose, narrow spikes, the fruits well separated and not at all overlapping; plants not aromatic; seeds without a pair of white spots at base.
WHITE VERVAIN (*Verbena urticifolia*) p. 148

19. Flowers in dense clusters in leaf axils along the stem, not terminating it.
FIELD MINT (*Mentha arvensis*) p. 153

18. Flowers in small heads that appear somewhat like individual flowers; fruits (achenes) 1-seeded, topped by a fine cluster of hairs or scales; stems not conspicuously square.

21. Flower heads with white petallike marginal (ray) flowers and a yellow center; leaves with 1 main midvein; plants annual.
SMALLFLOWER GALINSOGA
(*Galinsoga parviflora*) p. 210

21. Flower heads entirely white; leaves with 3 main veins; plants perennial.

22. Leaves broadly lanceolate, finely hairy; clusters of small leaves usually present in the axils of the main blades; heads usually with fewer than 15 flowers.
LATE EUPATORIUM
(*Eupatorium serotinum*) p. 209

22. Leaves ovate, concavely tapering to a point (acuminate), not hairy; clusters of small leaves not present in axils of main blades; heads usually with more than 15 flowers.
WHITE SNAKEROOT (*Eupatorium rugosum*) p. 208

1. Leaves alternate or sometimes most of them in a basal cluster (rosette).

23. Leaves, stems, or both prickly or spiny.

24. Flowers more than 2 inches (5 cm) in diameter; leaves with prickly teeth along edge.
BLUESTEM PRICKLEPOPPY (*Argemone intermedia*) p. 84

24. Flowers less than 1 inch (2.5 cm) in diameter; stem and leaf surfaces with yellowish thorns. HORSENETTLE (*Solanum carolinense*) p. 160

23. Leaves and stems not spiny, but fruits sometimes prickly or spiny.

25. Petals 4, placed at right angles to one another and presenting a cross-like appearance; fruits several-seeded.

26. Fruits flat.

27. Fruit triangular (or sometimes viewed as an upside down heart), plant covered with tiny (hand lens needed), branched (stellate) hairs.
SHEPHERD'S PURSE (*Capsella bursa-pastoris*) p. 91

27. Fruit circular; plants smooth or with unbranched hairs.

28. Fruit about ½ inch (1.3 cm) in diameter; seeds dark brown; leaves toothed.
FIELD PENNYCRESS (*Thlaspi arvense*) p. 104

28. Fruit ⅛ inch (3 mm) or less in diameter; seeds reddish-yellow; lower leaves pinnatifid (irregularly lobed, with lobes more or less at right angles to long midrib).
VIRGINIA PEPPERWEED (*Lepidium virginicum*) p. 98

26. Fruits inflated on one or both sides, or globular.

29. Plants densely hairy.

30. Pods short-cylindric, twice as long as wide; leaves entire (not toothed).
HOARY ALYSSUM (*Berteroa incana*) p. 87

30. Pods circular or broadly elliptic, nearly as broad as long; leaves wavy-toothed, or the lower somewhat lobed.

31. Plants perennial from creeping roots; pods inflated on both sides, with a distinct beak at tip.
HOARY CRESS (*Cardaria draba*) p. 92

31. Plants annual; pods flat on one side, inflated on the other, with little or no beak.
FIELD PEPPERWEED (*Lepidium campestre*) p. 96

29. Plants without hairs (glabrous) or with inconspicuous hairs.

32. Pods well over ¼ inch (6 mm) long, with a short beak (about ¼ the length of pod); seeds about 1/10 inch (2.5 mm) long.
LARGESEED FALSEFLAX (*Camelina sativa*) p. 90

32. Pods ¼ inch (6 mm) or less long, with a somewhat longer beak (about half the length of pod); seeds less than 1/16 inch (1.5 mm) long.
SMALLSEED FALSEFLAX (*Camelina microcarpa*) p. 90

25. Petals not 4 or, if so (rarely), not placed at right angles to one another; fruits various.

33. Plants vinelike, trailing, twining, or climbing; leaves heart- or arrowhead-shaped (cordate, hastate, or sagittate), or palmately lobed.

34. Plants with tendrils; leaves palmately lobed, the lobes acute tipped.

35. Plants pubescent (hairy); fruits in burlike clusters.
BUR CUCUMBER (*Sicyos angulatus*) p. 178

35. Plants nearly glabrous (smooth); fruits like a spiny gourd, solitary. WILD CUCUMBER (*Echinocystis lobata*) p. 177

34. Plants without tendrils; leaves not palmately lobed, or, if so, the lobes rounded.

36. Plants thick-stemmed (¼ to ½ inch [6 to 13 mm] in diameter), with a musky odor; flowers not morningglorylike; fruits with incurved beaks several inches long.
  DEVILSCLAW (*Proboscidea louisianica*) p. 168

36. Plants slender-stemmed (less than ¼ inch [6 mm] in diameter), not odoriferous; flowers, except for wild buckwheat, morningglorylike; fruits without a long beak.

37. Flowers small, clustered in upper leaf axils, greenish-white, not morningglorylike; fruit resembling a buckwheat seed, 3-angled (triangular in cross section), 1-seeded, not splitting open at maturity (indehiscent); young stems with membranous sheaths (ochreae) at attachment of leaf blades.
  WILD BUCKWHEAT (*Polygonum convolvulus*) p. 51

37. Flowers large, morningglorylike, fruit a capsule, ripening several large seeds; young stems without membranous sheaths at attachment of leaf blades.

38. Leaves deeply 3-lobed.
  IVYLEAF MORNINGGLORY
  (*Ipomoea hederacea*) p. 142

38. Leaves not deeply lobed, usually heart- or arrowhead-shaped (cordate, hastate, or sagittate).

39. Leaves arrowhead-shaped (sagittate or hastate) with pointed basal projections; plants perennial from slender creeping rootstocks.

40. Flowers roughly the size of a quarter; leaves lanceolate to oblong with narrow basal lobes, the blade continuing in essentially the same direction as the leaf stalk (petiole); plants more often trailing than climbing.
  FIELD BINDWEED
  (*Convolvulus arvensis*) p. 139

40. Flowers about the size of a silver dollar; leaves tending to be triangular with broad, basal lobes, the blade bent back at right angles to the petiole; plants twining and climbing.
  HEDGE BINDWEED
  (*Convolvulus sepium*) p. 140

39. Leaves heart-shaped (cordate) with rounded basal lobes; plants annual or perennial.

41. Flowers about 2 inches (5 cm) broad, not dark purple inside; plants annual, twining.
  TALL MORNINGGLORY
  (*Ipomoea purpurea*) p. 142

41. Flowers frequently 3 inches (7.5 cm) broad, dark purple inside of tube; plants perennial from very large roots, usually trailing on ground.
  BIGROOT MORNINGGLORY
  (*Ipomoea pandurata*) p. 143

33. Plant erect, ascending, or sometimes prostrate, but not vinelike; leaves various, usually not as above.

  42. Leaves (especially the lower ones) deeply palmately cleft (lobes dissected, fingerlike, to base of blade) or palmately compound, the segments in turn toothed or cleft.

    43. Leaf segments closely crowded together, the blade as a whole nearly circular in outline; flowers without a purple center; fruit slender and pointed.

      CAROLINA GERANIUM (*Geranium carolinianum*) p. 112

    43. Leaf segments not crowded together, the blade not circular in outline; flowers with a purple center; fruit nearly as thick as long.

      VENICE MALLOW (*Hibiscus trionum*) p. 123

  42. Leaves various, not palmately cleft or palmately compound (sometimes shallowly palmately lobed).

    44. Leaves pinnately compound (leaflets arising from an elongated midrib), or dissected into fine segments.

      45. Flowers in compound umbels, with numerous flower stalks arising from about the same point; fruits longitudinally ribbed, splitting into two 1-seeded segments at maturity.

        46. Leaves fernlike, dissected into ultimate segments often no more than 1/16 inch (1.5 mm) wide.

          47. Plants hairy (pubescent), annual; fruits bristly.

            WILD CARROT (*Daucus carota*) p. 132

          47. Plants smooth (glabrous), perennial; fruits not bristly.

            POISON HEMLOCK (*Conium maculatum*) p. 131

        46. Leaves not fernlike, the segments ¼ to ½ inch (6 to 13 mm) wide.

        SPOTTED WATERHEMLOCK

          (*Cicuta maculata*) p. 130

      45. Flowers in heads that look somewhat like individual flowers (but surrounded by numerous involucral bracts that flowers don't have), or in a spike; fruits various, not as above.

        48. Leaves compound with about 13 to 15 entire (not toothed) leaflets; flowers in a spikelike cluster (raceme); fruit a burlike prickly pod.

          WILD LICORICE (*Glycyrrhiza lepidota*) p. 108

        48. Leaves dissected into fine, fernlike segments; flowers in flowerlike heads; fruit not a burlike pod; plants usually strong-scented.

          49. Flower heads yellow in center, 1-2 inches (2.5-5 cm) wide; leaves bright green.

            50. Heads 1 inch (2.5 cm) wide or less; widely distributed, central and east.

              MAYWEED (*Anthemis cotula*) p. 186

            50. Heads distinctly more than 1 inch (2.5 cm) wide; north and west, primarily North Dakota.

            FALSE CHAMOMILE

              (*Matricaria maritima*) p. 226

49. Flower heads gray-white, smaller than above; leaves densely hairy or smooth.

    51. Flower heads erect in a flat-topped cluster rising above the leaves; plants usually hairy, perennial from a tangle of short rhizomes. COMMON YARROW
                        (*Achillea millefolium*) p. 180

    51. Flower heads usually drooping from leafy, spreading, or ascending branches; plants hairy or smooth, perennial or annual.

        52. Plant smooth, annual. ANNUAL WORMWOOD
                        (*Artemisia annua*) p. 189

        52. Plant silky or woolly-hairy, perennial. ABSINTH WORMWOOD
                        (*Artemisia absinthium*) p. 188

44. Leaves simple, not compound or dissected.

    53. Plants with a strong, onionlike odor, arising from a fleshy bulb; leaves fleshy, narrowly linear, mostly arising at or near base of stem; flowers umbellate (numerous flower stalks arising in close proximity); southern.

        54. Leaves mostly in a cluster at ground level. WILD ONION (*Allium canadense*) p. 46

        54. Leaves borne on stem as well as at ground level. WILD GARLIC (*Allium vineale*) p. 46

    53. Plants and flowers various, not as above.

        55. Stems and leaves gray- or white-woolly, at least on lower surface; flowers in white or gray-white cottony heads that look like individual flowers.

            56. Leaves spoon-shaped, mostly borne in basal clusters (rosettes) or on horizontal stolons (prostrate stems); heads dirty white, in small, erect clusters. PLANTAINLEAF PUSSYTOES
                        (*Antennaria plantaginifolia*) p. 185

            56. Leaves lanceolate, borne on an erect stem; heads clean white, frequently in rather dense clusters. FRAGRANT CUDWEED
                        (*Gnaphalium obtusifolium*) p. 211

        55. Stems and leaves not woolly; flowers or flower heads various, not as above.

            57. Flowers in heads having a yellow center (tubular flowers) and white petallike marginal (ray) flowers.

                58. Heads more than 1 inch (2.5 cm) across; basal leaves oblong or irregularly spoon-shaped, lobed (pinnatifid) or toothed with more or less rounded segments. OXEYE DAISY
                        (*Chrysanthemum leucanthemum*) p. 196

                58. Flower heads less than 1 inch (2.5 cm) across; leaves various, not as above.

59. Plants perennial from horizontal rhizomes, flowering in early fall; stems ordinarily bearing clusters of reduced leaves in axils of main blades, often considerably branched below inflorescence; flower heads often borne from one side of spreading or nearly horizontal inflorescence branches; fall-flowering.

60. Flower heads mostly ½ inch (1.3 cm) or more across; involucral bracts, under the heads, tending to be rolled up lengthwise at tip; stems glabrous or stiffly hairy, branched mostly in inflorescence.

WHITE HEATH ASTER
(*Aster pilosus*)[5] p. 191

60. Flower heads mostly less than ½ inch (1.3 cm) across; involucral bracts not rolled up, often bent backward; stems usually finely fuzzy (pubescent), diffusely branched throughout.

HEATH ASTER
(*Aster ericoides*)[5] p. 190

59. Plants annual or biennial from taproots, flowering in summer or fall; axillary clusters of reduced leaves not present; flower heads on erect ascending branches in dense or flat-topped clusters.

61. Flower heads about ¼ inch (6 mm) or less across, numerous in a dense, horsetaillike cluster (panicle); stem usually unbranched below inflorescence, very closely leafy with crowded, strap-shaped blades.

HORSEWEED
(*Conyza canadensis*) p. 204

61. Flower heads ½ inch (1.3 cm) or more across in a flat-topped cluster (corymb); stem branched or unbranched, loosely leafy with well-spaced, oblong to ovate, frequently toothed blades.

62. Stem hairs conspicuous, spreading; stem leaves mostly toothed, the lowermost strongly toothed or shallowly lobed.

ANNUAL FLEABANE
(*Erigeron annuus*) not illustrated

62. Stem hairs inconspicuous, upwardly appressed against stem (strigose); leaves, except for the lower, mostly untoothed.

ROUGH FLEABANE
(*Erigeron strigosus*) p. 207

---

[5] These are but two of the several species of *Aster* that are conspicuous in early fall.

57. Flowers not in heads, or if in headlike clusters, not colored as above.

    63. Leaves entire, neither toothed nor lobed.

        64. Fruit a capsule with an incurved or hooked beak several inches long; leaves cordate (heart-shaped), lobed or not; plant sprawling, robust, thick-stemmed; flowers large, about 1 inch (2.5 cm) long, speckled. DEVILSCLAW
           (*Proboscidea louisianica*) p. 168

        64. Fruit not having a long beak; leaves and plants various.

           65. Fruit a fleshy berry, purplish when mature, bearing black, shiny seeds; leaves borne on distinct stalks (petioled); plants often 3 feet (0.9 m) or more high. COMMON POKEWEED
              (*Phytolacca americana*) p. 69

           65. Fruit dry; seeds not as above; leaves narrowed to base, but without a distinct petiole; plants usually less than 3 feet (0.9 m) high.

              66. Plants prostrate or ascending, usually less than 1 foot (0.3 m) tall, not possessing a milky juice; flowers inconspicuous, in leaf axils; fruits 1-seeded, triangular.

                67. Plants prostrate, forming flat mats or ascending at tips; or completely ascending, but usually only a few inches high; leaves blue-green, oblong to narrowly elliptic; a very common urban and waste area weed. PROSTRATE KNOTWEED
                  (*Polygonum aviculare*) p. 49

                67. Plants ascending, frequently about 1 foot (0.3 m) high; leaves yellow-green, elliptic to broadly elliptic, less common than above. ERECT KNOTWEED
                  (*Polygonum erectum*) p. 49

           66. Plants erect, usually more than 1 foot (0.3 m) high, with a milky juice; flowers in terminal clusters; fruits 3-lobed, 3-seeded capsules.

              68. Plants annual; leaves, especially upper, with a white margin and greenish center; flower clusters small, somewhat hidden by the leaves; fruits hairy. SNOW-ON-THE-MOUNTAIN
                (*Euphorbia marginata*) p. 120

68. Plants perennial; leaves all green; flower clusters conspicuous, white; fruits smooth.
FLOWERING SPURGE
(*Euphorbia corollata*) p. 116

63. Leaves toothed or lobed.

69. Leaves as broad as or broader than long, roughly circular with a basal notch; fruits circular, dry, when mature breaking into several 1-seeded, wedge-shaped segments.
COMMON MALLOW
(*Malva neglecta*) p. 124

69. Leaves and fruits various, not as above.

71. Fruit a small berry, black when mature, green when immature; flowers look like tiny potato flowers; leaves wavy-toothed or shallowly lobed, almost always with insect holes.
EASTERN BLACK NIGHTSHADE
(*Solanum ptycanthum*) p. 162

71. Fruit a capsule, dry when mature; flowers not like potato flowers; leaves variable, some of them usually lobed or pinnatifid; insect injury usually not obvious.

72. Plants low or sprawling, flowering in early spring; leaves all deeply pinnatifid; capsule hairy, with four large seeds.
WATERPOD
(*Ellisia nyctelea*) p. 144

72. Plants erect, flowering in summer and fall; leaves variously lobed or toothed; capsules not as above.

73. Flowers large, 3 to 5 inches (7.5 to 12.5 cm) long; fruits large, spiny; plants rank, much branched, frequently becoming 5 feet (1.5 m) high.
JIMSONWEED
(*Datura stramonium*) p. 157

73. Flowers much smaller than above; fruits small, smooth; plants little branched, usually not more than 4 feet (1.2 m) high.
MOTH MULLEIN
(*Verbascum blattaria*) p. 165

KEY 3. PLANTS WITH RED, PINK, BLUE, LAVENDER, OR PURPLE FLOWERS

1. Plants (leaves, stems) spiny or thorny.
   2. Leaves opposite. TEASEL (*Dipsacus sylvestris*) p. 175
   2. Leaves alternate.
      3. Leaves attached directly to stem (sessile), edges prickly; flowers in dense, globular, flowerlike, prickly heads; fruit seedlike, dry; plants erect, 1 to 6 feet (0.3 to 1.8 m) tall, little branched with the main axis (stem) predominant, thistlelike.
         4. Stems, especially near base, white-woolly, not prickly.
            FLODMAN THISTLE (*Cirsium flodmani*) p. 201
         4. Stems green and smooth or hairy; or whitish and prickly.
            5. Plants perennial from creeping roots and without a basal cluster of leaves (rosette); stems usually 2 to 3 feet (0.6 to 0.9 m) high, crowded together; flower heads to 1 inch (2.5 cm) across (often less) when in flower.
               CANADA THISTLE (*Cirsium arvense*) p. 200
            5. Plants biennial, from a basal rosette (may be gone when plants reach flowering), with taller stems (2½ to 6 feet [0.75-1.8 m] high), often well separated; flower heads more than 1 inch (2.5 cm) across (except for plumeless thistle).
               6. Head very large, 1½ inches (3.8 cm) or more across, solitary, usually on a long stalk which is bent or somewhat recurved.
                  MUSK THISTLE (*Carduus nutans*) p. 199
               6. Heads less than 1½ inches (3.8 cm) across, usually several, scarcely stalked above uppermost leaves.
                  7. Stems not prickly; leaves white beneath, this color contrasting to the usually greenish stems; fruits (achenes, "seeds") with a wide yellow band at top.
                     TALL THISTLE (*Cirsium altissimum*) p. 202
                  7. Stems prickly (because the prickly leaves are decurrent); leaves not white or, if somewhat so, the stems of about the same color; fruits lacking a wide apical yellow band.
                     8. Prickly foliar wings on stems often ½ inch (1.3 cm) wide or more; foliage often green-grey; achenes ("seeds") strongly cross-wrinkled (rugose).
                        SCOTCH THISTLE (*Onopordum acanthium*) p. 203
                     8. Prickly wings on stems less than ½ inch (1.3 cm) wide (prickles may be longer); foliage usually greenish; achenes not rugose.
                        9. Heads less than 1 inch (2.5 cm) across; pappus bristles not branched.
                           PLUMELESS THISTLE (*Carduus acanthoides*) p. 198
                        9. Heads 1 inch (2.5 cm) or more across; pappus bristles feathery-branched (plumose) — use hand lens or hold up to light. BULL THISTLE (*Cirsium vulgare*) p. 202
      3. Leaves attached to stem with slender stalks (petioles), edges not prickly; flowers separate, resembling potato flowers; fruit a berry; plants rarely more than 1½ feet (0.45 m) tall, branched and spreading.
         10. Plants white-hairy; leaves lanceolate to oblong, wavy-margined but not lobed; flowers blue-purple.
            SILVERLEAF NIGHTSHADE (*Solanum elaeagnifolium*) p. 160

10. Plants greenish; leaves ovate to lanceolate, frequently lobed; flowers usually light lavender.
HORSENETTLE (*Solanum carolinense*) p. 160

1. Plants (leaves, stems) not spiny or thorny (fruits or fruit clusters sometimes spiny).

11. Leaves opposite (the uppermost rarely alternate).

12. Leaves entire, without teeth or lobes along the margin.[6]

13. Flowers in dense, often globelike clusters (umbels); fruit a soft pod several inches long; seeds flat, wind-borne by clusters of hairs.

14. Leaves usually 2 to 4 inches (5 to 10 cm) wide; flower clusters pinkish; pods 1/2 to 1 inch (1.3 to 2.5 cm) in diameter at base, soft-prickly; common in variety of habitats.
COMMON MILKWEED (*Asclepias syriaca*) p. 137

14. Leaves not more than 1 inch (2.5 cm) wide; flower clusters bright red; pods about 1/2 inch (1.3 cm) in diameter, smooth; poorly drained soil.
SWAMP MILKWEED (*Asclepias incarnata*) p. 136

13. Flowers not in clusters; fruit smaller than above.

15. Plants creeping with short, erect, flowering branches at most a few inches high.

16. Flowers not hidden by broad, overlapping bracts.
THYMELEAF SPEEDWELL (*Veronica serpyllifolia*) p. 166

16. Flowers partly hidden by broad, overlapping bracts.
HEAL-ALL (*Prunella vulgaris*) p. 155

15. Plants erect, 6 inches (15 cm) to several feet tall.

17. Leaves stalked (petioled); fruits 1-seeded or breaking into four 1-seeded segments (nutlets).

18. Leaves somewhat heart-shaped (cordate); plants usually about 2 feet (0.6 m) high; flowers 2 or 3 together, borne above a membranous "umbrella" (involucre).
WILD FOUR-O'CLOCK (*Mirabilis nyctaginea*) p. 68

18. Leaves not cordate; plants frequently less than 1 foot (0.3 m) high; flowers borne in a dense spike, and partly hidden by broad, overlapping bracts.
HEAL-ALL (*Prunella vulgaris*) p. 155

17. Leaves not stalked (sessile); fruits many-seeded capsules.

19. Plant hairy; flowers purple-red, not crowded together.
CORN COCKLE (*Agrostemma githago*) p. 72

19. Plants smooth; flowers pinkish, usually crowded together.

20. Calyx (the green hull around the base of the flower) tubular, round in cross section; plants perennial.
BOUNCINGBET (*Saponaria officinalis*) p. 75

20. Calyx becoming swollen, angular in cross section; plants annual.
COW COCKLE (*Vaccaria segetalis*) p. 81

12. Leaves toothed or lobed along margin, not entire.

---

[6] Two weeds in this group may have both entire and toothed leaves on the same plant. They are keyed out in both directions.

21. Leaves cut nearly to midrib (pinnatifid) into toothed segments or lobes; plants low, spreading, or nearly prostrate.
PROSTRATE VERVAIN (*Verbena bracteata*) p. 147

21. Leaves toothed or lobed (usually in palmate or fingerlike fashion) but the incisions not extending to midrib; plants usually either erect or strictly prostrate and rooting at nodes.

22. Plants prostrate, usually ascending at the tip, or with short erect branches.

23. Flowers borne usually 2 or 3 together in axils of ordinary foliage leaves; uppermost leaf pairs sessile and grown together (connate) at base.

24. Stems extensively trailing; leaves smooth, frequently broader than long; seeds with white spot at base.
GROUND IVY (*Glechoma hederacea*) p. 150

24. Stems short, prostrate to low-ascending; leaves finely hairy, frequently longer than broad; seeds without white spot at base.   HENBIT (*Lamium amplexicaule*) p. 151

23. Flowers borne in short, erect spikes in the axils of bracts or reduced leaves; uppermost leaves not connate.

25. Stems extensively trailing; flowers borne in the axils of narrow, alternate bracts.
THYMELEAF SPEEDWELL
(*Veronica serpyllifolia*) p. 166

25. Stems short, trailing or entirely erect; flowers borne in the axil of very broad bracts, and almost hidden from external view.   HEAL-ALL (*Prunella vulgaris*) p. 155

22. Plants erect or ascending.

26. Flowers in dense clusters in the axils of foliage leaves.

27. Lower leaves maplelike, broad, palmately lobed; flower clusters becoming spiny in fruit.
MOTHERWORT (*Leonurus cardiaca*) p. 152

27. Lower leaves not as above, ovate to lanceolate and toothed; flower clusters not becoming spiny.
FIELD MINT (*Mentha arvensis*) p. 153

26. Flowers in spikes, terminating stems above leaves.

28. Bracts accompanying flowers broad, conspicuous, prickly or marginally hairy (white), often partially hiding flowers.

29. Leaves barely toothed; bracts entire, marginally hairy but not prickly.
HEAL-ALL (*Prunella vulgaris*) p. 155

29. Leaves sharply toothed; bracts toothed, prickly.
DRAGONHEAD (*Dracocephalum parviflorum*) p. 149

28. Bracts accompanying flowers narrow or inevident.

30. Flowers distinctly 2-lipped (zygomorphic), the petals different in size and shape.

31. Leaves sharply toothed; flowers pinkish, crowded, usually overlapping.
AMERICAN GERMANDER
(*Teucrium canadense*) p. 156

31. Leaves vaguely toothed; flowers blue, widely spaced.
LANCE-LEAF SAGE
(*Salvia reflexa*) not illustrated

30. Flowers slightly 2-lipped (nearly actinomorphic), the petals of nearly the same size and shape.

32. Plants 2 to 3 feet (0.6 to 0.9 m) high, scarcely branched except for cluster of spikes at top; leaves very hairy; flowers ¼ inch (6 mm) across.
HOARY VERVAIN (*Verbena stricta*) p. 148

32. Plants frequently 3 to 4 feet (0.9 to 1.2 m) high, often branched; leaves inconspicuously hairy; flowers less than ¼ inch (6 mm) across.
BLUE VERVAIN (*Verbena hastata*) p. 148

11. Leaves alternate or mostly in a basal cluster.

33. Leaves compound with entire leaflets.

34. Leaves pinnately compound, terminated by tendrils; flowers pea-like (but considerably smaller).
NARROWLEAF VETCH (*Vicia angustifolia*) p. 110

34. Leaves palmately compound, not possessing tendrils; flowers not pealike.
ROCKY MOUNTAIN BEEPLANT (*Cleome serrulata*) p. 85

33. Leaves various, rarely compound (if so with lobed or toothed leaflets).

35. Plants vining, trailing, twining, or climbing; leaves with a pair of downwardly or outwardly pointed basal lobes (cordate, sagittate or hastate), or main body of blade divided into 3 segments.

36. Fruit a red berry with numerous small, flat seeds; flowers purple, shaped like potato flowers; plants irregularly sprawling or climbing, often woody at base; leaves frequently of several shapes. BITTER NIGHTSHADE (*Solanum dulcamara*) p. 161

36. Fruit a dry capsule with few, large seeds; flowers morning-glorylike; plants prostrate or climbing, not woody at base; leaves on a single plant consistent in shape.

37. Flowers pinkish to lavender; leaves with pointed basal corners (lobes) that stick outward or downward (sagittate or hastate); plants perennial from slender rootstocks.

38. Flowers roughly the size of a silver dollar; leaves tending to be triangular with broad basal lobes, the blade bent back at right angles to the petiole; plants twining and climbing.
HEDGE BINDWEED (*Convolvulus sepium*) p. 140

38. Flowers roughly the size of a quarter; leaves tending to be oblong with narrow basal lobes, the blade continuing in essentially the same direction as the leaf stalk (petiole); plants more often trailing than climbing.
FIELD BINDWEED (*Convolvulus arvensis*) p. 139

37. Flowers usually deep purple or blue; leaves cordate with rounded basal lobes or deeply 3-lobed; plants annual.

39. Leaves heart-shaped (cordate); calyx lobes (the lobes of the greenish hull at the base of the flower) abruptly pointed, relatively short.
TALL MORNINGGLORY (*Ipomoea purpurea*) p. 142

39. Leaves deeply 3-lobed; calyx lobes slender, drawn out, and gradually tapering to point (attenuate). IVYLEAF MORNINGGLORY

(*Ipomoea hederacea*) p. 142

35. Plants various, sometimes trailing, but not vinelike; leaves various, not as above.

40. Leaves about as broad as long, roughly circular in outline (although sometimes lobed into numerous segments); flowers pink to lavender, relatively small and inconspicuous; plants spreading or low ascending.

41. Leaf blades fingerlike, palmately dissected into lobed segments; fruit extended into a pointed beak. CAROLINA GERANIUM (*Geranium carolinianum*) p. 112

41. Leaf blades irregularly scalloped or shallowly lobed; fruit flat.

42. Petals evident, much longer than sepals (the greenish hull of the flower); fruit with a crenate (wavy) outline, usually hidden by the sepals, not reticulate (with a network of lines) on the outside. COMMON MALLOW (*Malva neglecta*) p. 124

42. Petals small, scarcely longer than sepals; fruit evenly circular, often hidden by sepals, reticulate at full maturity. DWARF MALLOW (*Malva rotundifolia*) p. 125

40. Leaves longer than broad, not circular; flowers and plants various.

43. Stems encircled by short membranous sheaths (ochreae) just above the attachment of each leaf; flowers bright pink or reddish to salmon-pink in short spikes; leaf blades entire; mature seeds black, smooth.

44. Plants perennial from creeping rhizomes; stems and leaves covered with fine, close-appressed hairs; plants usually growing in wet or poorly drained soil, especially along roadside ditches. SWAMP SMARTWEED (*Polygonum coccineum*) p. 50

44. Plants annual; stems and leaves smooth; plants common in all kinds of soil.

45. Flowers bright rose or pink; stem sheaths (ochreae) smooth or torn at the top; hulled achenes ("seeds") about ⅛ inch (3 mm) long. PENNSYLVANIA SMARTWEED

(*Polygonum pensylvanicum*) p. 52

45. Flowers dull pink to salmon-pink; ochreae topped by a line of hairs (ciliate); hulled "seeds" less than ⅛ inch (3 mm) long. LADYSTHUMB (*Polygonum persicaria*) p. 52

43. Stems not possessing ochreae; flowers blue to purple or lavender or, if pinkish, in globular, flowerlike heads; leaves and seeds various, usually not as above.

46. Fruit a red berry; flowers similar in shape to potato flowers; plant reclining or sprawling, somewhat woody at base; leaves heart-shaped or 2-lobed at base. BITTER NIGHTSHADE (*Solanum dulcamara*) p. 161

46. Fruit dry, not a berry; flowers not resembling potato flowers; plants erect or ascending; leaves not as above.

47. Fruits (or burlike hulls enclosing a cluster of fruits) spiny or prickly.

48. Mature fruits much less than 1 inch (2.5 cm) long, breaking into 2 to 4 prickly 1-seeded segments that readily stick to clothing.

49. Flowers blue, small (about ⅛ inch or 3 mm across); leaves narrow.
EUROPEAN STICKTIGHT
(*Lappula echinata*) p. 146

49. Flowers reddish to reddish-purple, ¼ to ½ inch (6 to 13 mm) across; lower leaves large and broad.
HOUNDSTONGUE
(*Cynoglossum officinale*) p. 145

48. Fruits about 1 inch (2.5 cm) long, enclosing numerous seeds; or burs containing several 1-seeded fruits.

50. Flowers large, 2 to 5 inches (5 to 12.5 cm) long; fruit a capsule, prickly with short, straight spines, bearing numerous rounded or kidney-shaped seeds; leaves irregularly wavy-toothed or lobed.
JIMSONWEED (*Datura stramonium*) p. 157

50. Flowers smaller than above, aggregated into burlike heads about 1 inch (2.5 cm) long; burs soft-prickly with hooked bristles, bearing several oblong, 1-seeded fruits (achenes); leaves mostly entire.
COMMON BURDOCK (*Arctium minus*) p. 187

47. Fruits not prickly.

51. Inflorescence an unbranched spike; flowers large with 5 petals; fruit a many-seeded capsule.
CREEPING BELLFLOWER
(*Campanula rapunculoides*) p. 179

51. Inflorescence various, branched; flowers small, in flowerlike heads; fruits 1-seeded achenes, several to a head.

52. Plants with a milky juice; individual flowers in the head strap-shaped and petallike.

53. Flowers pink; leaves small, entire; stem conspicuously ridged, the upper portion practically leafless.
SKELETONWEED
(*Lygodesmia juncea*) p. 225

53. Flowers blue; leaves (at least the basal ones) large, pinnatifid, or coarsely toothed; stem not conspicuously ridged.

54. Plant with numerous well-developed stem leaves, the upper narrowly strap-shaped and entire (usually with no

teeth); stems straight, ordinarily branched only at top; "seeds" (achenes) flattened, with a short beak.
BLUE LETTUCE
(Lactuca pulchella) p. 223

54. Plant with well-developed leaves mostly at base, the upper ones reduced; stem much branched; achenes neither flattened nor beaked.
CHICORY *(Cichorium intybus)* p. 197

52. Plants not possessing a milky juice; individual flowers tubular, not petallike.

55. Flower heads ½ inch (1.3 cm) or more across; lower leaves pinnatifid or irregularly toothed, the upper essentially entire or with slender divisions; plants usually less than 3 feet (0.9 m) high.

56. Plants perennial from creeping roots; heads not dark-spotted on outside; "seeds" (achenes) ivory-colored, without a crown of bristles at top.
RUSSIAN KNAPWEED
(Centaurea repens) p. 195

56. Plants biennial from a taproot; heads dark-spotted on outside; achenes dark, with an oblique notch at base and a crown of bristles at top.
SPOTTED KNAPWEED
(Centaurea maculosa) p. 194

55. Flower heads about ¼ inch (6 mm) across; lower and upper leaves essentially similar with numerous even teeth; plants often more than 3 feet (0.9 m) high.

57. Lower surface of leaves covered with dense film of fine hairs; greenish bracts on outside of flower heads (involucral bracts) recurved at tips.
WESTERN IRONWEED
(Vernonia baldwini) p. 239

57. Lower surface of leaves smooth or sparsely hairy; involucral bracts not recurved.
TALL IRONWEED
(Vernonia altissima) p. 239

KEY 4. PLANTS WITH GREENISH FLOWERS, GRASSES OR GRASSLIKE

1. Plants with a strong onionlike odor, arising from a fleshy bulb, bearing clusters of small scaly bulblets below flowers.

   2. Leaves mostly in a cluster at ground level.
             WILD ONION (*Allium canadense*) p. 46

   2. Leaves borne on stem as well as at ground level.
             WILD GARLIC (*Allium vineale*) p. 46

1. Plants not possessing an onionlike odor, not bearing aerial bulblets.

   3. Stems triangular in cross section; leaves harsh and somewhat stiff, arising in 3 rows.

      4. Plants arising from heavy, creeping rhizomes (underground stems); fruits usually borne in broad spikes; "seeds" (1-seeded fruits) produced within an inflated, saclike structure (perigynium).
             HOP SEDGE (*Carex lupulina*)[7] p. 43

      4. Plants with slender, stringlike rhizomes and small tubers; fruits borne in narrow, clustered, yellowish-green spikes; "seeds" (1-seeded fruits) hidden by closely overlapping bracts, but not in saclike structures.
             YELLOW NUTSEDGE (*Cyperus esculentus*) p. 44

   3. Stems not triangular in cross section, but round or flattened; leaves various, usually arising in 2 rows from opposite sides of the stem.

      5. Fruit a spiny bur.
             LONGSPINE SANDBUR (*Cenchrus longispinus*) p. 20

      5. Fruit not a spiny bur.

         6. Plants low and wiry, rarely found in tilled soil; flowers numerous in nearly flat-topped clusters with tiny, green petals and sepals; fruits bearing many very small, dustlike seeds.
             SLENDER RUSH (*Juncus tenuis*) p. 45

         6. Plants various; flowers not in flat-topped clusters, without petals and sepals, usually hidden from external view by enclosing hulls; fruit (the grain) 1-seeded, much larger than above.   (GRASSES)[8]

           7. Stem or its main branches terminated by a single flowering spike (like wheat); spikes neither borne in clusters at stem tip nor arising from leaf axils along the stem.

              8. "Seeds" (spikelets), when "shucked" from the spikes, rounded or elliptic, not sharply pointed or terminated by a bristle; spikes usually dense and cylindric, bristly from clusters of stiff hairs that surround the seeds (but are not borne by the seed hulls).

                9. Spikes stickery and readily adhering to clothing or hands if touched; plants of only local abundance.
             BRISTLY FOXTAIL (*Setaria verticillata*) p. 37

---

[7] Numerous sedges (*Carex* spp.) are minor agricultural weeds. They are usually conspicuous in the spring, growing in wet, low meadows and along ditches. They are rare in tilled soil. All species of *Carex* have the seed borne within the saclike perigynium. The size, appearance, and arrangement of the perigynia are variable.

[8] Although many grasses are easily recognized, it is difficult to identify them in a key without the use of technical characteristics. This key, avoiding the use of exact (and more technical) terms, is necessarily less precise than if such terms were employed. Reference to the illustrations may facilitate keying grasses.

9. Spikes neither stickery nor adherent; plants widespread, common weeds.

    10. Spikes erect; "seeds" (spikelets) broadly oval, ⅛ inch (3 mm) or more long; hard inner hull (lemma) coarsely cross-wrinkled; bristles tawny yellow; a few long, slender hairs present on upper side of blade at base; sheaths not finely hairy (ciliate) along overlapping margins.
        YELLOW FOXTAIL (*Setaria lutescens*) p. 36

    10. Spikes somewhat or much drooping at tip; "seeds" (spikelets) narrowly oval, less than ⅛ inch (3 mm) long; inner hull (lemma) granular or faintly cross-wrinkled; bristles green or pale yellow when dry; leaves without hairs on upper surface, or entirely covered with fine, short hairs; sheath marginally hairy, or ciliate (hand lens will help).

        11. Leaves without hairs (glabrous) on upper surface; spikes slightly drooping at tip; plants usually less than 3 feet (0.9 m) high.
            GREEN FOXTAIL (*Setaria viridis*)[9] p. 38

        11. Leaves finely hairy on upper surface; spikes drooping at tip; plants sometimes 6 feet (1.8 m) high or more.
            GIANT FOXTAIL (*Setaria faberi*) p. 35

8. "Seeds" (spikelets or florets), when "shucked" from spike, oblong to lanceolate, pointed at tip (or entire spike fragmenting into seed-containing bony joints — JOINTED GOATGRASS, lead 12); hulls frequently terminated by bristles; spikes various, bristly or not bristly.

    12. Spike axis with hard, bony joints, the seeds contained within these joints; bristles few, 3 or 4 long ones protruding from tip of spikes, the ones below becoming progressively shorter to base; plant occurring mostly in southern part of our range. JOINTED GOATGRASS (*Aegilops cylindrica*) p. 13

    12. Spike axis not as above; seed-bearing units produced in various manners but not inside of joints of spike axis.

        13. Spikes dense, bristly or plumelike with numerous bristles arising between the "seeds" (florets) as well as from the tips of them; bristles mostly considerably longer than the seeds.

            14. Spikes plumelike with numerous long, green or silvery bristles protruding in all directions.
                FOXTAIL BARLEY (*Hordeum jubatum*) p. 27

            14. Spikes stiff (like a small head of barley) with rigid, ascending bristles about as long as or slightly longer than the seeds.
                LITTLE BARLEY (*Hordeum pusillum*) p. 27

        13. Spikes looser, the seed-bearing units (spikelets) usually clearly separate from one another; bristles absent, or, if present, relatively short, and arising only from the tips of the seeds.

---

[9] This weed seems to cross with foxtail millet (*Setaria italica*). The hybrids are common in some areas and may be as tall as giant foxtail. Some have lobed, strongly drooping spikes.

15. Seed-bearing units (spikelets) placed with narrow edge against spike axis; plants annual, primarily small grain weeds.　　DARNEL (*Lolium temulentum*) p. 28

15. Seed-bearing units (spikelets) placed with the broader, flat edge against spike axis; plants perennial from scaly, creeping rhizomes, abundant throughout most of north central states.

QUACKGRASS (*Agropyron repens*) p. 14

7. Stems not terminated by a single spike; inflorescences various — if spikelike, the spikes borne in leaf axils along stem or clustered together in fingerlike fashion at tip.

16. Inflorescence of 2 to 5 spikes, which arise in fingerlike fashion from tip of stems; bristles (awns) not present.

17. Plants perennial with short, ascending branches arising from extensively creeping stolons (prostrate stems); leaves at base of erect branches much reduced; seed-bearing units (spikelets) not hairy, 1-seeded.

BERMUDAGRASS (*Cynodon dactylon*) p. 21

17. Plants annual, ascending or sprawling and rooting from lower nodes; none of leaves reduced; spikelets finely hairy or several-seeded.

18. Spikes mostly less than ⅛ inch (3 mm) wide; seed-bearing units (spikelets) finely hairy, 1-seeded; a fine row of hairs (ligule) present at base of upper side of blade where it joins the sheath.

19. Stems and leaf sheaths hairy; seeds (spikelets) narrowly oval, the inner hull brownish.

LARGE CRABGRASS (*Digitaria sanguinalis*) p. 22

19. Stems and leaf sheaths almost without hairs; spikelets broadly oval, the inner hull (when mature) black.

SMOOTH CRABGRASS (*Digitaria ischaemum*) p. 22

18. Spikes broader than ⅛ inch (3 mm); spikelets smooth, bearing several seeds; ligule a fine membrane rather than a row of hairs.　GOOSEGRASS (*Eleusine indica*) p. 24

16. Inflorescences not of 2 to 5 spikes or, if spikelike, bristly or long-hairy.

20. Seed-bearing units (spikelets) without bristles (awns), sometimes with sharp points to ⅛ inch (3 mm) long.

21. Spikelets oblong, several-seeded, with several or numerous hulls (lemmas) overlapping in shinglelike fashion.

22. Spikelets with about 6 overlapping hulls, leaves without glands; turf weed.

ANNUAL BLUEGRASS (*Poa annua*) p. 34

22. Spikelets with more than 10 overlapping hulls, conspicuously flattened, leaves with small, bumpy glands, especially along edges (hand lens); waste area weed.

STINKGRASS (*Eragrostis cilianensis*)[10] p. 25

21. Spikelets oval, 1-seeded, without a series of shinglelike hulls.

_____

[10] Two additional species of *Eragrostis* are common late-summer, waste area or roadside weeds; usually in dry soil.

23. Inflorescences diffusely branched (a panicle), the spikelets usually separated from one another at the tips of the ultimate branchlets; plants annuals.

24. Spikelets (seeds) about the size of sorghum seeds or a bit smaller, ¼ inch (6 mm) or more long.

25. Spikelets paired, one larger and hard, the other short-stalked and soft; spikelets and axis with fine hairs (hand lens needed).
SHATTERCANE (*Sorghum bicolor*) p. 39

25. Spikelets not paired, all of the same kind; spikelets without hairs (glabrous).
WILD PROSO MILLET
(*Panicum miliaceum*) p. 33

24. Seeds about the size of bluegrass seeds, much smaller than sorghum seeds and less than ¼ inch (6 mm) long.

26. Plant erect or ascending, densely hairy.
WITCHGRASS (*Panicum capillare*) p. 31

26. Plant prostrate-spreading or ascending, smooth.
FALL PANICUM
(*Panicum dichotomiflorum*) p. 32

23. Inflorescences various but not a diffuse panicle; sometimes a series of spikes or appearing almost spikelike (the branches ascending and pressed together), or the spikelets irregularly congested.

27. Inflorescences sticking up beyond leaves, irregularly congested and lopsided, or consisting of an aggregation of short spikelets, each shelling down to a hard, broad, shiny hull; plant annual, husky, with stems usually more than ¼ inch (6 mm) in diameter; ligule absent.
BARNYARDGRASS (*Echinochloa crusgalli*) p. 23

27. Inflorescences usually overtopped by some of the leaves, not lopsided, but narrow and spikelike in appearance or a series of spikes; plants often wiry or slender-stemmed; ligule present.

28. Plants perennial from scaly rhizomes; seed head usually evident; weeds of cultivated soil.

29. Inflorescence axis hairy; spikelets ("seeds") nearly ¼ inch (6 mm) wide.
WOOLLY CUPGRASS
(*Eriochloa villosa*) p. 26

29. Inflorescence axis without hairs; spikelets tiny, less than ⅛ inch (3 mm) wide.
WIRESTEM MULHY
(*Muhlenbergia frondosa*) p. 29

28. Plants annual, without rhizomes; seed head spikelike, often nearly hidden in upper leaf sheaths; a weed usually of dry, sterile areas.
ANNUAL DROPSEED
(*Sporobolus neglectus*) p. 41

20. Spikelets with short or long bristles or awns.
  30. Inflorescences with dense, long, silky hairs, resembling a series of separate or congested plumes.
    31. Plants 2 to 4 feet (0.6 to 1.2 m) tall, in small, erect clumps or bunches, without conspicuous rhizomes, lower portion of stem flattened with keeled edges.
      BROOMSEDGE (*Andropogon virginicus*) p. 15
    31. Plants 4 to 12 feet (1.2 to 3.6 m) tall from creeping rhizomes.
      SILVER PLUMEGRASS
        (*Miscanthus sacchariflorus*) not illustrated
  30. Inflorescences not silky-hairy; pubescence (hairs), if present, relatively short; plants various.
    32. Bristles (awns) 3-branched (shorter unbranched bristles may also be present).
      PRAIRIE THREEAWN (*Aristida oligantha*) p. 16
    32. Awns unbranched.
      33. Some or all awns spirally twisted at base.
        34. Awn 3 to 4 inches (7.6 to 10 cm) long, several times length of seed, frequently twisted for much of its length.
          PORCUPINEGRASS (*Stipa spartea*) p. 42
        34. Awn scarcely more than 1 inch (2.5 cm) long, up to about twice the length of seeds, usually twisted near the base.
          35. Spikelets about ¾ inch (1.9 cm) long (excluding awns), gaping open at the tip when mature, 2- to 3-seeded; plants annual, oat-like in appearance; primarily western part of range.
            WILD OAT (*Avena fatua*) p. 17
          35. Spikelets (excluding awns) about ¼ inch (6 mm) long, not opening at tip, 1-seeded; "seeds" (spikelets) plump, elliptic, straw-colored to shiny black; plants perennial or annual, resembling sorghum or sudangrass; primarily southern part of range.
            36. Plants perennial from creeping rhizomes usually 3 to 6 feet (0.9-1.8 m) high; ripe spikelets ("seeds") with inner black hulls.
              JOHNSONGRASS
                (*Sorghum halepense*) p. 40
            36. Plants annual, 4 to 8 feet (1.2 to 2.4 m) high, sometimes to 12 feet (3.6 m); ripe spikelets various in color, commonly tan.
              SHATTERCANE
                (*Sorghum bicolor*) p. 39
      33. Awns not spirally twisted.
        37. Inflorescence open, branched (a panicle), sometimes appearing somewhat plumelike, the

spikelets usually well separated from one another; spikelets large, oblong, ½ to ¾ inch (1.3-1.9 cm) long (excluding awns), with a series of hulls overlapping in shinglelike fashion and breaking into several seeds at maturity.

38. Stems essentially smooth and without hairs; awns usually rather short.
CHEAT (*Bromus secalinus*) p. 18

38. Stems finely hairy; awns long and conspicuous.

    39. Spikelets and seeds finely hairy; panicle rather dense, often turning reddish-purple at maturity and appearing plumelike; spring-flowering.
DOWNY BROME
(*Bromus tectorum*) p. 19

    39. Spikelets and seeds not hairy; panicle more open, neither becoming reddish nor appearing plumelike; late spring to summer flowering.
JAPANESE BROME
(*Bromus japonicus*) p. 18

37. Inflorescence not open-branched, usually irregularly congested or very slender, the spikelets crowded together; spikelets broadly or narrowly elliptic, 1-seeded, less than ½ inch (1.3 cm) long (excluding awns).

    40. Plants annual, ascending or sprawling, husky, growing in the open; stems usually more than ¼ inch (6 mm) in diameter; inflorescence an irregular, often lopsided cluster of broadly rounded spikelets that are often covered with short bristles; ligule absent; annual of agricultural soil.
BARNYARDGRASS
(*Echinochloa crusgalli*) p. 23

    40. Plants commonly prostrate, rooting at nodes with ascending branches, often growing in partial shade; stems less than ¼ inch (6 mm) in diameter; inflorescence long and narrow; spikelets small, narrowly elliptic; ligule present; perennial, usually of shady turf.
NIMBLEWILL
(*Muhlenbergia schreberi*) p. 30

KEY 5. PLANTS WITH GREENISH FLOWERS, NOT GRASSES

1. Stem not leaf-bearing; leaves all in a basal cluster (rosette) at ground level.
    2. Leaves broadly ovate or elliptic; flower-producing portion of spike longer than stalk (peduncle); seeds irregular in shape, several in each seed pod (capsule).
        3. Leaves glossy-green, almost without hairs; petioles usually purple at base; seeds black when mature (immature ones brownish).
            BLACKSEED PLANTAIN (*Plantago rugelii*) p. 171
        3. Leaves dull green or gray-green, covered with fine hairs; petioles not purple; seeds brown when mature.
            BROADLEAF PLANTAIN (*Plantago major*) p. 171
    2. Leaves lanceolate to linear; flower-producing portion of spike about as long as, or much shorter than peduncle; seeds 2 in each capsule, and boat-shaped.
        4. Plants perennial, usually appearing smooth; leaves narrowly elliptic to lance-shaped; flowering spike less than 1/5 as long as stalk (peduncle); mature seeds glossy, without a white line on the concave side.
            BUCKHORN PLANTAIN (*Plantago lanceolata*) p. 170
        4. Plants annual; usually appearing hairy or woolly; leaves narrowly oblong to linear; flowering spike $\frac{1}{2}$ as long or nearly as long as peduncle; mature seeds not glossy, with an elliptic, white line on concave surface.
            5. Bracts much longer than flowers and giving the spike a bristly appearance; plants loosely hairy (villous) or occasionally smooth; most common in the southern part of our range.
                BRACTED PLANTAIN (*Plantago aristata*) p. 169
        5. Bracts mostly shorter than flowers and hidden by them; entire plant, including spike, woolly; most common in western portion of our range.   WOOLLY PLANTAIN (*Plantago purshii*) p. 172
1. Stem leaf-bearing with opposite or alternate blades at time of flowering (a basal rosette of leaves may or may not also be present).
    6. Leaves palmately compound with 5 to 7 narrow leaflets arising fingerlike from the same point at end of leaf stalk.   HEMP (*Cannabis sativa*) p. 47
    6. Leaves various, not palmately compound.
        7. Leaves fernlike, divided into numerous, narrow segments (1- or 2-pinnatifid); plants ragweedlike, topped by a spike (raceme) of yellowish-green, sterile, pollen-producing flowers (flower heads).
            8. Leaves woolly beneath or on both sides; fruit a spiny bur, usually with 2 or 3 seeds; plants primarily of western portion of our range.
                9. Leaves woolly beneath; stamen-producing flowers (flower heads) short-stalked; fruits with straight spines.
                    SKELETONLEAF BURSAGE (*Ambrosia tomentosa*) p. 184
                9. Leaves woolly on both sides; stamen-producing flowers (flower heads) slender-stalked; fruits with curved spines.
                    WOOLLYLEAF BURSAGE (*Ambrosia grayi*) p. 184
            8. Leaves not woolly; fruit 1-seeded, not a spiny bur; plants abundant throughout our range.
                10. Plants annual, very common; leaves smooth above, usually much divided, the main segments being cut into secondary divisions (2-pinnatifid); fruits with a distinct crown of points at tip.
                    COMMON RAGWEED (*Ambrosia artemisiifolia*) p. 181
                10. Plants perennial from creeping roots (first-year plants appear annual), similar in appearance to above, but much less common;

leaves rough on upper surface, less divided than in above species, the main segments frequently lobed but not again divided (1-pinnatifid); fruits with a very short crown of points or nearly smooth at tip. WESTERN RAGWEED (*Ambrosia psilostachya*) p. 182

7. Leaves not fernlike; entire, toothed, or lobed but not pinnatifid (rarely lowermost leaves pinnatifid but the middle stem ones not); plants various.

  11. Plant a twining or prostrate vine with tendrils.

    12. Plant a twining vine; leaves arrowhead- or spear-shaped; fruit not burlike.
WILD BUCKWHEAT (*Polygonum convolvulus*) p. 51

    12. Plant a prostrate vine with tendrils; leaves not arrowhead-shaped; fruit a prickly bur. BUR CUCUMBER (*Sicyos angulatus*) p. 178

  11. Plant not a twining or tendril-bearing vine.

    13. Stem encircled by a white or brownish membranous sheath (ochrea) for a short distance just above attachment of each leaf (this sheath is easily seen on younger parts of stem — it is frequently broken and partly destroyed on older portions); "seeds" (achenes) 3-angled.

      14. Plants with a basal rosette of leaves as well as stem leaves (rosette blades may mostly be gone on old plants); flowers in a terminal branched spike; seeds (achenes) shiny.

        15. Leaves arrowhead-shaped (hastate) with pointed basal lobes; plants with creeping rootstocks; fruit hulls (calyx lobes) tightly appressed to fruit.
RED SORREL (*Rumex acetosella*) p. 53

        15. Leaves not hastate; plants not possessing creeping rootstocks; fruit hulls loose around fruit.

          16. Leaves smooth and even, neither closely wavy along margin nor lobed at base; fruiting hulls, when mature, about 1/4 inch (6 mm) long.
PALE DOCK (*Rumex altissimus*) p. 54

          16. Leaves either closely wavy-crisped along margin or slightly basally lobed (cordate); fruiting hulls less than 1/4 inch (6 mm) long.

            17. Leaves ovate to oblong, mostly somewhat cordate at base, frequently with reddish veins; fruit hulls toothed along margin.
BROADLEAF DOCK (*Rumex obtusifolius*) p. 55

            17. Leaves oblong, with crisped or wavy-curved edges, rarely red-veined; fruit hulls not toothed.
CURLY DOCK (*Rumex crispus*) p. 55

      14. Plants not possessing a basal rosette; flowers axillary; "seeds" (achenes) usually dull.

        18. Plants prostrate, forming flat mats or ascending at tips, or completely ascending, but only a few inches high; leaves blue-green, oblong to narrowly elliptic; a very common urban weed.
PROSTRATE KNOTWEED (*Polygonum aviculare*) p. 49

        18. Plants ascending, frequently about 1 foot (0.3 m) high; leaves yellow-green, elliptic to broadly elliptic; less common. ERECT KNOTWEED (*Polygonum erectum*) p. 49

13. Stem not encircled by a sheath as above described; fruits various, not as above.

19. Leaves entire, neither toothed nor lobed.

20. Plants spiny.

21. Upper leaves narrow, hardened, and spine-tipped; seeds snaillike in appearance.
RUSSIAN THISTLE (*Salsola kali*) p. 61

21. Leaves all normal, the spines arising in pairs at base of leaf stalks; seeds lens-shaped, black.
SPINY AMARANTH (*Amaranthus spinosus*) p. 66

20. Plants not spiny (fruit sometimes a spiny bur).

22. Plants with a milky juice; leaves without stalks (sessile) or very short-stalked, strap-shaped or oblong; flower clusters yellowish-green or greenish-white.

23. Flowers with small greenish-white petals; leaves with very short stalks; fruit long and slender.
HEMP DOGBANE (*Apocynum cannabinum*) p. 134

23. Flowers borne above yellowish-green bracts; leaves without stalks, strap-shaped; fruit as wide as long.

24. Leaves about ⅛ inch (3 mm) wide.
CYPRESS SPURGE
(*Euphorbia cyparissias*) p. 117

24. Leaves usually ¼ to ½ inch (6-13 mm) wide.
LEAFY SPURGE (*Euphorbia esula*) p. 118

22. Plants not possessing milky juice; leaves stalked or sessile; flower clusters not yellow-green.

25. Plant prostrate, forming a mat on ground.
PROSTRATE PIGWEED
(*Amaranthus blitoides*) p. 63

25. Plants erect or ascending.

26. Plants woolly.
WOOLLY CROTON (*Croton capitatus*) p. 115

26. Plants smooth or hairy, but not woolly.

27. Plants perennial from creeping rootstocks; leaves elliptic to oblong, not stalked (sessile), 2-veined; flower clusters borne in leaf axils; mostly western portion of our range.
POVERTYWEED (*Iva axillaris*) p. 221

27. Plants annual; leaves various, not as above described; flower clusters (except for bushy-branched *Amaranthus albus*, below) in terminal branched spikes; plants widely distributed.

28. Leaves not stalked (sessile), narrowly strap-shaped (linear) to lanceolate; seed brownish, longer than wide.
KOCHIA (*Kochia scoparia*) p. 60

28. Leaves stalked (petioled), ovate to lanceolate; seeds black when mature, circular.

29. Plants bushy-branched, the main axis not dominating; flowers borne in clusters in leaf axils.
TUMBLE PIGWEED
(Amaranthus albus) p. 62

29. Plants branched or not, but the main axis predominant; flowers in dense terminal spikes.

30. Spikes dense, bristly in appearance and somewhat prickly to touch; leaves finely hairy, usually broadly lanceolate and upwards of 1½ inches (3.8 cm) in width.

31. Spikes thick, the main portion more than ½ inch (1.3 cm) thick (this plant is not always clearly distinguishable from the following).
REDROOT PIGWEED
(Amaranthus retroflexus) p. 65

31. Spikes narrow, the main portion less than ½ inch (1.3 cm) across.
SMOOTH PIGWEED
(Amaranthus hybridus) p. 64

30. Spikes often interrupted, and not especially dense, not bristly or prickly to touch; leaves smooth, usually narrowly lanceolate and less than 1 inch (2.5 cm) wide.
TALL WATERHEMP
(Amaranthus tuberculatus)[11] p. 67

19. Leaves, at least the lower, toothed (the teeth sometimes small or scattered) or lobed.

32. Fruit a bur covered with numerous hooked spines; leaves long-stalked, irregularly shallowly lobed and toothed, rough.
COMMON COCKLEBUR *(Xanthium strumarium)* p. 240

32. Fruit not a spiny bur; leaves various.

33. Plants with milky juice, rarely more than 1 foot (0.3 m) high; leaves frequently with dark blotches or spots, all opposite.

34. Plants prostrate.
PROSTRATE SPURGE
(Euphorbia maculata) p. 119

34. Plants ascending, usually with slanting stems which frequently recurve at tip.
SPOTTED SPURGE *(Euphorbia preslii)* p. 119

33. Plants not possessing milky juice; leaves various, not spotted — if all opposite, the plants usually much taller than above described.

[11] Some of the waterhemp found in the region is probably a hybrid complex among various species of waterhemp.

35. Leaves all alternate or the lowest in a basal cluster (a rosette as in pepperweed); the lower leaves not opposite.

36. Fruits circular, flat, each 2-seeded; flowers usually with tiny white petals (close examination required).
GREENFLOWER PEPPERWEED
(*Lepidium densiflorum*) p. 97

36. Fruits variously shaped, not flat, usually 1-seeded; flowers lacking petals.

37. Fruits produced in irregularly branched spikes that protrude beyond leaves, 1-seeded; seeds lens-shaped, usually black after being rubbed to remove scurf; plants not restricted to southern part of range.

38. Fruits (actually fruits plus enveloping calyx) with a marginal wing; upper portion of stem often nearly naked at maturity; leaves sharply sinuate-toothed; mostly limited to western portion of our range.
WINGED PIGWEED
(*Cycloloma atriplicifolium*) p. 59

38. Fruits without a marginal wing; leaves retained at maturity, i.e., stem not becoming naked; leaves variously toothed; plants not restricted to western portion of north central states.

39. Plants strongly aromatic; leaves oblong, wavy-toothed or shallowly lobed, not white-mealy beneath.
MEXICANTEA
(*Chenopodium ambrosioides*) p. 57

39. Plants not aromatic; leaves ovate to oblong, irregularly lobed, toothed or nearly entire, often white-mealy beneath.

40. Seeds (easily rubbed out of hulls) about 1/16 inch (1.5 mm) in diameter; leaves dull green to green, often scurfy-whitish beneath, the large blades usually not longer than 2 to 3 inches (5-7.5 cm); common weed.
COMMON LAMBSQUARTERS
(*Chenopodium album*) p. 57

40. Seeds 1/16 to ⅛ inch (1.5 to 3 mm) in diameter; leaves bright green, the larger blades often 4 inches (10 cm) or more long; only locally common.
MAPLELEAF GOOSEFOOT
(*Chenopodium hybridum*) p. 58

37. Fruits solitary or in small clusters at base of upper leaves, often mostly hidden by the leaves, forming 2 to 4 seeds; seeds usually turtle-shaped; plants restricted to southern portion of our range.
TROPIC CROTON
          (Croton glandulosus) p. 115

35. Lower leaves opposite, the upper becoming alternate, or all leaves opposite. (If lowest leaves have fallen off, their position can be verified by noting leaf scars at stem nodes.)

41. Flower clusters produced in leaf axils and not protruding above leafy stem.

  42. Leaves all opposite; stems frequently more than 2 feet (0.6 m) high, with stinging hairs; flower clusters slender, catkinlike, drooping from leaf axils.
  STINGING NETTLE *(Urtica dioica)* p. 48

  42. Leaves mostly alternate, usually with insect holes; stems usually less than 2 feet (0.6 m) high, without stinging hairs; flower clusters mostly hidden by toothed bracts in leaf axils.
  VIRGINIA COPPERLEAF
          (Acalypha virginica) p. 114

41. Flower clusters in simple or branched spikes (racemes or panicles), entirely or in part borne apically on stem above leaves.

  43. Seeds circular in outline, blackish, borne within a pair of pointed husks, which fit together in clamshell-like fashion; leaves often arrowhead-shaped (hastate).
  SPREADING ORACH
          (Atriplex patula) p. 56

  43. "Seeds" (fruits) not circular, not borne as above described; leaves not hastate.

    44. Leaves narrow, usually with 1 or 2 upward-pointing teeth on each side; plants low, usually not much more than 1 foot (0.3 m) high, restricted to southern portion of our range.
    LANCELEAF RAGWEED
          (Ambrosia bidentata) p. 181

    44. Leaves broad and large, with numerous teeth, or 3- to 5-lobed; plants tall, often more than 3 feet (0.9 m) high.

      45. Leaves, except sometimes for the uppermost, 3- to 5-lobed; fruits with a crown of points at tip.
      GIANT RAGWEED
          (Ambrosia trifida) p. 183

      45. Leaves unlobed; fruits seedlike without a crown of points.
      MARSHELDER
          (Iva xanthifolia) p. 222

KEY 6. PLANTS WOODY

Only four woody plants are illustrated in this circular. However, a number of shrubs and trees often occur as brush in pastures and, under these conditions, are considered weeds. The following key includes some common brushy weeds.

Warning — Poison ivy and poison oak have compound leaves with three leaflets. Don't pick or handle leaves of this type.

1. Plants thorny or spiny.
  2. Leaves simple.
    3. Leaves entire; fruit the size of a large orange, green.
      OSAGEORANGE (*Maclura pomifera*)
    3. Leaves toothed or lobed; fruits like small crabapples, usually reddish.
      HAWTHORN (*Crataegus* spp.)
  2. Leaves compound.
    4. Leaflets toothed; shrubby plants.
      5. Stipules (appendages at the base of the leaves) fused to petioles; flowers 1 inch (2.5 cm) or more across, roselike.
        6. Robust bush, or tangle-forming shrub 6-10 feet (1.8-3 m); flowers usually white, the styles (see glossary if necessary) united into a single column, protruding and evident; commonly weedy in brushy pastures.   MULTIFLORA ROSE (*Rosa multiflora*)
        6. Bushes or low shrubs much smaller than above; flowers usually pink, the styles separate and not evident; rarely weedy.
          Other *Rosa* spp. including
        ARKANSAS ROSE (*Rosa arkansana*) p. 107
      5. Stipules essentially free from petioles; flowers less than 1 inch (2.5 cm) across.   BRAMBLES, WILD BLACKBERRIES (*Rubus* spp.)
    4. Leaflets entire; trees.
      7. Some of leaves twice-compound (i.e., the main divisions of the leaves, in turn compound); thorns various, becoming more than 1 inch (2.5 cm) long and branched.   HONEYLOCUST (*Gleditisa triacanthos*)
      7. Leaves all once-compound; thorns (spines) less than 1 inch (2.5 cm) long, unbranched.   BLACK LOCUST (*Robinia pseudoacacia*)
1. Plants not thorny or spiny.
  8. Leaves compound.
    9. Leaves opposite.
      10. Plant a vine with trumpet-shaped, orange-red flowers 2 to 3 inches (5-7.6 cm) long.   TRUMPETCREEPER (*Campsis radicans*) p. 167
      10. Plants shrubs or trees; flowers small.
        11. Flowers white, in conspicuous flat- or convex-topped clusters (corymbs) appearing in summer; fruit a small fleshy berry; twigs with conspicuous, light-colored bumps (lenticels).
          ELDER (*Sambucus* spp.)
        11. Flowers greenish-yellow, inconspicuous, appearing with or before leaves; fruit dry, winged (a samara); twigs not as above.
          12. Leaflets 3-5, conspicuously toothed or lobed; young twigs usually with a whitish-waxy covering.
            BOXELDER (*Acer negundo*)

12. Leaflets 5 to 7, entire or finely toothed; twigs not whitish waxy. ASH (*Fraxinus* spp.)

9. Leaves alternate.

13. Leaflets 3; fruits berrylike, white; plants trailing, climbing or forming small shrubs (poisonous to touch!).
POISON IVY (*Rhus radicans*) p. 121

13. Leaflets 5 or more, fruits not white; plants large shrubs or trees.

14. Fruits small, reddish "berries" in dense clusters at branch tips; leaves mostly with more than 9 leaflets. SUMAC (*Rhus* spp.)

14. Fruits hickory nuts; leaves of common kinds with 5 to 7 leaflets.
HICKORY (*Carya* spp.)

8. Leaves simple, not divided into leaflets.

15. Plants evergreen, with needlelike or scalelike leaves.

16. Leaves needlelike, in clusters of 2 to 5; fruit a cone.
PINE (*Pinus* spp.)

16. Leaves overlapping scales, or, on young plants, sometimes like short needles (but not in clusters); fruit berrylike.
EASTERN REDCEDAR (*Juniperus virginiana*)

15. Plants with deciduous leaves (falling off in winter) that are neither scalelike nor needlelike.

17. Leaves opposite.

18. Leaves broad, palmately lobed; fruit dry. MAPLE (*Acer* spp.)

18. Leaves elliptic, entire; fruit a berry.

19. Stems viny or forming mats on the ground.
JAPANESE HONEYSUCKLE (*Lonicera japonica*)

19. Stems erect; plants forming low shrubs.
BUCKBRUSH (*Symphoricarpos* spp.)

17. Leaves alternate.

20. Plants vinelike, trailing or climbing; fruit a berry.

21. Plants with tendrils; leaves palmately lobed.
WILD GRAPE (*Vitis* spp.)

21. Plants without tendrils; leaves ovate and entire or with 1 or 2 irregular lobes at base; flowers resembling those of potatoes.
BITTER NIGHTSHADE (*Solanum dulcamara*) p. 161

20. Plants shrubs or trees; fruit various, usually not a berry.

22. Leaves lobed.

23. Leaves densely white-hairy beneath.
WHITE POPLAR (*Populus alba*)

23. Leaves not white-hairy underneath.

24. Leaves both lobed and serrate; fruit fleshy; plants with milky juice. MULBERRY (*Morus* spp.)

24. Leaves not serrate; fruit an acorn; juice not milky.
OAK (*Quercus* spp.)

22. Leaves not lobed.

25. Leaves 3 to 5 times as long as wide (in common species); buds covered by a single hoodlike scale.
WILLOW (*Salix* spp.)

25. Leaves less than 3 times as long as wide; buds various, usually with several overlapping scales.

    26. Leaves palmately veined with 3 (sometimes 5) main veins from base of blade.

        27. Leaves lopsided or asymmetric at base; fruit fleshy, 1-seeded; bark usually with distinctive narrow ridges or bumps. HACKBERRY (*Celtis* spp.)

        27. Leaves essentially symmetric; fruit if fleshy with several seeds.

            28. Juice milky; fruits fleshy, several-seeded; leaf petioles scarcely flattened.

                MULBERRY (*Morus* spp.)

            28. Juice not milky; fruits dry with tiny air-borne seeds; petioles often flattened.

              COTTONWOOD, POPLAR (*Populus* spp.)

    26. Leaves pinnately veined, with one main vein from base of blade.

        29. Leaves asymmetric (lopsided) at base.

            ELM (*Ulmus* spp.)

        29. Leaves symmetric.

            30. Leaves nearly as broad as long, abruptly pointed; petioles flattened; buds sticky.

              COTTONWOOD (*Populus* spp.)

            30. Leaves various, but distinctly longer than wide; petioles not flattened; buds not sticky.

                31. Leaf petioles with 1, 2, or several small glands at upper end; flowers white, conspicuous; fruits fleshy.

                  WILD CHERRY (*Prunus* spp.)

                31. Leaf petioles not bearing glands; flowers greenish, some of them in catkins; fruit dry.

                    32. Some of leaves crowded together on short spurs; fruits in conelike clusters. BIRCH (*Betula* spp.)

                    32. Leaves alternate, not crowded together; fruit a nut enclosed in a husk.

                      HAZEL (*Corylus* spp.)

COMMON WEED SEEDLINGS OF CORN AND SOYBEANS

These short keys list only the most common weed seedlings of the middle North Central states. The explanatory footnotes are grouped together following the keys.

Seven Annual Grasses[1]

1. Leaf sheaths (of all leaves, or just the lower) conspicuously pubescent.
    2. All leaves pubescent.
        3. Seedlings slender, the first leaves usually less than ⅛ inch (3 mm) wide; ligule a fringe of hairs (hard to see on first leaves); surface of leaf blades often without hairs.[2] WITCHGRASS (*Panicum capillare*)
        3. Seedlings quickly robust, second to third leaves usually ¼ to ⅜ inch (6 to 9 mm) wide; ligule a membrane; surface of leaf blades usually hairy.[3] LARGE CRABGRASS (*Digitaria sanguinalis*)
    2. Only lower two leaf sheaths pubescent, the remainder essentially without hairs. FALL PANICUM (*Panicum dichotomiflorum*)
1. Leaf sheaths not pubescent or the hairs inconspicuous.
    4. Seedlings with inconspicuous hairs on leaf sheath or blade as described below (foxtails).
        5. Leaf blade with fine hairs over entire upper surface.[4] GIANT FOXTAIL (*Setaria faberi*)
        5. Leaf blade without hairs or with a few restricted to basal portion.
            6. Leaf sheaths ciliate (with a line of hairs along edges).[5] GREEN FOXTAIL (*Setaria viridis*)
            6. Leaf sheaths not ciliate; instead a few filmy hairs present at base of blade (second to third leaf stage). YELLOW FOXTAIL (*Setaria lutescens*)
    4. Seedlings without hairs.
        7. Ligule present.[6, 7] FALL PANICUM (*Panicum dichotomiflorum*)
        7. Ligule absent.[8] BARNYARDGRASS (*Echinochloa crusgalli*)

Seven Broadleaf Weeds

1. Cotyledons ⅝ to 1¼ inches (1.5 to 3 cm) long, more than ¼ inch (6 mm) wide; leaves (above cotyledons) paired or nearly so.
    2. Cotyledons more than 1 inch (2.5 cm) long.[9] COMMON COCKLEBUR (*Xanthium strumarium*)
    2. Cotyledons less than 1 inch (2.5 cm) long.[10] COMMON SUNFLOWER (*Helianthus annuus*)
1. Cotyledons usually smaller than above; leaves plainly alternate when expanded (may appear paired when just starting to develop).
    3. Cotyledons nearly as broad as long.[11] VELVETLEAF (*Abutilon theophrasti*)
    3. Cotyledons much longer than wide.
        4. Cotyledons about ⅝ inch (1.5 cm) long, ⅛ inch (3 mm) wide; midvein scarcely discernible; surface even, not blotched.[12] PENNSYLVANIA SMARTWEED (*Polygonum pensylvanicum*)
        4. Cotyledons about ⅜ inch (1 cm) long, 1/16 inch (2 mm) wide, not possessing above combination of surface characters.

5. Cotyledons with good midvein, surface finely blotched; first leaves not as below.

6. Stem soon becoming hairy.

REDROOT PIGWEED (*Amaranthus retroflexus*)

6. Stem remaining glabrous.

TALL WATERHEMP (*Amaranthus tuberculatus*)

5. Cotyledons not possessing an evident midvein, surface not blotched; first leaves, especially undersurface, granular-mealy.

COMMON LAMBSQUARTERS (*Chenopodium album*)

Footnotes

1. Grass seedlings look alike. The identification characters are small, requiring good eyes or a hand lens and some knowledge of the structure of the grass leaf.

2. The grass leaf consists of three parts: (1) the blades; (2) the sheath, which is rolled into a tube around the stem, the edges usually overlapping; and (3) the ligule, which is a fringe of hairs or a narrow membrane, positioned at the juncture of the blade and sheath (on side next to stem). To see the ligules on grass seedlings, you must usually pull the leaf away from the stem and use a hand lens.

3. Seedlings of witchgrass and crabgrass are easily confused.

4. The first leaf of giant foxtail seedlings lacks the hairs but subsequent ones have them. The hairs form a dense but inconspicuous covering. The young eyes of undergraduate students see them easily. Others can hold the leaf up to the light or use a hand lens. The furry covering on leaves of older plants can be felt by rubbing your finger over the upper surface — but this is a "no go" on seedlings.

5. The hairs are readily evident on well-developed plants, less so on seedlings. Hand lens may be necessary. If you can't see them, pull leaf off stem. Sometimes, the first sheath may have tiny hairs on surface as well as margin.

6. The ligule in fall panicum is a tiny fringe of hairs. It's necessary to pull the leaf away from the plant and use magnification to see it.

7. We have two crabgrasses. Large crabgrass is entered in the outline above. Smooth crabgrass (*Digitaria ischaemum*) lacks hairs entirely or, at the third to fourth leaf stage, has filmy hairs on margin of base of leaf blade. It will key out here, but differs from fall panicum in having a membranous ligule; that of fall panicum is a fringe of hairs.

8. Barnyard grass is unusual in not possessing a ligule. The juncture of the leaf and blade is well marked by a whitish, almost bony area — but there is no ligule.

9. Common cocklebur seedlings are big, often with purple stems, and the cotyledons are inconspicuously glandular. The stem is somewhat hairy.

10. The stem below the cotyledons is smooth; that above is strongly hairy.

11. Velvetleaf seedlings are finely downy; the cotyledons are nearly as broad as long, have several veins, and are stalked.

12. We have several kinds of smartweeds. All have a membrane (ochrea) around stem just above the node; the ochreae are easily evident after 2 or 3 leaves have developed but not at the cotyledon stage. Ladysthumb (*Polygonum persicaria*) is second to Pennsylvania smartweed in abundance. It has somewhat smaller seedlings. The upper edges of the ochreae have a fringe of hairs on ladysthumb but not on Pennsylvania smartweed.

GLOSSARY

Alternate (leaf arrangement). One leaf at each node of the stem.

Annual. A plant that lives a year or less.

Aromatic. Having an odor; fragrant.

Anther. The pollen-producing part of the stamen.

Auricle. One of a pair of lateral projections at juncture of sheath and blade of certain grass leaves.

Awn. A bristlelike tip; most frequently used to denote projections from glumes, lemmas, or paleas of grass spikelets.

Axil. The angle between a leaf and a stem in which branches or flowers may arise.

Axillary. Of or related to the axil.

Biennial. A plant that lives two years.

Bract. A modified, reduced leaf that subtends a flower or portion of an inflorescence.

Bulb. An underground, perennial storage organ consisting of a stem axis and numerous overlapping leaf scales.

Calyx. The outer whorl of flower parts; the sepals. The calyx is usually greenish and covers the other flower parts in bud.

Capsule. A dehiscent, dry, several-seeded fruit.

Caryopsis. The grass fruit; one-seeded, indehiscent; also called a grain.

Collar. Junction of the leaf blade and leaf sheath in grasses.

Complete flower. A flower possessing all flower parts: sepals, petals, stamens, and pistil(s).

Compound (leaf). A leaf divided into two or more distinct leaflets.

Cordate. Heart-shaped; usually used to describe leaves with a pair of rounded basal lobes.

Corolla. The petals; the usually colored flower parts immediately inside the calyx.

Cotyledons. Seed leaves; the first leaflike structures, usually paired, appearing above ground in most dicotyledonous plants; e.g., cocklebur, soybean. The cotyledons are often thick and fleshy and serve as food storage organs for the embryo plant. The so-called cotyledon (scutellum) of monocotyledons; e.g., foxtails, corn, does not emerge from the seed.

Culm. The stem of a grass.

Decumbent. Sprawling, prostrate, but usually with young growth ascending.

Dehiscent. Referring to a dry fruit that splits open at maturity, releasing the seeds; e.g., milkweed pods.

Dentate. Toothed, with the teeth directed at right angles to the edge; usually employed with reference to leaf margins.

Digitate. Having several parts or branches arising at or near the same point; fingerlike.

Dioecious. Referring to a plant with unisexual flowers, the pistillate and staminate flowers being borne by different individuals.

Disk. The central portion of flower heads of members of the composite family; it is composed of tubular flowers.

Dissected (leaf). A leaf whose blade is cut up into numerous, narrow lobes.

Entire. A leaf margin that is untoothed, smooth.

Filament. The stalklike portion of a stamen.

Floret. A grass flower and its surrounding lemma and palea; the word floret is sometimes also used for a small flower in a dense cluster.

Genus. A group of similar species such as the clovers (*Trifolium*) or the bluegrasses (*Poa*).

Glabrous. Without hairs.

Glaucous. Having a waxy whitish covering, a "bloom."

Glume. One of the two sterile bracts at the base of a grass spikelet.

Grain. The grass fruit; characterized by being one-seeded, indehiscent; also called a caryopsis.

Hastate. Spearhead-shaped; used especially to describe leaves with a pair of basal lobes, these lobes directed outward.

Head. An inflorescence in which the sessile flowers arise essentially at more or less the same level from an enlarged stem tip; e.g., Canada thistle.

Herbaceous. Soft; lacking woody tissue. Used with respect to plants without woody tissue or with reference to the above-ground parts that do not live over winter.

Imperfect flower. A flower lacking either stamens or pistils; unisexual.

Indehiscent. Referring to a fruit that does not split open and release the seed or seeds at maturity; e.g., a peanut.

Inflorescence. A cluster of flowers, or the flower-bearing portion or portions of a plant.

Internode. Portion of a stem between nodes.

Involucre. A circle of bracts surrounding a flower cluster or single flower.

Irregular. A flower with petals that differ in size; e.g., a bean flower.

Lanceolate. Narrow and tapering from the base to the tip; e.g., a willow leaf.

Leaflet. A secondary division of a compound leaf.

Lemma. The larger of the two bracts surrounding a grass flower.

Ligule. An appendage (a short membrane or row of hairs) on the upper side of the grass leaf at the juncture of the leaf and blade.

Linear. Long and narrow, with parallel margins, as the blade of a grass leaf.

Lobed. Shallowly or deeply divided into usually rounded sections or divisions; ordinarily employed with respect to leaves or leaf margins.

Lyrate (leaf). Deeply cut, with a large rounded terminal lobe and lateral lobes becoming smaller toward the base.

Membranous. Like a membrane, commonly brownish and translucent.

Monoecious. A plant with unisexual flowers and both pistillate and staminate flowers borne by the same individual.

Node. That part of the stem from which leaves and branches arise.

Nutlet. Seedlike fruit segment of the mints and related families. The fruit splits longitudinally into four sections; each segment, shaped like a quarter section of an apple, is a nutlet.

Oblanceolate. Relatively narrow but broadening from the base to the tip.

Obovate. Inversely ovate, egg-shaped in two dimensions, with the broadest end upward.

Ochrea. A membranous sheath surrounding the stem immediately above attachment of the leaves in members of the smartweed family.

One-celled. Referring to a pistil or ovary containing but a single chamber or cell inside.

Opposite (leaves). The leaves paired at each node.

Ovary. The basal portion of the pistil containing the ovules.

Ovate. Egg-shaped in two dimensions with the broad end at the attachment end; usually used to describe shape of leaves.

Palea. The smaller of the two bracts surrounding a grass flower.

Palmately compound. A compound leaf in which the leaflets all arise from the same point.

Panicle. A branched inflorescence.

Pappus. A cluster of fine hairs or scales born by the "seeds" (achenes) of some members of the composite family: e.g., dandelion or thistles.

Pedicel. The stalk of an individual flower.

Peduncle. The stalk of an inflorescence or part of an inflorescence, but not of an individual flower.

Perennial. A plant that may live several years.

Perfect (flower). A flower that contains both stamens and pistils.

Perigynium. A saclike structure surrounding the flower and fruit of plants belonging to the *Carex* genus.

Petal. A single member of the usually colored flower parts, collectively the corolla.

Petiole. The stalk of a leaf.

Pinnately compound (leaf). A compound leaf in which the leaflets are arranged feather-fashion along an elongate axis.

Pistil. The central female part of the flower that develops into the fruit.

Pubescent. Possessing hairs; hairy.

Pungent. With an acrid or biting flavor.

Raceme. An unbranched, elongating inflorescence in which the flowers are stalked.

Rachilla. A short stalk, usually appressed against the lower portion of the palea of certain grass "seeds" (florets). Rachilla-possessing florets originate from several-flowered spikelets. The rachilla represents that portion of the spikelet axis lying between the two contiguous florets.

Rachis. An axis bearing flowers or leaflets.

Ray (flower). Strap-shaped irregular flowers characteristic of the heads of certain members of the composite family. Ray flowers may constitute the entire head (e.g., dandelion) or make up the marginal petal-like flowers in head types possessing both ray and tubular flowers (e.g., daisy).

Regular. Referring to flowers in which petals are of the same size, the flower thus being radially symmetrical.

Rhizome. An underground creeping stem; most frequently characteristic of perennial grasses.

Rosette. A basal cluster of leaves not separated by evident internodal stem elongation.

Rootstock. The underground overwintering part of a perennial herb; a rootstock may be either a rhizome (a stem) or a root.

Sagittate. Arrowhead-shaped; used especially to describe leaves having a pair of basal lobes, these lobes usually directed downward.

Scape. A leafless flowering stem arising from the ground; e.g., onions.

Sepal. A member of the outer whorl of flower parts, collectively the calyx. Usually the sepals are greenish and cover the other flower parts in bud.

Serrate. Toothed, the teeth slanting somewhat forward; usually employed with reference to leaf margins.

Sessile. A leaf or flower attached directly to the axis; without petiole or pedicel.

Sheath. The tubular lower portion of a grass leaf surrounding the stem.

Silique. The fruit of the mustard family; typically two-chambered, dry, usually dehiscent.

Simple (leaf). The leaf blade in one piece; not divided into separate leaflets.

Sinuate. Wavy; used especially to describe leaf margins.

Spatulate. Spoon-shaped.

Species. A distinct kind of plant, such as wheat, alfalfa, buckhorn plantain, or common ragweed.

Spike. An unbranched inflorescence in which the flowers or flowering units are sessile.

Spikelet. The basic flowering unit within a grass inflorescence; consisting of a condensed stem apex bearing a pair of sterile bracts (glumes) at base and one or more florets above.

Stamen. One of the male, pollen-producing organs of the flower.

Stigma. The terminal pollen-receptive portion of the pistil.

Stipules. Appendages, usually paired, arising from the stem at either side of petiole attachment; particularly characteristic of legume family.

Stolon. A prostrate stem or runner that roots at the nodes; e.g., strawberry or bermudagrass.

Striation. A fine longitudinal line or streak.

Style. The stalklike part of the ovary that bears the stigma.

Subtend. To bear above; used especially with reference to a bract or a leaf that bears a flower in its axil.

Tuber. A swollen underground storage stem; e.g., a potato.

Tubular (flower). Regular flowers characteristic of many members of the composite family; such flowers may constitute the entire head, or form only the center portion of the head.

Umbel. An inflorescence in which the pediceled flowers arise essentially from the same point.

Utricle. A one-seeded fruit with a thin wall, often dehiscent with the top part (lid) falling off.

Whorled. A leaf arrangement in which three or more leaves are borne at each stem node.

Winter annual. An annual plant that usually initiates growth in the fall, lives over winter, and produces seed the following spring.

INDEX TO SPECIES

COMMON NAMES

Velvetleaf, 122
Venice mallow, 123
Vervain, blue, 148
  hoary, 148
  prostrate, 147
  white, 148
Vetch, narrowleaf, 110
Virginia copperleaf, 114
  pepperweed, 98

Waterhemlock, spotted, 130
Waterhemp, tall, 67
Waterpod, 144
Western ironweed, 239
  ragweed, 182
  salsify, 238
White cockle, 74
  heath aster, 191
  snakeroot, 208
  vervain, 148
Wild buckwheat, 51
  carrot, 132
  cucumber, 177
  four-o'clock, 68
  garlic, 46

Wild licorice, 108
  mustard, 89
  oat, 17
  onion, 46
  parsnip, 133
  proso millet, 33
  radish, 100
Winged pigweed, 59
Wirestem muhly, 29
Witchgrass, 31
Woodsorrel, common yellow, 111
Woolly croton, 115
  cupgrass, 26
Woollyleaf bursage, 184
Woolly plantain, 172
Wormseed mustard, 95
Wormwood, absinth, 188
  annual, 189

Yarrow, common, 180
Yellow foxtail, 36
  hawkweed, 220
  nutsedge, 44
  rocket, 86
  toadflax, 164

SCIENTIFIC NAMES

Abutilon theophrasti, 122
Acalypha virginica, 114
Achillea millefolium, 180
Aegilops cylindrica, 13
Agropyron repens, 14
Agrostemma githago, 72
Allium canadense, 46
  vineale, 46
Amaranthus albus, 62
  blitoides, 63
  hybridus, 64
  retroflexus, 65
  spinosus, 66
  tuberculatus, 67
Ambrosia artemisiifolia, 181
  bidentata, 181
  grayi, 184
  psilostachya, 182
  tomentosa, 184
  trifida, 183
Ampelamus albidus, 135
Andropogon virginicus, 15
Antennaria plantaginifolia, 185
Anthemis cotula, 186

Apocynum cannabinum, 134
Arctium lappa, 187
  minus, 187
Argemone intermedia, 84
Aristida oligantha, 16
Artemisia absinthium, 188
  annua, 189
Asclepias incarnata, 136
  syriaca, 137
  verticillata, 138
Aster ericoides, 190
  pilosus, 191
Atriplex patula, 56
Avena fatua, 17

Barbarea vulgaris, 86
Berteroa incana, 87
Bidens bipinnata, 192
  frondosa, 193
Brassica juncea, 88
  kaber, 89
  nigra, 88
Bromus japonicus, 18
  secalinus, 18
  tectorum, 19

INDEX TO FAMILIES